INTRODUCTION TO
THE BIOCHEMISTRY OF FOODS

INTRODUCTION TO
THE BIOCHEMISTRY
OF FOODS

BY

J. B. S. BRAVERMAN, D.SC.

Late Professor of Food Technology, Technion,
Israel Institute of Technology,
Haifa (Israel)

FOREWORD BY PROF. S. A. GOLDBLITH

Department of Nutrition
Food Science and Technology, Massachusetts Institute
of Technology, Cambridge, Mass. (U.S.A.)

ELSEVIER PUBLISHING COMPANY

AMSTERDAM / LONDON / NEW YORK

1963

SOLE DISTRIBUTORS FOR THE UNITED STATES AND CANADA

AMERICAN ELSEVIER PUBLISHING COMPANY, INC.

52 VANDERBILT AVENUE, NEW YORK 17, N.Y.

SOLE DISTRIBUTORS FOR GREAT BRITAIN

ELSEVIER PUBLISHING COMPANY LIMITED

12B, RIPPLESIDE COMMERCIAL ESTATE

RIPPLE ROAD, BARKING, ESSEX

LIBRARY OF CONGRESS CATALOG CARD NUMBER 62-13013

WITH 55 ILLUSTRATIONS AND 12 TABLES

FOREWORD

In this era of *exploding technology*, the need for high standards in pedagogy and in the tools of teaching is obvious. The present volume is a definite step in this direction since it is hoped it will greatly aid the teaching of the expanding field of food science and technology.

Introduction to the Biochemistry of Foods is a descriptive title and while it well defines the field of interest covered, the contents of the book are broader than the title indicates. The work represents an approach to biochemistry directed towards foods, their components, and the changes occurring in these during the growth, harvest, process, and storage stages.

These are important considerations for any food scientist to have at his finger tips, knowledge of the basic chemistry of the complex products with which he is dealing, in order that he may explore, with wisdom, keen perception, and sound judgment, the potentialities of an *exploding technology* by means of a logical and direct approach.

This book, written by a scientist who is endowed with an above-average amount of common sense and sagacity, synergized with years of experience, provides a fulcrum of basic science from which a student can "enter to grow in wisdom" in food science and technology.

While many American texts are replete with respect to their references to the American literature in their own particular field, and, likewise, many European texts are replete with European literature citations, relatively few texts exhibit the cosmopolitanism that actually exists in the particular field of interest of the text. In this book, the references and bibliography indicate the universality of food science.

In addition, the presentation of the pertinent historical background adds much to making this an effective pedagogical tool.

Dr. Braverman has achieved very high standards in his own academic background with formal degree work at Harvard and at the Sorbonne. A world-renowned expert on citrus and citrus products, he has published extensively in this field, including an excellent text, *The Chemistry and Technology of Citrus Products* (Interscience Publishers), which appeared in 1949.

Since 1953 he has been Professor of Food Technology and Head of the Department of Food- and Biotechnology at the Technion (Israel Institute of Technology) at Haifa, Israel.

During 1960–1961, Dr. Braverman was Visiting Professor of Food Technology in the Department of Nutrition, Food Science and Technology at the Massachusetts Institute of Technology. He presented to our students an excellent course in advanced food technology centered around basic principles. This course, presented by an individual possessing the uncommon gifts of an excellent comprehensive theoretical knowledge, and 30 years of practical experience, integrated with a genetic teaching ability inherited through many generations in his own family, provided a wonderful experience for our graduate students.

This text personifies the cosmopolitanism of food science as presented by a keen intellect.

S. A. GOLDBLITH

DEDICATED

TO

THE MANY THOUSANDS

WHO DEVOTED THEIR LIVES TO

THE STUDY OF THIS FASCINATING SCIENCE,

THUS MAKING THIS BOOK

POSSIBLE

PREFACE

"Il n'y a pas de science appliquée mais seulement des applications de science."

LOUIS PASTEUR

One of the fundamental disciplines usually included in the curriculum of a good food technologist is biochemistry. However, practically all the existing good English textbooks on biochemistry deal mainly with medical, clinical and nutritional aspects, while very little mention is made of various important components, present in foods, which are of fundamental importance to the changes occurring during the preparation, processing and storage of foods and feeds. Very little attention has been given in these textbooks to components such as pectins, tannins, pigments, essential oils, etc., or to such phenomena as browning, colloidal state, rheological properties, changes in color, flavor or texture.

The present volume has been written to fill this gap. The chemical and enzymatic phenomena occurring in food are related to the properties required from foods as far as their nutritional value, flavor, color or texture are concerned. The various chapters that follow are concerned, therefore, with the composition of foods, the biosynthesis of their components and their breakdown or decomposition. When dealing with the decomposition of various food components, the main stress is laid on changes which such foods undergo during processing. No mention is made of the metabolic changes in the human body, for these are part and parcel of the science of nutrition with which this book is not concerned.

Starting with the major anabolic process, photosynthesis, the author endeavors to impress upon the student the vital importance of various scientific disciplines in the search and understanding of such biochemical problems in food and biotechnology. Here the stress is laid on basic principles from organic chemistry, physics, enzymology and biotechnology, as well as on the use of modern methods of biochemical research such as spectrophotometry, chromatography and the use of tracer elements. In this and other chapters the author has made use of the historic approach, as far as possible. Both the stress laid on basic scientific principles and the historic approach are, in the view of the author, important from the didactic point of view.

The other metabolic processes, having a direct relation to the changes in foods, which are described more fully, are: fermentation, respiration and the KREBS' cycle, the PASTEUR effect, biological oxidation, enzymatic and non-enzymatic browning.

The book is intended primarily for food technologists, students in agriculture and agricultural engineering.

Since this text is regarded only as an introduction to the subject of its title, it is the opinion of the author that in order to broaden his knowledge on a specific item, the student should be referred to authoritative reviews rather than to original reports of investigators. As far as possible, this principle was adhered to throughout the book. This book has been written along the lines of an earlier edition in Hebrew by the author published in 1960.

1962, Technion, Haifa (Israel).   J. B. S. BRAVERMAN

Professor J. B. S. BRAVERMAN passed away on March 21st, 1962, in Tel-Aviv after a long illness.

The proofs of the first chapters of his *Introduction*, so dear to him, reached him at a time when he was still in full working capacity. He added improvements here and there in order to make the text more perfect and up to date. His intellectual integrity uncorrupted by a rapidly failing health encouraged me to undertake proof corrections. I am sure that my late teacher, Professor BRAVERMAN, would have done better.

I feel certain that the Publishers, so devoted to bringing out this book on a high standard, will gladly accept suggestions and criticisms in order to make out of this book in editions to follow a living memorial for those to whom it has been dedicated as well as for its pioneering author.

Department of Food and Biotechnology, Technion, M.I.T.,   G. ZIMMERMAN
        Haifa (Israel)

ACKNOWLEDGEMENTS

I wish to acknowledge my sincere thanks to many of my colleagues and friends at the Massachusetts Institute of Technology and at the Technion, Israel Institute of Technology, Haifa, who helped me in producing this book. Special thanks are due to Prof. SAMUEL A. GOLDBLITH for his continuous interest during the preparation of the manuscript and for its critical evaluation, to Prof. J. T. R. NICKERSON, Prof. EMILY WICK, and Prof. MARCUS KAREL all of M.I.T. and to Prof. GIDEON ZIMMERMAN of the Technion, each of whom reviewed several of the chapters and offered criticisms and advice. Finally, I wish to record my gratitude to Mr. LOUIS RONSIVALLI, who prepared all the drawings, to Mrs. K. FARNHAM for her diligence in typing the manuscript and to Miss VIRGINIA POCHETTI, who assisted in various ways to make this book a reality.

J. B. S. BRAVERMAN

CONTENTS

CONTENTS

CHAPTER I

INTRODUCTION

Enter to grow in wisdom

HARVARD

The world in which we live is composed of two main classes of matter: the inanimate matter and the organized living matter. While the former, which comprises rocks, stones and minerals, is made of such patterns as atoms, molecules and crystals, in themselves well organized entities, it does not, by and large, change appreciably except perhaps owing to erosion, weathering or to natural cataclism. On the other hand, living matter, which comprises microorganisms, plants, animals and human beings, while also built of the same atoms, molecules and crystals, is composed of extremely complex, highly organized patterns, which have the ability to grow, to support themselves and to reproduce. In addition, living matter is in a state of constant metabolic change.

Living matter should, in its turn, be divided into two general groups: the *autotropic* and the *heterotropic* organisms. Organisms belonging to the first group embody all green plants and a limited number of microorganisms. These are capable of growth and reproduction by preparing for themselves all the required complex materials from very simple inorganic compounds: carbon dioxide, water and a few minerals. With these the autotropic organisms are able to provide the necessary energy for themselves from the sun: some by means of the photosynthetic apparatus, the others by chemosynthesis.

The *heterotropic* organisms, on the other hand, are strongly servile towards the former group: they can not subsist, grow or reproduce without "food", which they have to acquire mainly from the autotropic organisms or at least by devouring other members of their own group. In other words, the heterotropic organisms get the required energy for their subsistence only by decomposing foodstuffs which are ultimately derived from the autotropic group, namely plants. It should be pointed out that heterotropic organisms are indeed capable of building up in their bodies certain components such as their own proteins, for instance; however, in order to do so they require the "building blocks", in this case "essential" amino acids, from external sources. Other organisms of this group often lack vitamins or other important ingredients for their development. This group of heterotropic organisms embraces all the animals, including man, as well as most of the micro-organisms. It is clear that this group represents a long chain of parasitism, beginning with man and ending with the smallest microorganisms, all hanger-ons with respect to green plants.

In spite of this striking difference existing between autotropic and hetero-tropic organisms, and in spite of the multitude of varieties of the different living species, it has been definitely established, on the strength of com-paratively recent discoveries, that the number of fundamental biochemical mechanisms, by which these apparently different organisms operate, is rather limited and that these mechanisms are in many cases identical, or at least very similar, no matter whether these are taking place in the lowest organized living cell or in a highly organized form of life, such as human. Such a vital process as respiration, for instance, is identical in plants and in animals; and, again, the very same eight steps necessary for fermenting plant sugars by yeast cells are identical with the anaerobic breakdown of glycogen in the human body. All this shows that, notwithstanding the enormous evolutionary changes which have taken place during millions of years, a plant- or a yeast-cell and the human cell, all of which had their starting point in some premordial material, preserved some basic reaction mechanisms in order to achieve their fundamental needs.

As mentioned above, the heterotropic organisms require their food to be supplied by others, and so man seeks to obtain his supplies from plants and animals. However, at a very early stage in his development, man was confronted with the problem of how to preserve his food from deterioration as well as from deleterious changes in color, taste, flavor, texture and in nutritional value. Through the ages, he learned this art of food preservation by trial and error and much of his knowledge for selecting suitable foods came to him by intuition.

Food science, or *bromatology*, however, is a comparatively new science. One should probably attribute its beginning to Louis Pasteur. During the last 150 years much has been achieved in elucidating the nature of the chemical and biochemical changes occurring in foods. These changes in the constitu-tion of the numerous components of foods and feeds may be caused by chemical or biochemical reactions. The latter are reactions catalyzed by a great number of specific biological catalysts, called enzymes. Contrary to chemical reactions, biochemical processes occur under ordinary conditions of temperature and pressure, as is the case for all enzymatic reactions.

Biochemistry of foods, therefore, is engaged in the study of the composition of foods, their formation (biosynthesis) and their decomposition:

(A) The *compositions* of interest are those of the basic nutrients (carbohydrates, proteins and fats) as well as those of a large number of secondary compounds, which may affect the color (chlorophyll, carotenoids, anthocyanins and bioflavanoids), the taste (organic acids, bitter substances, tannins, etc.), the aroma (*e.g.*, essential oils, terpenoids, etc.), the texture (*e.g.*, pectins, and other hydrocolloids), as well as the compositions of a number of accessory compounds, which are important in organizing the complex systems constituting foods (enzymes, vitamins, growth factors and hormones).

(B) The formation or *biosynthesis* of all these compounds is performed by a series of *anabolic processes* capable of creating complex organic matter from less complicated compounds. Examples of these are *photosynthesis* (during which the energy of the sun is bound to the carbohydrates formed from the simple oxides H_2O and CO_2), *synthesis of proteins* (whereby the nitrates are reduced to nitrites and finally to amines, which enter into the composition of amino acids; the latter combining to form numerous proteins), *synthesis of lipids* (formation of glycerol, the synthesis of fatty acids and the esterification of these to form lipids). These are only examples of the synthesis of the main nutrients, there being many others.

(C) The *decomposition or catabolism* of all nutrients during processes such as digestion, respiration, or fermentation. Throughout all these catabolic processes complex nutrients are decomposed into simpler compounds, whereupon energy is evolved and supplied to the living matter for purposes of growth, subsistence and reproduction.

Some of these changes are not necessarily undesirable, *e.g.*, the activity of certain enzymes is called for when the food technologist is interested, for instance, in the production of cheeses from milk, or in the clarification of food products, or in the creation of citric acid from sugar by mycological methods or the production of beer from starch-containing cereals, or the utilization of plant waste materials for the production of antibiotics, etc.

All these are subjects with which biochemistry is generally concerned. The following chapters describe the composition as well as the metabolic processes (both anabolic and catabolic) in a manner pertaining primarily to the various foods before they are utilized by man or animal, since the metabolic processes engaged in the utilization of the foods themselves are governed by the science of nutrition.

References p. 4/5

SELECTED BIBLIOGRAPHY TO CHAPTER 1

(i) Chemistry and Biochemistry

BALDWIN, E., *Dynamic Aspects of Biochemistry*, 3rd edn., Cambridge Univ. Press, 1957.
BATE-SMITH, E. C., *Food Science*, Cambridge Univ. Press, 1952.
BONNER, J., *Plant Biochemistry*, Academic Press, New York, 1950.
FOX, B. A. AND CAMERON, A. G., *A Chemical Approach to Food and Nutrition*, Univ. of London Press, 1961.
FREAR, D. E. H., *Agricultural Chemistry*, 2 Vols., Van Nostrand Co., New York, 1951.
FRUTON, J. S. AND SOFIA SIMMONDS, *General Biochemistry*, 2nd edn., J. Wiley & Sons, New York, 1958.
GREEN, D. E., *Currents in Biochemical Research*, Interscience Publishing Co., New York, 1946 and 1956.
HARRISON, K., *A Guide-Book to Biochemistry*, Cambridge Univ. Press, 1959.
KARLSON, P., *Kürzes Lehrbuch der Biochemie*, 3. Aufl., Thieme Verlag, Stuttgart, 1962.
MALLETTE, M. F., ALTHOUSE, P. M. AND CLAGETT, C. O., *Biochemistry of Plants and Animals*, J. Wiley, New York, 1960.
MEYER, L. H., *Food Chemistry*, Reinhold Publishing Co., New York, 1960.
MRAK, E. AND STUART, G. F., *Advances in Food Research*, Vol. 1–10, Academic Press, New York, 1948–1960.
SCHOENHEIMER, R., *The Dynamic State of Body Constituents*, Harvard Univ. Press, Cambridge, Mass., 1942.
SCHORMÜLLER, J., *Lehrbuch der Lebensmittelchemie*, Springer-Verlag, Berlin, 1961.
WEST, E. S. AND TODD, W. R., *Textbook of Biochemistry*, Macmillan Publishing Co., New York, 1951.

(ii) Selected Bibliography on Food Technology

Fundamental aspects of the dehydration of foodstuffs, *Aberdeen Conf. Soc. Chem. Ind., London, 1958.*
ALTSCHUL, A. M., *Processed Plant Protein Foodstuffs*, Academic Press, New York, 1958.
BARTHOLOMEW, E. T. AND SINCLAIR, W. B., *The Lemon Fruit*, Univ. of California Press 1951.
BAUMGARTNER, J. G. AND HERSOM, A. C., *Canned Foods; an Introduction to their Microbiology*, Churchill, London, 4th edn., 1956.
BINSTEAD, R. AND DEVEY, J. D. *Soup Manufacture (Canning, Dehydration and Quick-freezing)*, 2nd edn., Food Trade Press, London, 1960.
BLANK, F. C., *Handbook of Food and Agriculture*, Reinhold Publishing Co., New York, 1955.
BRAVERMAN, J. B. S., *Citrus Products*, Interscience Publishing Co., New York, 1949.
CHARLEY, V. L. S., Recent advances in fruit juice production, *Commonwealth Bur. Hort., Tech. Commun. No. 21,* London, 1950.
CRUESS, W. V., *Commercial Fruit and Vegetable Products*, 3rd edn., McGraw-Hill Publishing Co., New York, 1948.
HANNAN, R. S., *Food Preservation by Ionizing Radiation*, Chemical Publishing Co., New York, 1956.
HIND, H., *Brewing Science and Practice*, Chapman & Hall, London, 1943.
JACOBS, M. B., *The Chemistry and Technology of Food and Food Products*, 3 Vols., 2nd edn., Interscience Publishing Co., New York, 1951.
JENNESS, R. AND PATTON, S., *Principles of Dairy Chemistry*, J. Wiley & Sons, New York, 1959.
JONES, O. AND JONES, T. W., *Canning Practice and Control*, Chapman & Hall, London, 1941.
JOSLYN, M. A., *Methods in Food Analysis Applied to Plant Products*, Academic Press, New York, 1950.

KRAMER, A. AND TWIGG, B. A., *Fundamentals of Quality Control for the Food Industry*, Avi Publishing Co., Westport, Conn., 1962.

LOWE, B., *Experimental Cookery*, J. Wiley & Sons, New York, 1955.

MATZ, S. A., *Bakery Technology and Engineering*, Avi Publishing Co., Westport, Conn., 1960.

MORRIS, T. N., *Principles of Fruit Preservation*, Chapman & Hall, London, 1933.

PARKER, M. E., STATELER, E. S. AND HARVEY, E. H., *Elements of Food Engineering*, Reinhold Publishing Co., New York, 1952.

SMOCK, R. M. AND NEUBERT, A. M., *Apples and Apple Products*, Interscience Publishing Co., New York, 1950.

TRESSLER, D. K. AND JOSLYN, M. A., *The Chemistry and Technology of Fruit and Vegetable Juice Production*, Avi Publishing Co., New York, 1961.

VAN SLYKE, L. L. AND PRICE, W. V., *Cheese*, Orange Judd Publications, New York, 1952.

VON LOESECKE, H. W., *Outlines of Food Technology*, Reinhold Publishing Co., New York, 1942; *Bananas*, Interscience Publishing Co., New York, 1950.

WHITTIER, E. O. AND WEBB, B. H., *Byproducts from Milk*, Reinhold Publishing Co., New York, 1950.

WINTON, A. L. AND WINTON, K. B., *The Structure and Composition of Foods*, 4 Vols., J. Wiley & Sons, New York, 1946.

CHAPTER 2

CHLOROPHYLL

The green thralldom

TANG PEI-SUNG

The most important of all anabolic processes is photosynthesis, namely, the synthesis of organic matter of high potential energy from the simple oxides, CO_2 and H_2O, of very low energy, by green plants containing *chlorophyll* in the presence of light. This green pigment, chlorophyll, is the major agent capable of absorbing light energy and transmitting it to the carbohydrates synthesized during thi sprocess. To these carbohydrates we owe the maintenance of life on this planet and it is no wonder that the physiologist, TANG PEI-SUNG[1], while writing a book on chlorophyll, expressed our un-reserved subordination to this pigment as the "green thralldom".

Occurrence

Most of the plants have the chlorophylls in their leaves (before their senescent stage) and in their fruits (before they ripen). The chlorophylls are concentrated in the spongy region under the leaf or fruit cuticle—in the plastids, called *chloroplastids* as long as they are green, and *chromoplastids* after they have changed color. A simple microscopic examination shows that chlorophyll is not dissolved in the cells but has a granular structure. The plastids are relatively large, cup- and plate-like bodies, 3–10 μ in diameter and 1–2 μ in thickness. They are built of smaller particles, *grana*, which, because of their size (0.2–2 μ in diameter) lie in the border region of possible detection by the optical microscope.

The grana of spinach, for example, are 0.6 μ in diameter and 0.1 μ thick. It is possible by means of an electron microscope to detect even smaller structures, *laminae*, of which the grana are composed. The size range of laminae is only 0.01 μ–0.02 μ (Fig. 1).

Between these laminae lie the molecules of the chlorophylls, apparently bound in some way to the proteins, lipids and lipoproteins. Carotenoids, yellow companions of the chlorophylls, and some mineral salts are also found in these positions. The exact orientation of chlorophyll molecules in

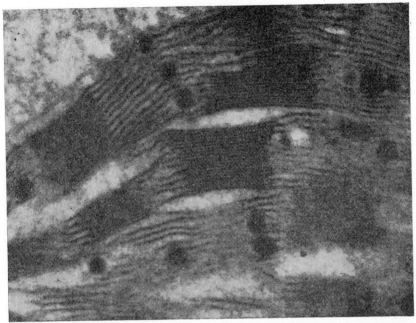

Fig. 1. *Grana* and *Laminae* in the chloroplasts of *Zea* as seen by the electron microscope (Courtesy of A. HODGE, *Rev. Mod. Phys.*, 31 (1959) 331).

the laminae is yet unknown. However, there is no doubt that this spongy environment is most appropriate for the specific function of the chlorophylls —the absorption and storage of light energy. (It has been shown, for instance, that the transfer of the excitation energy from chlorophyll a to chlorophyll b is only possible when these molecules[2] are spaced within the area of about 10^3 Å. Apparently this range is allotted by nature to each of the chlorophyll molecules so that their efficiency of energy transfer is about 96%.)

In the green leaves of higher plants the chlorophyll content is about 0.1 % of the fresh weight. In green algae there appears to be considerable variation in the total content of the green pigment.

Structure

WILLSTAETTER[3] and his school were the first to make a thorough study of these pigments and their related compounds and, although they did not establish their final structure, most of their conclusions hold good upto the present.

WILLSTAETTER found that leaf chlorophyll is, in fact, composed of two substances, chlorophyll a and chlorophyll b, which are always found together in the ratio of about $1:2.5$. The difference in their empirical formulae is merely an extra atom of oxygen in the b form in lieu of two hydrogen atoms in chlorophyll a:

$$C_{32}H_{30}ON_4Mg\diagup^{COOCH_3}_{\diagdown COOC_{20}H_{39}} \qquad\qquad C_{32}H_{28}O_2N_4Mg\diagup^{COOCH_3}_{\diagdown COOC_{20}H_{39}}$$

chlorophyll a chlorophyll b

The two chlorophylls are always accompanied by yellow pigments, carotene ($C_{40}H_{56}$) and xanthophyll ($C_{40}H_{56}O_2$)—see further Chapter 3.

In their attempt to elucidate the structural formulae of the chlorophylls, WILLSTAETTER and his collaborators ascertained, in addition to the above, the following important facts:

(a) that the molecule of chlorophyll contains one atom of magnesium connected to the rest by a conjugated bond. (WILLSTAETTER suggested that Mg acts here in the same manner as in the Grignard reagent and he successfully used this idea when attempting in 1906 a partial synthesis of the tetra-pyrrole ring.) It may be pointed out that 100 years before that, DE SAUSSURE[4] (1804) showed that Mg is indispensable for the growth of plants.

(b) that the chlorophyll molecule consists of four substituted pyrrole rings which are linked together by methine bridges (now conventionally labeled α, β, γ and δ). It is of interest to remark here that the presence of such pyrrole groups in petroleum has finally solved the long-standing dispute among scientists regarding the origin of oil, namely, that petroleum is formed from plants.

(c) that the tetra-pyrrole structure of chlorophyll is very similar to that of *hemin*, the red pigment in hemoglobin, with the exception that hemin contains iron instead of magnesium.

Structural formula of Chlorophyll a [1,3,5,8-tetramethyl,2-vinyl,4-ethyl,7-propionyl (phytyl)ester,9-oxo,10-carb-methoxy phorbin]

(d) that chlorophyll is the diester formed from a dicarboxylic acid (chlorophyllin), methanol (CH_3OH) and phytyl alcohol ($C_{20}H_{39}OH$); in other words, it is a methyl-phytylchlorophyllide.

(e) that this magnesium-containing molecule is quite stable in weak alkalis but is easily attacked by even weak acids which cause the cleavage of Mg from the molecule, thereby leaving a substance with a brownish-olive color (pheophytin).

The structural formula was definitely established by WILLSTAETTER's pupil, FISCHER[5], in 1937. The total synthesis was accomplished only in 1960 by STRELL[6], using a method originally proposed by FISCHER, and by WOODWARD[7] from monocyclic pyrroles.

Chlorophyll *b* differs from chlorophyll *a* only by having an aldehyde group (—CHO) on carbon atom 3 instead of a methyl group.

The special terminology used in chlorophyll chemistry comprises, among others, the following terms:

porphin—the tetra-pyrrole skeleton, consisting of four pyrrole rings connected by four methine bridges;

porphyrin—same skeleton substituted by various groups, methyl, ethyl, vinyl, etc.;

phorbin—the above with the addition of a C_9–C_{10} ring;

chlorin—a phorbin with the C_9–C_{10} ring open;

phorbide—ester of a phorbin;

phaeophorbide—the methyl ester of a phorbin;

phaeophytin—the phytyl ester of a phorbin without the Mg;

phyllin—a derivative of a phorbide or a chlorin with Mg in the center;

chlorophyllin—the dicarboxylic acid:

$$R\begin{cases} COOH \\ COOH \end{cases}$$

methyl chlorophyllide—the methyl ester of the above:

$$R\begin{cases} COOCH_3 \\ COOH \end{cases}$$

chlorophyll *a* or *b*—the above esterified by both methyl and phytyl alcohols:

$$R\begin{cases} COOCH_3 \\ COOC_{20}H_{39} \end{cases}$$

FISCHER[8] also determined that phytol has an isoprenoid structure (composed

of molecules of isoprene
$$CH_2=C-CH=CH_2$$
$$|$$
$$CH_3$$

bound in a head to tail arrangement).

$$CH_3 \cdot CH \cdot CH_2 \cdot CH_2 \cdot CH_2 \cdot CH \cdot (CH_2)_3 \cdot CH \cdot (CH_2)_3 \cdot CH = CH \cdot CH_2OH$$
$$\qquad | \qquad\qquad\qquad\qquad | \qquad\quad | \qquad\qquad\qquad\quad |$$
$$\qquad CH_3 \qquad\qquad\qquad CH_3 \quad CH_3 \qquad\qquad\qquad CH_3$$

phytyl alcohol (phytol) molecule

This isoprenoid structure is found in many natural products, such as carotenoids, terpenoids, steroids, etc., as will be seen in later chapters. Isoprene is insoluble in water, as are most isoprenoids, including phytol. Because of this, chlorophyll is insoluble in water so long as the phytol moiety is attached to it. However, removal of phytol by hydrolysis yields the water-soluble methyl chlorophyllide.

The structural formula of hemin (the chloride of *heme*) shows its similarity to the chlorophyll. It differs, however, in that a vinyl group has replaced an ethyl group at C_4, iron has replaced magnesium, two propionic acid groups are present at C_6 and C_7 of the pyrrole rings, and the C_9–C_{10} ring is absent.

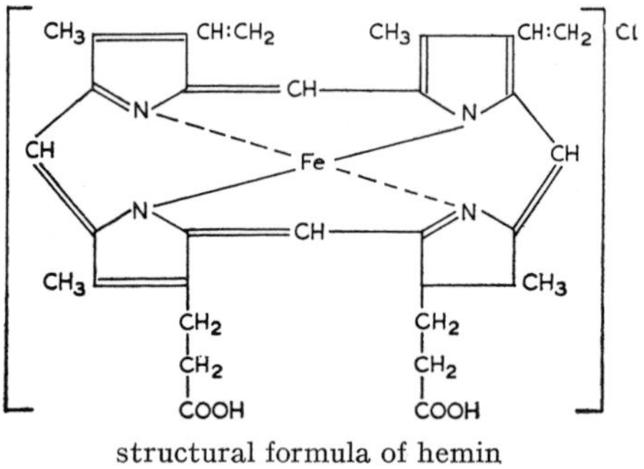

structural formula of hemin

The above iron porphyrin molecule is quite widespread in nature and constitutes a part of the important oxidative enzymes, catalase, peroxidase and cytochromes (see Chapter 12).

Biogenesis

While the problem of the structure of the chlorophyll molecule can now be considered as completely solved, the mode of its creation in the green parts of plants is still a matter for conjecture. Botanists have, for a long time, believed that plants form, in their plastids, some simpler substances from which the green pigment is later synthesized. In fact, the buds of most of etiolated plants show no traces of chlorophyll, although it can be detected immediately after the buds have been exposed to light for a few seconds. It is, therefore, suggested that a precursor of chlorophyll, is formed in some leuco form (sometimes called protochlorophyll) in the plastids of the plant. There is also evidence for the view that chlorophyll is bound to protein in plastids. However, it has not been possible thus far to separate from the plant tissue a chlorophyll–protein complex of uniform composition that may be considered with certainty to represent a native conjugated protein.

A colorless phase is common to all chlorophyll-containing higher plants with the exception of a few species of cryptogams and conifers, as well as several varieties of *Citrus* in which the cotyledons of the seeds are green when inside the fruit. Apparently a certain amount of iron is necessary for transforming the colorless phase into the green chlorophyll. (A well-known plant disease, *chlorosis*, which causes the green leaves to turn yellow, can usually be overcome by treating the affected leaves with a solution of iron salts, the leaves regaining their green color in a few hours.)

The importance of iron in the formation of chlorophyll is supported by the following considerations of its biosynthesis. SHEMIN AND RUSSEL[9] suggested a scheme for the biosynthesis of iron porphyrins in which the iron is further replaced by magnesium.

The first step in this scheme is the formation of δ-aminolevulinic acid from α-amino-β-ketoadipic acid by decarboxylation. The latter is synthesized from coenzyme A activated succinate (see further) and glycine:

$$HOOC \cdot CH_2 \cdot CH_2 \cdot C \cdot CH \cdot COOH \qquad \longrightarrow \qquad HOOC \cdot CH_2 \cdot CH_2 C \cdot CH_2 \cdot NH_2$$

α-amino-β-ketoadipic acid   δ-aminolevulinic acid

Two molecules of δ-aminolevulinic acid condense then to form a pyrrole ring:

Condensation of four such pyrrole rings in the presence of ferrous ions as catalysts together with elimination of four molecules of NH_3 is postulated to give the following structure:

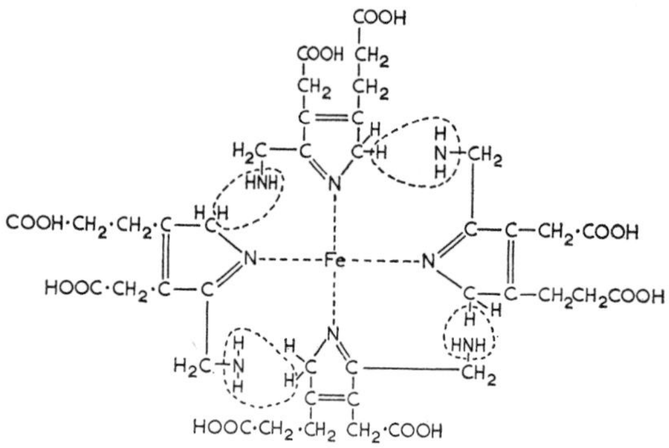

Dehydration and appropriate substitution yield iron porphyrin. Then, since iron is present in the plant in too small quantities to react with all the molecules formed, magnesium reacts to form chlorophylls[10].

Behavior of chlorophyll during food processing

On the basis of our knowledge of the chlorophyll structure, it is important to summarize the changes that may occur in various food products during processing operations. Some general considerations have been presented by ARONOFF[11] from which practical applications may be deduced.

When it is desirable to retain the full green color of chlorophyll in food products, such as in the case of dehydrated or canned vegetables, the possible changes in the chlorophyll molecule should be kept in mind so as to avoid deterioration of the color.

As mentioned earlier, the action of even a weak acid results in the removal of magnesium from the chlorophyll molecule, and formation of pheophytin, which possesses a brownish-olive color. Although practically every green plant tissue is naturally quite acid, chlorophyll, *in situ*, is apparently bound to lipoproteins which in some way protect it from the acid action.

On the other hand, when heat is applied in food processing, the proteins tend to coagulate and, in thus, the chlorophyll becomes more exposed to the adverse action of the acids. Blanching, therefore, always causes some chlorophyll to be converted into pheophytin. Numerous attempts have been made to protect the chlorophyll by neutralizing a portion of the acid and thus raising the pH of the plant tissue in question by the addition of alkali. However, in most cases, such procedures did not succeed because of marked changes in flavor or in texture. This occurred even when magnesium hydroxide was used as an alkali to reduce acidity in commercially canned green peas[12].

In contrast to the above, blanching by the so-called Thomas process can be very successfully applied to spinach which preserves its good green color if blanched by steam at exactly 77°C, notwithstanding the fact that after such blanching this product is processed at 120°C. However, if canned directly at boiling temperature without previous blanching, it will not retain its green color. An explanation of this curious effect is not readily available; some authors think that the enzyme *chlorophyllase* is not inactivated at the temperature of 77°C, and therefore continues to convert chlorophyll into chlorophyllin which possesses a green color.

The enzyme *chlorophyllase* is normally present in plant tissue. Its action is to detach the phytol moiety from the chlorophyll molecule, thereby causing dissolution of the green pigment in water. The behavior of this enzyme is rather strange: at certain seasons of the year chlorophyllase remains active at 65° to 75°C, a temperature at which most other enzymes are inactivated, while at other times the same chlorophyllase appears to be relatively inactive. For instance, the chlorophyllase in spinach is practically inactive during the summer months; in the spring, however, the same enzyme will convert chlorophyll into phyllin even after the vegetable has been heated for 20 minutes. Some vegetables, such as peas, string beans and asparagus apparently do not contain the chlorophyllase enzyme at all. (For inactivation of enzymes by heat see Chapter 12.)

The following scheme summarizes the various changes which may occur in the chlorophylls:

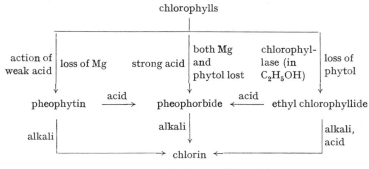

general scheme of chlorophyll breakdown

Some additional phenomena in connection with chlorophyll should be mentioned. Cooking in copper vessels may cause substitution of the magnesium in the chlorophyll molecule by copper. Alkaline oxidations will cause *porphyrins* to be formed.

In addition, photo-oxidation and the actual disappearance of chlorophyll is observed when fruits and vegetables, previously treated with SO_2, are dried in the sun; whereas, when dehydrated in tunnels in the dark, their color is still preserved. This phenomenon is rather inconsistent with the prevailing assumption that the disappearance of chlorophyll is due to oxidation[13]. Green vegetables which have been treated with SO_2 should, therefore, be dehydrated in the dark.

Artificial ripening of fruits

During the ripening of fruits, the chlorophylls become colorless, thus permitting other colors to show. So far, no readily identifiable fragments of the chlorophyll molecule associated with this phase of complete color disappearance have been found. The chlorophyll molecule appears to break up completely.

Some fruits, however, cannot be left to ripen on the tree since they become so sweet that they soon attract many insects or, at the best, their color will not be uniform. This is the case with bananas, figs, certain varieties of citrus fruits and some others. The public consuming these fruits usually judges the maturity of various fruits by their color. However, it is a well established fact that the color alone is by no means always a reliable indication of maturity. Consequently, methods of artificial ripening and coloring of fruit have been extensively used for many years. These methods actually add no color to that which has been attained naturally by the fruit; they merely cause the green chlorophyll to disappear and permit the previously masked yellow and orange pigments to become fully evident. It is, therefore, an indispensable condition for the coloring of citrus fruit, especially oranges, that the fruit be sufficiently mature. When this process is employed for ripening other fruits (such as bananas) or vegetables (tomatoes, celery), some physiological changes occur, affecting not only the color but also the degree of ripeness.

It has been customary to hasten the coloration of green citrus fruits by means of blue-flame kerosene stoves placed directly in the room in which the fruit is stored, the so-called "sweat rooms". For some time it was thought that the change in color is brought about by heat, but it has been found that the products of combustion are responsible for the hastening of coloration. Further experiments disclosed that the gases responsible for the ripening of the fruit were unsaturated hydrocarbons the specific gravity of which was approximately equal to that of air. These facts suggested ethylene (C_2H_4), and later experiments proved that this gas, or a mixture of other unsaturated hydrocarbons, could effectively bring about the desired change in color in fruits. The mechanism of this reaction is not yet known. The gases merely stimulate the fruit to renewed life activity. During this period, lasting from five to ten days, the fruit continues to respire by inhaling oxygen and expelling carbon dioxide and, as a result, brings about the discoloration of its green pigment.

It is assumed that the presence of ethylene and acetylene affects the permeability of cell membranes and therefore hastens the respiration process[14]. Even one part by volume of ethylene in five million parts of air can produce the effect. The suitable concentration of the gas, however, depends on the time required for coloration, the location where the process is conducted, and the relative quantity of air present in the space not occupied by the fruit (to provide sufficient oxygen for the respiration of the fruit).

Artificial ripening of fruit, a physiological process, requires careful attention to the atmospheric conditions. The temperature must be carefully controlled and kept uniform. The high temperatures that were formerly thought necessary are now known to be actually injurious to the fruit.

The question of humidity is also very important. During the process the fruit loses some water and thus the atmosphere of the coloring room must contain sufficient humidity to prevent shrinkage of the fruit.

Generally it has been found that the CO_2 output during coloring is increased by about 150–250% compared with the normal output. Obviously a sufficient supply of oxygen is necessary for the process. It is recommended, therefore, that the coloring rooms should be thoroughly ventilated at least once daily for a period of 1–2 hours.

In this connection it is interesting to note that the vapors from moldy lemons inoculated with green mold (*Penicillium digitatum* Sacc.) cause a very marked increase in the rate of carbon dioxide evolution and greatly accelerate the color development of sound green lemons. Emanations from a single moldy lemon can produce these effects in as many as 500 fruits[15]. Ethylene has been identified as one of the volatile substances given off by fruits during respiration[16].

The atmospheric conditions necessary for the coloring process, as described above, create at the same time optimum conditions for the development of various diseases in fruits which contain the spores of the organisms responsible for these diseases, such as *Penicillia* (blue and green molds) or *Diplodia* (stem-end rot). In other words, since the fruit continues its normal processes at a quicker pace in the coloring room than on the tree, the spores will also act more quickly if they are present in the fruit.

The latest improved methods of ripening fruits require rooms equipped with air-conditioning apparatus to maintain the requisite constant atmos-

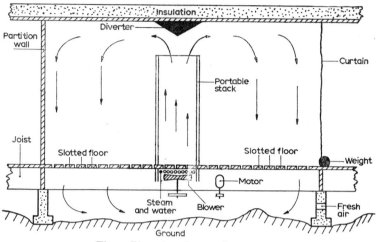

Fig. 2. Plan of modern curing room.

pheric conditions. The ethylene gas, accurately measured by a special metering trickle device, is released into the entering air which is blown through the slotted floor. The constantly changing air, which is humidified, prevents the accumulation of CO_2 and excessive humidity and thereby lessens the danger of decay. The whole process may take 24–48 hours.

REFERENCES

[1] TANG PEI-SUNG, *Green Thralldom*, Allen & Unwin, London, 1949.
[2] I. B. THOMAS, *Endeavour*, 17 (1958) 156; *Progress in Biophys. and Biophys. Chem.*, 5 (1955) 109.
[3] R. WILLSTAETTER AND A. STOLL, *Untersuchungen über das Chlorophyll*, Springer-Verlag, Berlin, 1913.
[4] N. TH. DE SAUSSURE, *Recherches chimiques sur la végétation*, Nyon, Paris, 1804.
[5] H. FISCHER, *Chem. Rev.*, 20 (1937) 41.
[6] M. STRELL et al., *Angew. Chem.*, 72 (1960) 167.
[7] R. B. WOODWARD et al., *J. Am. Chem. Soc.*, 82 (1960) 3800.
[8] H. FISCHER, "Progress of chlorophyll chemistry", *Naturwissenschaften*, 28 (1940) 401.
[9] D. SHEMIN AND C. S. RUSSEL, *J. Am. Chem. Soc.*, 75 (1953) 487.
[10] E. J. HAERTL AND A. E. MARTELL, "Metal Chelates in Plant and Animal Nutrition", *J. Agr. Food Chem.*, 4 (1956) 26.
[11] S. ARONOFF, "The Chemistry of Chlorophyll with Special Reference to Foods", *Advances in Food Research*, 4 (1953) 133.
[12] J. S. BLAIR AND T. B. AYRES, "Protection of Natural Green Pigment in the Canning of Peas". *J. Ind. Eng. Chem.*, 35 (1943) 85.
[13] E. I. RABINOWITCH, *Photosynthesis*, Interscience Publishing Co., New York, 1956.
[14] F. F. NORD, *Ergeb. Enzymforsch.*, 1 (1932) 77.
[15] J. B. BIALE AND A. D. SHEPHERD, "Respiration of Citrus Fruits in Relation to Metabolism of Fungi: I. Effects of Emanations of *Penicillium digitatum* Sacc. on Lemons", *Am. J. Botany*, 28 (1941) 263.
[16] E. V. MILLER, J. R. WINSTON AND D. F. FISHER, *J. Agr. Research*, 60 (1940) 269.

SELECTED BIBLIOGRAPHY TO CHAPTER 2

ARONOFF, S., "The Chemistry of Chlorophyll with Special Reference to Foods", *Advances in Food Research*, 4 (1953) 134.

BLAIR, J. S. AND AYRES, T. B., "Protection of Natural Green Pigment in the Canning of Peas", *Ind. Eng. Chem.*, 35 (1943) 85.

FISCHER, H., "Progress of Chlorophyll Chemistry", *Naturwissenschaften*, 28 (1941) 401.

MacKINNEY, G. AND WEAST, C. A., "Color Changes in Green Vegatables", *Ind. Eng. Chem.*, 32 (1940) 392.

TANG PEI-SUNG, *Green Thralldom*, Allen and Unwin, London, 1949.

WILLSTAETTER, R. AND STOLL, A., *Untersuchungen über das Chlorophyll*, Springer-Verlag, Berlin, 1913.

CHAPTER 3

CAROTENOIDS

The yellow companions

R. WILLSTAETTER

Occurrence

During the discussion of chlorophyll (Chapter 2) mention was made of two yellow–orange pigments which constantly accompany it in the plastids, namely, carotene and xanthophyll. The two belong to a large group of pigments, the carotenoids, widely distributed in the plant and animal kingdoms. The carotenoids are yellow–orange to purple in color, insoluble in water but soluble in fats and organic solvents; they are classed, therefore, as lipochrome pigments.

The carotenoids embrace two groups:

(a) *carotenes*—hydrocarbons, soluble in petroleum ether but only slightly soluble in ethanol;

(b) *xanthophylls*—oxygenated derivatives of the carotenes; these compounds are alcohols, aldehydes and acids, soluble in ethanol but not in petroleum ether.

In the higher plants the carotenoids are found in the leaves, together with chlorophyll, as well as in many other parts of the plant. They are found in squash, in carrots (from which the name carotene was derived) and in sweet potatoes; these generally accumulate hydrocarbons (β-carotene) rather than xanthophylls. They are also found in fruits, *e.g.*, tomatoes, peaches, all citrus fruits, banana skins, squashes, paprika, red peppers, rose-hips and many others.

Fruits containing carotenoids may be divided into four main categories:

(a) those containing in their plastids small concentrations of normal "plastid carotenoids" in addition to chlorophyll *a* and *b*, *e.g.*, elderberries;

(b) those in which ripening causes a marked synthesis of acyclic carotenoids, such as lycopene, but little β-carotene, *e.g.*, tomatoes, watermelons and apricots;

(c) fruits in which the main pigment is β-carotene or a mixture of xanthophylls accompanied by only small amounts of acyclic carotenoids, *e.g.*, red palm, citru ς fruit;

(d) fruits in which the main constituents of the carotenoid pigment are specific xanthophylls such as *capsanthin*, while both cyclic or acyclic carotenes are only minor components.

Carotenoids constitute, also, the principal pigments of certain yellow, orange and red flowers and of many microorganisms (red and green algae, fungi and photosynthetic bacteria). They are also found in all animals. While plants and microorganisms synthesize their carotenoids, those present in the tissues of higher animals are derived from dietary sources. Animal products, therefore, such as milk, butter and egg yolk, contain carotenoids in their lipoid tissues. An interesting carotenoid, *astexanthin*, constitutes the red principle in shrimp, lobster and salmon.

Structure

Carotene was first extracted from carrots in 1831 by WACKENRODER, but another 100 years elapsed before its structure was definitely established by KARRER in 1930. All carotenoids belong to the class of "polyenes" in organic chemistry, namely, long chains of conjugated double bonds. KUHN AND WINTERSTEIN, working on series of compounds containing many conjugated bonds, have shown that the longer such molecules are the more intense is their color, as shown by the following series synthesized by them:

$$C_6H_5 \cdot CH = CH \cdot C_5H_5,$$
diphenyl ethylene—colorless;

$$C_6H_5 \cdot CH = CH - CH = CH \cdot C_6H_5,$$
diphenyl butadiene—yellowish;

$$C_6H_5 \cdot CH = CH - CH = CH - CH = CH \cdot C_6H_5,$$
diphenyl hexatriene—greenish;

$$C_6H_5 \cdot CH = CH - CH = CH - CH = CH - CH = CH \cdot C_6H_5,$$
diphenyl octatetraene—chrome yellow;

$$C_6H_5 \cdot CH = CH - CH = CH - CH = CH - CH = CH - CH = CH \cdot C_6H_5,$$
diphenyl decapentaene—orange.

The work of these investigators greatly advanced the knowledge of this field, but real progress was achieved only recently with the introduction of chromatography, which permits the separation of individual carotenoids. By this method, several scientists, notably KARRER, KUHN, LEDERER and ZECHMEISTER, have been able to determine the structure of many carotenoids.

References p. 27

The second consideration to be taken into account regarding the structure of all carotenoids is their isoprenic nature. Similar to the phytyl group in the chlorophyll molecule, carotenoids are built of isoprene units:

$$CH_2 = C - CH = CH_2$$
$$|$$
$$CH_3$$

isoprene

However, while no double bonds are present in phytol, the carotenoids show the characteristic isoprenic unsaturation.

It is also obvious from the structure of carotenoids that in unsaturated compounds of this type a very large number of geometrical isomers of the *cis* and *trans* configurations are possible. However, as has been shown by ZECHMEISTER[1] and his collaborators, to whom we owe most of our present knowledge of carotenoids, the bulk of carotenoids found in nature appear to have an all-*trans* configuration and only very few *cis* isomers are known.

The carotenoids are characterized by the possession of a bilaterally symmetrical C_{40} skeleton, each half of which can be considered from the formal structural stand-point to consist of four isoprene units joined head to tail, so that the projecting methyl groups assume a 1:5 relationship. These two C_{20} halves, however, are joined tail to tail so that the two central methyl groups of the molecule are brought into a 1:6 relationship.

The following are the structural formulae of α-, β-, and γ-carotene and of lycopene:

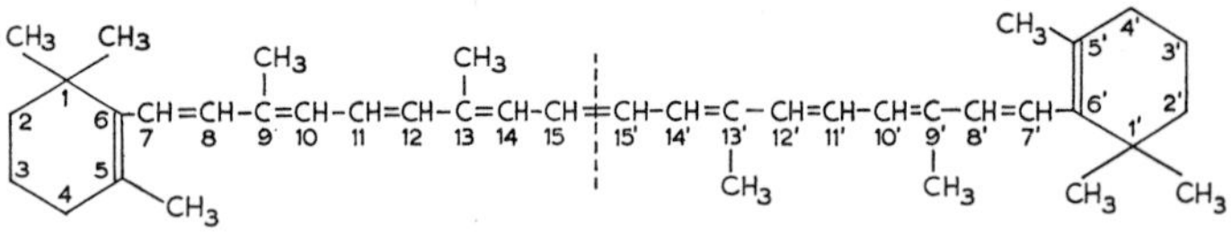

β-carotene (provitamin A)

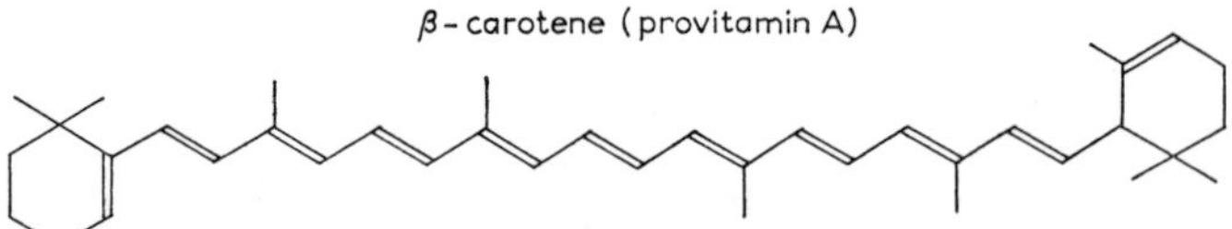

α-carotene

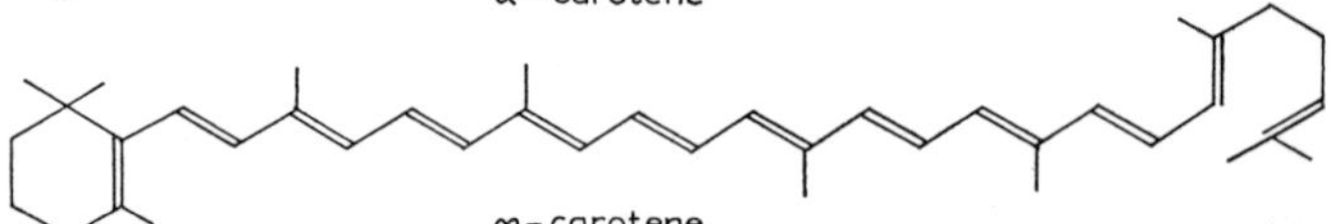

γ-carotene

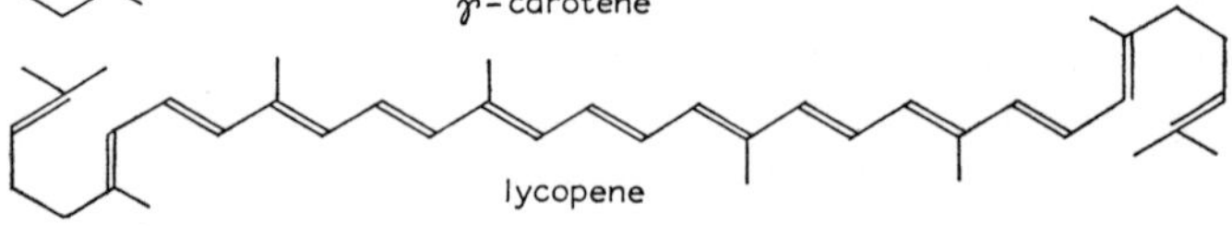

lycopene

It will be noted that the differences between the four formulae are relatively slight, mainly involving the position of the terminal double bonds. However, these slight differences have a profound effect on the nature of these substances. While β-carotene has two complete ionone rings at each end of the molecule, γ-carotene has one of these rings open, and lycopene has no ionone rings. Possession of at least one complete ionone ring is necessary for a carotenoid substance to give rise to vitamin A which is, in fact, an alcohol made up from half of the β-carotene molecule:

vitamin A

This is the reason why β-carotene is often designated as "provitamin A". While theoretically one molecule of β-carotene should give rise to two molecules of vitamin A, in reality somewhat more than one molecule is created. Vitamin A, the vitamin concerned with growth and prevention of *xerophthalmia* (night blindness) (*cf.* Chapter 14), is not found in plants except in the form of its precursor, β-carotene. Animals, however, are able to transform carotene into vitamin A with the aid of intestinal mucose. It is then carried by the blood into the liver where it is stored. Therefore, herbivorous animals obtain their requirement for vitamin A from carotenes in plants, while carnivorous animals obtain their requirement by eating the liver or meat of other animals or fish.

OLCOTT AND McCAMIN[2] have reported the isolation from liver extract of an enzyme *carotenase*, which is capable of converting carotenes into vitamin A *in vitro*. This, however, has not been definitely confirmed.

Xanthophyll ($C_{40}H_{56}O_2$), the second yellow companion of chlorophyll, is a dihydroxy derivative of β-carotene, the two hydroxyl groups being attached to the ionone rings. Xanthophyll (which is found in egg yolk) occurs in two isomeric forms, α and β. The structural formula of β-xanthophyll (lutein) is:

β-xanthophyll (lutein)

Cryptoxanthin, which contains only one hydroxyl group, is another example of a xanthophyll. It is one of the chief pigments in yellow corn, paprika, papaya and mandarin orange.

Cryptoxanthin and β-xanthophyll were shown by ZECHMEISTER AND TURZON[3] to be present in the pigments of orange peel (*Citrus aurantium*) in

cryptoxanthin

the form of esters. Saponification, followed by fractional extraction of these pigments with petroleum ether and methanol (90%) yielded a carotene fraction (28.1 mg/kg peel) and a xanthophyll fraction (49.8 mg/kg peel). Both fractions were examined chromatographically. The bulk (95%) of the carotene fraction was identified as crystalline cryptoxanthin ($C_{40}H_{56}O$); this fraction also contained β-carotene and traces of α-carotene. β-Xanthophyll was found to constitute about a third of the xanthophyll fraction.

A more recent investigation of a similar nature is that of CURL[4] who separated the pigments of "Valencia Orange Juice" by counter-current distribution in a petroleum ether–methanol (99%) system. A large number of carotenoids were isolated, some of them in quite high proportions:

carotenoids containing no free OH
$$\begin{cases} \text{α-carotene} & 0.6\%; \\ \text{β-carotene} & 1.3\%; \\ \text{zeta carotene} & 3.1\%; \\ \text{violaxanthin} & 34.9\%; \end{cases}$$

carotenoids containing one free OH
$$\begin{cases} \text{cryptoxanthin} & 4.8\%; \\ \text{lutein} & 7.4\%; \\ \text{zeaxanthin} & 5.6\%; \\ \text{antheroxanthin} & 8.2\%; \\ \text{luteoxanthin} & 15.3\%, \text{ etc.} \end{cases}$$

Whereas here the hydrocarbon carotenes are about 40% and the oxygenated xanthophylls constitute the remaining 60% of the total carotenoids, other investigators[4a] found that natural orange juices and concentrates from various sources contain only about 2 to 5% of true carotenes the remaining being the xanthophylls.

All xanthophylls are invariably present in the cell as esters of linoleic, oleic, palmitic, linolenic, stearic and myristic acids. In fruits, the xanthophylls occur as *psysalien* and *helenien*, *i.e.* dipalmitic esters of zeaxanthin and lutein, respectively.

Biosynthesis

A probable biosynthetic pathway for carotenoids has been recently indicated by GOODWIN[5]. The appearance of mevalonic acid among the breakdown products of β-carotene indicates that this compound is an effective precursor of β-carotene. Mevalonic acid in its turn is most probably synthesized from acetic acid by the aid of coenzyme A, as follows:

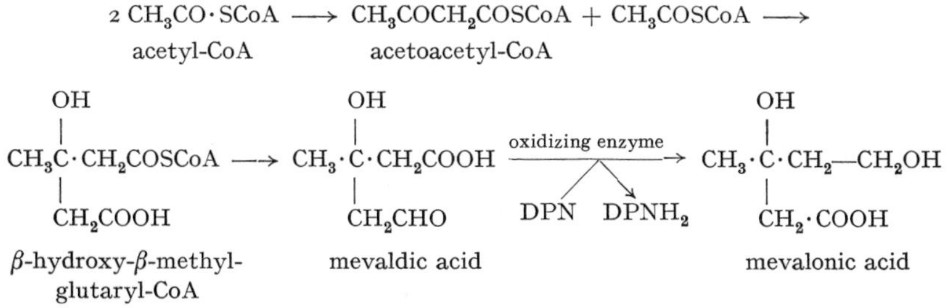

$$2\ CH_3CO \cdot SCoA \longrightarrow CH_3COCH_2COSCoA + CH_3COSCoA \longrightarrow$$

$$\text{acetyl-CoA} \qquad\qquad \text{acetoacetyl-CoA}$$

$$\underset{\substack{|\\CH_2COOH}}{\overset{\substack{OH\\|}}{CH_3C \cdot CH_2COSCoA}} \longrightarrow \underset{\substack{|\\CH_2CHO}}{\overset{\substack{OH\\|}}{CH_3 \cdot C \cdot CH_2COOH}} \xrightarrow[\text{DPN}\quad\text{DPNH}_2]{\text{oxidizing enzyme}} \underset{\substack{|\\CH_2 \cdot COOH}}{\overset{\substack{OH\\|}}{CH_3 \cdot C \cdot CH_2 - CH_2OH}}$$

β-hydroxy-β-methyl-glutaryl-CoA   mevaldic acid   mevalonic acid

The incorporation of mevalonate into isoprenoid polymers may be represented by three alternative schemes:

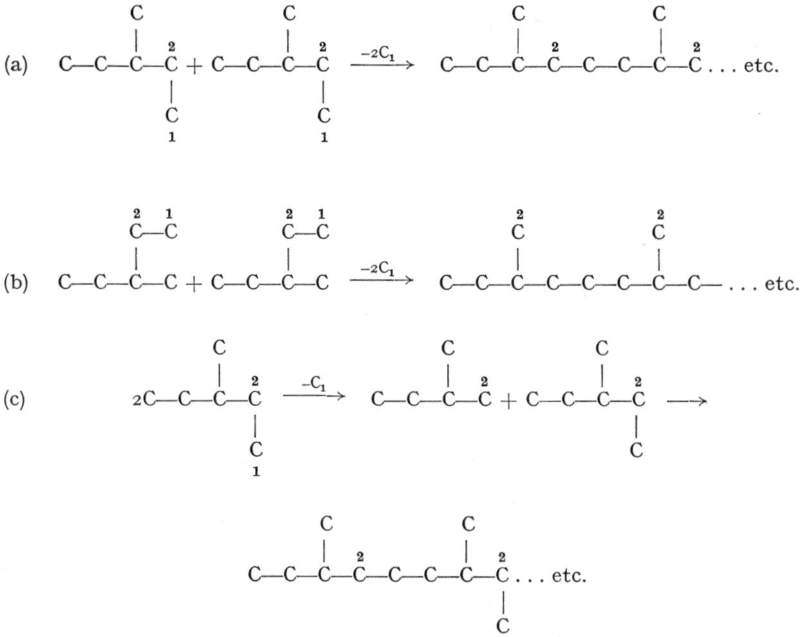

(a)

(b)

(c)

As has already been mentioned, many natural products in addition to the carotenoids have isoprenic structures. Phytol, the terpenes, rubber, and parts of the molecules of the vitamin E and the vitamin K groups are isoprenoid. It will be shown further (Chapter 14), that there is now ample evidence that all steroids originate from isoprenic compounds.

RUZICKA[6] called attention to the fact that in the biosynthesis of these isoprenoid substances the isoprene units may be linked in a "regular" (head-to-tail) arrangement as in terpenes and the halves of the β-carotene molecule, or in an "irregular linkage" as illustrated by the linkage between two symmetrical halves of carotenoid compounds:

$$
\begin{array}{c}
\text{C} \qquad\qquad\qquad\qquad \text{C} \\
| \qquad\qquad\qquad\qquad | \\
\text{regular arrangement} \quad -\text{C}-\text{C}-\text{C}-\text{C}\text{------}\text{C}-\text{C}-\text{C}-\text{C}-
\end{array}
$$

$$
\begin{array}{c}
\text{C} \qquad\qquad\qquad\qquad \text{C} \\
| \qquad\qquad\qquad\qquad | \\
\text{irregular arrangement} \quad -\text{C}-\text{C}-\text{C}-\text{C}\text{------}\text{C}-\text{C}-\text{C}-\text{C}-
\end{array}
$$

This "isoprene rule" has been valuable in the determination of the structure of terpenes and more recently in the study and biosynthesis of carotenoids and also squalene, the apparent precursor of cholesterol. The available data on the synthesis of rubber give further support to the hypothesis that the biosynthesis of all isoprenoids involves the initial conversion of C_2 units derived from acetic acid (as acetyl-coenzyme A) to a compound such as mevalonic acid followed by the formation of larger isoprenic compounds[7].

The existence of a number of hydrogenated derivatives (the phytoene series) of lycopene as minor polyene components of tomatoes led to the suggestion that they were intermediates in the biosynthesis of lycopene.

The breakdown of carotenoid substances

When the fruit ripens, the green chlorophyll disappears, or its degradation products become colorless, and its permanent yellow companions, carotenes and xanthophylls manifest themselves. The possibility that the phytyl group in chlorophyll may directly dehydrogenate to form carotenoids is refuted by the fact that the amount of carotenoids present often exceeds the corresponding amount of phytol, which was contained in the chlorophyll. Table I illustrating the autumn change of color in the leaves of sycamore trees after plucking supports the fact that carotenoids are not created at the expense of chlorophyll:

TABLE I

Days after plucking	Color of leaf	% of original quantity		
		Chlorophyll	Xanthophyll	Carotene
0	green	100	100	100
3	light green	59	89	100
5	yellow	16	72	95
7	brown	2	45	63

Owing to the unsaturated nature of the carotenoids, they are apt to oxidize very quickly, particularly at the double bonds thus forming epoxides. There is, however, some indication that the oxidation and subsequent disintegration of the carotenoid is initiated at the end of the molecule and does not occur at random; the process always takes place at the open end rather than at the terminal ionone ring. The final breakdown of the carotenoid molecule results in the formation of ionone, a ketone with the smell of violets:

β-ionone

This disintegration takes place when molecular oxygen is available. Thus, hay which has been dried in a field in the sun smells of ionone, its total carotene content having been practically destroyed. Alfalfa, for instance, which is particularly valuable as chicken feed or cattle fodder due to its carotene content, is nowadays dried in mobile rotary dryers in the field immediately after harvest using the combustion gases to prevent oxidation of the carotenes.

The effect of heat treatment on some plant carotenoids has been studied by JOYCE[8] who showed that carotenoids undergo alteration in their molecular shape whereby unstable poly-*cis* forms are changed into all-*trans* forms, these latter giving unstable mono- and di-*cis* configurations. Both the color of the plant tissues as well as the provitamin A potency are altered during such treatments. The mechanisms by which the carotenoids are destroyed during processing are still unknown.

Dehydrated vegetables, such as carrots, are quickly oxidized if they are not protected by air-tight containers. A method has been devised by the Western Regional Research Branch of the U.S.D.A. in Albany, Calif. which prevents destruction of carotene in dehydrated carrots by coating them with a thin monomolecular film of starch.

References p. 27

The bleached color of the carotenoids, caused by oxidation, is often a very important indication of the deterioration of a particular food product containing these pigments. Such is the case, for instance, in the deterioration of essential oils which, in the natural state, are usually colored by carotenoids but which become bleached upon oxidation.

In general, carotenoid pigments present few problems during canning processes. However, since they are lipochromes distributed in the chromoplasts in close proximity to oil droplets, and since they are often bound to lipids as esters of fatty acids, care should be taken to prevent deterioration of the lipid moiety. Such deterioration is usually caused by the lipoxidase enzyme. To prevent this occurring, antioxidants may be used where practicable[9] (see also Chapter 16).

Another product of the breakdown of carotenoids is probably *crocetin*, a water-soluble yellow compound which seems to be fairly widespread in the plant kingdom as a sugar ester:

crocetin

Crocetin, a dicarboxylic acid with the general formula $C_{20}H_{24}O_4$, is not a carotenoid in the strict sense, but it is most probably derived in the cell from a true carotenoid by oxidation at both ends of the molecule[10].

It has generally been suggested that the color changes occurring in ripening fruits have much in common with the fading of foliage in its senescent stages. Unfortunately, the composition of "autumn carotenoids" is still insufficiently known.

Functions of carotenoids

For a long time carotenoids have been regarded, as have many other secondary products, as plant waste products or, at best, as compounds created by the plant to invite insects for cross-polination. However, such theories could not explain the invariable presence of carotenoids in chloroplasts alongside chlorophyll. The carotenoids are constantly synthesized and are specifically incorporated into the structure of the photosynthetic apparatus. It was demonstrated long ago that *all* the plastid pigments, and not merely chlorophyll, could mediate photosynthetic oxygen evolution and it is now generally accepted that light absorbed by the so-called "accessory pigments", the carotenoids, contributes to photosynthesis through the ability of these pigments to transmit the accumulated light energy to the chlorophyll.

Recently, it has been shown that in the absence of carotenoid pigments the photosynthetic apparatus is rapidly destroyed by chlorophyll-catalyzed photooxidation and it is suggested, therefore, that the essential function of carotenoids in the photosynthetic apparatus is to prevent or minimize photooxidative damage by chlorophyll.

REFERENCES

[1] L. ZECHMEISTER, *Chem. Rev.*, 34 (1944) 267.

[2] H. S. OLCOTT AND D. C. McCAMIN, "Carotenase; Transformation of Carotene in Vitamin A *in Vitro*", *J. Biol. Chem.*, 94 (1931) 185.

[3] L. ZECHMEISTER AND P. TURZON, "Über das Pigment der Orangenschale". *Naturwissenschaften*, 19 (1931) 307.

[4] A. L. CURL, *Food Research*, 20 (1955) 371.

[4a] H. ROTHER, "Über die Bestimmung von Carotin und Carotinoiden in Orangensäften", *Mineralwasser-Zeitung*, Stuttgart, 11 (1961) 40.

[5] T. W. GOODWIN, "The biosynthesis and function of the carotenoid pigments", *Advances in Enzymol.*, 21 (1959) 295.

[6] L. RUZICKA, *Experientia*, 9 (1953) 357.

[7] R. STANIER, "Carotenoid pigments: problems of synthesis and function", *Harvey Lectures*, Ser. LIV, (1960) 219.

[8] A. JOYCE, The effect of heat treatment on some plant carotenoids, *Proc. Symp. Color in Foods*, National Academy of Sciences, November, *1953*.

[9] T. E. WEIER AND C. R. STOCKING, Histological changes induced in fruits and vegetables by processing, *Advances in Food Research*, 2 (1949) 297.

[10] K. PAECH, Colour development in flowers, *Ann. Rev. Plant Physiol.*, 6 (1955) 273.

SELECTED BIBLIOGRAPHY TO CHAPTER 3

GOODWIN, T. W., *The Comparative Biochemistry of the Carotenoids*, Chapman & Hall London, 1952; Biosynthesis and function of carotenoid Pigments, *Advances in Enzymol.*, 21 (1959) 295.

ISLER, O., OFHER, A. AND SIEMERS, G. F., Synthetic carotenoids for use as food colors, *Food Technol.*, 12 (1958) 520.

KARRER, P. AND JUCKER, E., *The Carotenoids*, Van Nostrand, Princeton, 1950.

MacKINNEY, G. AND CHICHESTER, C. O., The color problem in foods, *Advances in Food Research*, 5 (1954) 301; *Proc. Symp. Color in Foods*, National Academy of Sciences, November, *1953*.

STANIER, R., Carotenoid pigments: problems of synthesis and function, *Harvey Lectures*, Ser. LIV, (1960) 219.

ZECHMEISTER, L. AND DEUEL JR., H. J., Stereochemical configuration and provitamin A activity, *Arch. Biochem. and Biophys.*, 36 (1952) 81.

CHAPTER 4

PHOTOSYNTHESIS

Production of vital air

INGEN-HOUSZ, 1779

It is well-known that green plants are capable of converting light energy into chemical energy by assimilating simple inorganic substances, H_2O and CO_2, of very low potential energy and transforming them into carbohydrates of high potential energy; this is achieved with the aid of the green plant pigments, the chlorophylls.

The transformation of light energy into chemical energy is not a rare occurrence—it always takes place to some extent when light falls on a body capable of absorbing it. However, when this happens, the compounds formed during such a photochemical reaction, are very unstable and decompose quickly by liberating the absorbed energy in the form of heat. An example of such a reaction are textiles colored by organic dyestuffs which soon become bleached in the sun. While such photochemical reactions are reversible, photosynthesis is not reversible and the new compounds created during this process are stable, energy-rich organic compounds which steadily accumulate in the cells in which they are formed.

Activation energy

In relation to this photosynthetic process, two questions present themselves:

(a) Could the organic matter upon this planet have been synthesized from CO_2 and H_2O by means of heat alone without the aid of light rays?

The answer to this question is negative, for when the Earth was created from premordial dust the prevailing temperature was so high that any organic matter, in itself an extremely unstable configuration, would have decomposed into CO_2 and H_2O. Furthermore, under those conditions there would have been hardly any free oxygen available since the oxygen would have been bound to many other elements in the form of stable oxides. It is obvious, therefore, that *the only possible source of the free oxygen present today in the atmosphere surrounding our planet derives its origin from green plants.*

(b) Why does not the organic matter, created by photosynthesis, oxidize quickly into CO_2 and water?

Let us consider a simple example of an organic gas, such as methane in a mixture with an appropriate amount of oxygen exposed to light in a suitable glass container at ordinary temperatures. Nothing will ever happen to such a mixture. To start the reaction between the organic matter (methane) and the oxygen, one needs to add "activation energy" in the form of heat or an electric spark. This is due to the fact that at ordinary prevailing temperatures the velocities at which the molecules of gas move about are rather low, and at small distances the molecules repel each other. Raising the temperature will increase the number of impacts of the molecules, since the kinetic energy is directly proportional to the absolute temperatures. With increase in their kinetic energy the molecules will then be capable of overcoming the repelling forces and of approaching the centers of gravitation of each other so that the given reaction may take place. In the absence of such "activation energy" any reaction is said to face a "potential barrier".

Let us exemplify this mechanically: A ball (Fig. 3) brought up to the top

Fig. 3.

of a hill possesses quite considerable potential energy and could transform it into kinetic energy and heat by rolling down the hill, if it were not for the small barrier placed in front of it. In order to roll down, the ball has to overcome this "potential barrier" and, in order to do so, a small amount of "activation energy" is required.

The same state of affairs exists in the example of the chemical reaction between methane and oxygen gases: in order to oxidize the organic matter into CO_2 and H_2O, two stable oxides, a minimum energy is required before any change will take place The activation energy of a single reaction can be described as a barrier of potential energy of a definite level, which separates

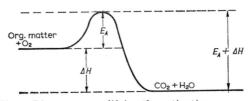

Fig. 4. Diagram exemplifying the activation energy.

two minima of potential energy, those of the initial and final stages of the reaction (Fig. 4).

In the reaction:

$$CH_4 + 2 O_2 \rightarrow CO_2 + 2 H_2O$$

E_a is the activation energy and ΔH the heat of reaction. For this reaction to run in the opposite direction, the total energy required will be $E_a + \Delta H$. The configuration of the three atoms at the top of the "potential barrier" depends on the atoms themselves, and on their energy relationship. This is the so-called *"activated state"*.

The velocity of a chemical reaction is, therefore, proportional not to the total number of molecules present but, instead, to the number of molecules which possess the necessary activation energy. Such activation energy may be caused by thermal collision, which normally raises the rate of a reaction. The relationship between the rate of a reaction, the activation energy and temperature is expressed by the formula of ARRHENIUS:

$$K = A e^{-E_a/RT}$$

where K = rate of reaction quotient;
A = constant;
e = the natural logarithmic base;
E_a = activation energy;
R = the gas constant (1.99 cal/mol);
T = absolute temperature.

The rate of a reaction is, therefore, an exponential function of the activation energy and a reciprocal exponential function of the temperature. In other words, the slightest change in the activation energy or in the temperature will bring about enormous changes in the rate of the reaction.

All this does not, however, answer the third question:

(c) If every reaction requires activation energy, usually in the form of heat, how can the reactions in our body proceed at the comparatively low temperature of about 37°C, at which our foods are "burned" into CO_2 and H_2O, while supplying our bodies with the required energy for work, growth, etc.?

The answer to this question is that this is possible only if the reaction can be divided into several stages and if catalysts can be used at each step of the reaction, since catalysts, particularly biological catalysts, called *enzymes*, have the peculiar property of *appreciably lowering the activation energy required* by a given reaction.

Let us assume that for the reaction:

$$A_2 + B_2 \rightarrow 2 AB$$

a catalyst (enzyme) has been found which will first combine with one of the reactants to form the complex:

$$A_2 + E \rightarrow A_2E$$

which, in its turn, will react with the second reactant thus freeing the catalyst again:

$$A_2E + B_2 \rightarrow 2\,AB + E$$

The original reaction thus takes place in two stages and the required activation energy was in each step considerably smaller.

Photosynthesis is, in fact, one such reaction, catalyzed by a number of enzymes, which starting at the lower energy level forms with CO_2 and water organic matter of high potential energy (see Fig. 5).

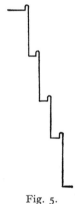

Fig. 5.

Light

Photosynthesis needs light energy, however the first requirement for it is that light rays should be absorbed by the plant. A light ray meeting a body can be either *reflected* (if the body is white), or *penetrative* (if the body is transparent), or *absorbed* (if the body is colored, *i.e.*, contains some pigments that absorb a part of the light spectrum). In the green tissues of the plant, this role of light absorbance is performed by the green pigments, chlorophyll *a* and *b* and their yellow companions, carotene and xanthophyll. Up-to-now, no reaction has been found in which photosynthesis can proceed in the absence of chlorophyll.

The visible spectrum comprises electromagnetic rays the wave length of which ranges from approx. 4000 Å at the violet end of the spectrum up to 8000 Å at its red end. Photosynthesis takes place approximately in this range.

References p. 45

Light energy, however, is not infinitely divisible. Light energy, in the same way as the atoms of the matter, has its smallest indivisible particle, the *photon*. The amount of energy possessed by each photon, the *quantum*, is directly proportional to the frequency of a given wave and is, therefore, inversely proportional to the wave length: the larger the wave length the smaller is its quantum. In the red waves of the visible spectrum, which are longer, this light energy is only some 100 times greater than the Brownian movement. On the other hand, the quanta of the blue part of the spectrum is about 200 times larger and that of the ultraviolet even more.

According to EINSTEIN, a photochemical reaction can take place only if the light is absorbed in quantities of one quantum per molecule and if this quantum is large enough to perform the task. For example, the photosynthetic reaction cannot take place in the presence of infrared waves since they are long and, therefore, their quanta are too small, even at high intensities. Considering monochromatic light and moving slowly in the direction of the blue end of the spectrum a wave length should be found whose quanta are sufficiently large to start the photosynthetic reaction. In fact, only visible light is suitable for this. Outside the range of visible light, we have at one end the infrared waves, whose quanta are too small for photosynthesis, and on the other side the ultraviolet waves, with large quanta, most of which are, however, screened off by the ozone layer in the upper ionosphere before the sun rays reach the Earth.

On their path to Earth the visible rays are not absorbed by the atmosphere containing oxygen, nitrogen, CO_2 and water vapors as they would, for instance, be absorbed by chlorine gas, which is green (this is why a mixture of Cl and H will explode on exposure to light rays with the resultant HCl formation). The green color of chlorophyll acts as such an absorbent for the visible rays when they reach the Earth. A simple question presents itself, however: chlorophyll itself is a complicated organic compound, and if, as we rightly assume, photosynthesis is the only source of organic matter on earth, how then could photosynthesis have occurred before chlorophyll ever put in its appearance?

There is only one possible answer to this baffling question: there must have been some other process capable of creating organic matter before photosynthesis, let it be called *"proto-photosynthesis"*. At that time, there was no chlorophyll, but there was no oxygen either and, therefore, no ozone layer to prevent the passage of the ultraviolet rays through the atmosphere. At that time, the ultraviolet rays, whose quanta are quite large, could easily give the activation energy to the CO_2 and to the water needed to start the photosynthetic reaction, without necessitating the presence of the green pigment. It is true that as the organic matter could be formed so easily under

these conditions it could also easily disintegrate under the influence of the
same ultraviolet rays. If, however, this reaction took place in water the
ultraviolet rays could not very easily destroy the organic matter. Thus
biologists of today are of the opinion that life was first created in water.

  This theory of the possible existence of a proto-photosynthetic period
recently received support from the simple experiments performed by MILLER
of the University of Chicago.

  MILLER[1] enclosed in a sealed glass tube the gases methane, ammonia,
hydrogen, CO_2 and water vapor (a mixture which was probably the prevailing atmosphere during the proto-photosynthetic period), and rotated
the tube in front of a weak light source obtained by repeated electrical
discharges. A source of this kind is rich in ultraviolet rays which were
probably prevailing at that time on the Earth. At the end of the first week,
MILLER found in his tube amino acids, the "building stones" of proteins,
the most important constituents of all living matter. Similar experiments
were performed by ELLENBOGEN at the University of Pittsburgh using direct
illumination with ultraviolet rays. Although these experiments have not
created life synthetically as yet they give ample support for the assumption
that in some way, on similar lines to these, life was started for the first time
on earth.

  The chlorophylls and carotenoids are those pigments which absorb most
of the light spectrum except the green and the yellow colors, as shown in the
accompanying graphs. The absorption spectra of chlorophyll a and that of
β-carotene are shown in Fig. 6 and a combination of graphs A and B are
represented as graph A in Fig. 7. HAXO AND BLINKS[2] measured the effectiveness of photosynthesis using the same amount of light but different wave

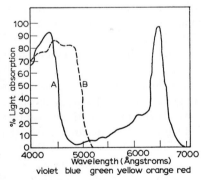

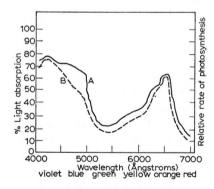

Fig. 6. Absorption spectra of the chlorophylls (A) and of β-carotene (B).

Fig. 7. Absorption spectra of green algae
Ulva (A) compared with the effectiveness of photosynthesis (B) (ref. 2).

References p. 45

lengths and obtained graph B in Fig. 7, which is very similar to the sum of absorption spectra of both pigments.

This experiment shows that the total quantity of light absorbed during the process is all engaged in photosynthesis. Furthermore, by comparing graphs A and B, one can see that at wave lengths of 4800–5000 Å, where the maximum absorption is caused by carotenoids, the photosynthetic reaction was stronger than would have been expected with chlorophyll alone. This indicates that the "yellow companions" also play a definite role. However, since no photosynthesis has ever been discovered in the absence of chlorophyll, one is compelled to assume that the carotenoids, although they absorb light energy, transfer it immediately to the chlorophyll. This transfer of energy from one pigment to another is already known in chemistry.

When light energy is absorbed by a certain material, several things may happen:

(1) The absorbed energy affects only the thermal energy of the molecules (Brownian movement). This is the case, for instance, when rays of long wavelength, such as infrared waves, are absorbed. This results only in temperature elevation and obviously it is not the case in photosynthesis.

(2) When, however, visible rays are absorbed by a given compound, their action affects the atom: they may displace one of the electrons from its regular path around the nucleus of the atom. The displaced electron will now move in an orbit further away from the center of the atom, having acquired a higher potential energy. If the quantum of the ray which struck the atom is large enough the dislocation of the electron may be larger and the atom may ultimately lose the electron completely—this is the *photoelectric effect*.

(3) An electron displaced not too far from the center of the atom will sooner or later return to its orbit and will then give up its extra energy in one of two ways. If this happens soon after the absorption of the ray, the phenomenon caused is *fluorescence*. If some time elapses between the light absorption and the return of the energy, it will cause *phosphorescence*. Both phenomena are of a *photochemical effect*. This is the most common effect occurring during photosynthesis.

The chlorophylls possess the capacity for fluorescence and, in so far as this can be measured, one can obtain an idea of how much energy has been invested during the photochemical reaction. If the photosynthetic reaction stops or slow downs, the fluorescence will proportionally alter. After the molecule has absorbed a quantum of light, the displaced electron shatters the entire molecule, which now becomes quite unstable and, as a result, the molecule may undergo some important changes in quite another part of it. The true mechanism of the photochemical effect in the chlorophyll molecule during the photosynthesis has not yet been elucidated.

The various stages of photosynthesis

The overall reaction of photosynthesis may be expressed as follows:

$$CO_2 + H_2O \xrightarrow[\text{chlorophyll}]{Nh\nu} (CH_2O) + O_2 \qquad (1)$$

where $Nh\nu$ is the number of quanta required per mol and the term (CH_2O) designates "organic matter", without stating, at the moment, its exact nature.

One could assume from this equation that only one atom of oxygen may be derived from water while the other one may come from CO_2, or that both atoms may be derived from carbon dioxide. The fact is, however, that the only source of oxygen is water, as has been successfully demonstrated by experimentally using water containing the O^{18} isotope. The correct equation will therefore be:

$$CO_2 + 2 H_2O^{18} \xrightarrow{Nh\nu} (CH_2O) + H_2O + O_2^{18} \qquad (2)$$

This is an oxidation–reduction reaction in which one compound is oxidized by another one which is simultaneously reduced. In biochemistry it is customary to present oxidation as a detraction of hydrogen instead of an addition of oxygen. Accordingly, oxidation can be presented as hydrogen transfer, as follows:

$$\underset{\text{acceptor}}{A} + \underset{\substack{\text{hydrogen} \\ \text{donor}}}{DH_2} \rightarrow \underset{\substack{\text{reduced} \\ \text{acceptor}}}{AH_2} + \underset{\substack{\text{oxidized} \\ \text{donor}}}{D} \qquad (3)$$

In photosynthesis the water (DH_2) is the hydrogen donor and CO_2 is the hydrogen acceptor (A). At this point it is relevant to mention that some microorganisms and algae are capable of carrying out photosynthesis with compounds other than water. Thus, for instance, green sulfur bacteria are known to convert H_2S into organic matter:

$$CO_2 + 2 H_2S \rightarrow (CH_2O) + H_2O + 2S \qquad (4)$$

From the energy point of view it is important to note that the potential chemical energy of organic compounds depends on the measure of their state of reduction. Thus, CO_2 has practically no potential energy while a configuration such as $—(CH_2O)$ is of a very high potential energy. Since the total sum of the energies contained in the compounds on the right side of the above equations is much higher than that on the left, external energy must be

References p. 45

supplied for these reactions to take place. In photosynthesis this energy comes from light, however, such reactions may also occur in the dark, provided the required energy is supplied from the outside as, for example, through the oxidation of ammonia by the nitrification bacteria in the soil. In such cases the reduction of CO_2 organic substances is called *chemosynthesis*. The number of microorganisms which use this process is small in comparison with those using photosynthesis.

From the above, one can see now that reaction (2) actually consists of two separate reactions, of which the first is engaged in binding hydrogen by some unknown acceptor, while the second reaction is engaged in the reduction of CO_2. We can, therefore, write now:

$$2 \, H_2O + 2 \, A = 2 \, (AH_2) + O_2 \tag{5}$$

$$CO_2 + 2 \, (AH_2) = (CH_2O) + H_2O + 2 \, A \tag{6}$$

The first of these two reactions, (5), (the *"photolysis"* of water) proceeds in the presence of light and, although its details are not exactly known, the hydrogen acceptor is assumed to be α-lipoic acid (6:8 thioctic acid) which is initially reduced as follows:

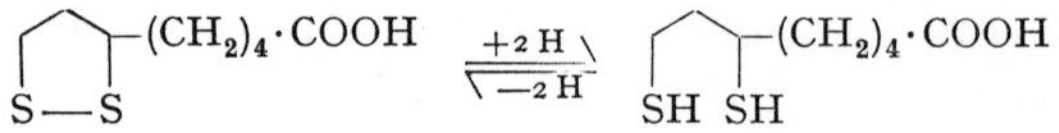

The reduced lipoic acid apparently transfers the hydrogen to an important enzyme, DPN, some of which, when oxidised through the flavoprotein–cytochrome pathway, furnishes ATP. These important compounds will be dealt with in later chapters.

While this reaction of photolysis is taking place in the light, it has been shown by BLACKMAN[3] that the next step, (6), the actual reduction of CO_2, can proceed in the dark. BLACKMAN found that, while the intensity of light speeds up the rate of photosynthesis, this is only true up to a limited extent, since the reaction attains a state of saturation during illumination and can continue further in the dark. One may compare this situation with the state of affairs when some merchandise is transported by trains to a port to be further shipped by steamers: to increase the number of trains will not speed up the shipment so long as the number of steamers remains the same. Also in photosynthesis there appears to be two distinct phases: if a green plant is illuminated by a short flash of light, for say 0.0001 of a second, the oxygen will continue to form for another 0.02 second in the dark. Apparently, the intermediate compounds formed at this stage are not quite stable and their final stabilization takes place only in the dark. It has been found that for every 2000 molecules of chlorophyll, only one molecule of oxygen is formed every 0.02 second[4].

All this refers, however, to undamaged green plant tissues. It is sufficient to prick a simple green cell containing chlorophyll to stop this cell from proceeding with photosynthesis. This is the reason why, so far, nobody has been able to demonstrate the photosynthetic reaction *in vitro*. On the other hand, HILL[5] has succeeded in performing only the first stage (reaction (5) above) with isolated chloroplasts in the presence of a suitable hydrogen acceptor. HILL used for that purpose a ferric salt which was reduced to a ferrous compound.

$$4 \ Fe^{3+} + 2 \ H_2O \ \xrightarrow[\text{chloroplasts}]{Nh\nu} \ 4 \ Fe^{2+} + 4 \ H^+ + O_2$$

Instead of a ferric salt, one could use some other suitable oxido-reducing pigment, such as methylene blue or 2:6 dichlorophenol indophenol, by means of which it is possible to measure the degree of reduction in a colorimeter by means of the change in color.

The total energy required for all these reactions is designated $(Nh\nu)$ and is termed an *Einstein*, where N represents $6.06 \cdot 10^{23}$ photons, *i.e.*, the number of photons which one mole of substance absorbs in a photochemical reaction; h is Planck's constant $(6.55 \cdot 10^{-27}$ erg second); and ν is the frequency of the light wave. The frequency is the reciprocal of the wave length $(1/\lambda)$ and the product $h\nu$ (or the quantum value) is the energy of a photon.

Formation of primary carbohydrates

The main problem confronting scientists during the last hundred years has been the question: which is the primary organic substance formed during the photosynthetic reaction?

It was ninety years ago, in 1870, that VON BAEYER suggested that the primary substance created as a result of photosynthesis is formaldehyde, HCOH:

$$CO_2 + H_2O \ \longrightarrow \ HCOH + O_2$$

which should, in its turn, give by aldol condensation, a monosaccharide, $(C_6H_{12}O_6)$. WILLSTAETTER, who made careful measurements, found that the ratio of CO_2, reduced during the reaction, to oxygen, is one: $CO_2/O_2 = 1$. He therefore supported VON BAEYER's hypothesis *per exclusionem* on the assumption that no other simple organic substance, such as oxalic acid, glycolic acid or formic acid could possibly be formed for, in all these cases, the above ratio of CO_2 to O_2 would differ from unity. WILLSTAETTER assumed, therefore, that photosynthesis is a photochemical reaction proceeding on the surface of the chloroplasts in which both chlorophyll *a* and *b* take part.

Other investigators supporting Von Baeyer's theory assumed it to be a reaction in which Mg took part.

Von Baeyer himself suggested the possibility that formaldehyde formed during the photosynthesis might undergo quick polymerization to form *inositol*. This compound, as will be seen later (Chapter 14), has been verified to exist in green leaves. Von Baeyer thought that by the migration of a hydrogen atom from one carbon to its neighbor a monosaccharide, such as glucose, might be formed.

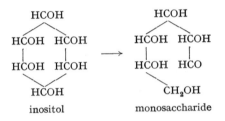

inositol   monosaccharide

For over half a century, all of these and many other theories on the formation of primary sugars have been investigated. The formaldehyde theory has been finally abandoned, however, since it was never possible to demonstrate the presence of this compound which, in addition, has been found to be toxic to the plant.

In general, the predominant carbohydrate in the leaves of dicotyledone plants is starch, while in monocotyledones glucose is the main carbohydrate. On the other hand, some green algae produce lipids and in the green leaves of wheat a large accumulation of proteins is found right after illumination in the presence of CO_2. Experiments with the green leaves of sunflowers showed the presence of about 50% sucrose, 10% hexoses and 30% starch.

Recently, with the advent of modern methods of investigation, and especially with the use of isotopes and paper chromatography, scientists have succeeded in solving most of the problems connected with this intricate and most valuable process of nature. We owe most of our present-day knowledge regarding the mechanism of CO_2 fixation during photosynthesis to Calvin and his associates[6]. These investigators elaborated a special technique, using both isotope tracers and paper chromatography. For the purpose of these studies, monocellular green algae such as *Chlorella* and *Scenedesmus* were used. The algae were exposed to carbon dioxide, in which the carbon was labeled as the C^{14} isotope, for various periods of illumination. After short periods, which lasted for 5, 30 and 90 seconds and 5 minutes, the algae suspensions were thrown into boiling alcohol which immediately stopped all vital processes, enzymatic and others. The resulting mixtures were now subjected to two-dimensional paper chromatography and the newly formed components, which contained the radioactive carbon, were easily detected by placing the chromatogram on a sheet of photographic paper: wherever compounds containing C^{14} were absorbed onto the chromatogram they affected the photographic paper, leaving spots of varying sizes (Fig. 8).

The most important finding during these early investigations was the fact that, after the very first few seconds of illumination, a three-carbon compound, namely 3-phosphoglyceric acid (PGA) was formed to the extent of

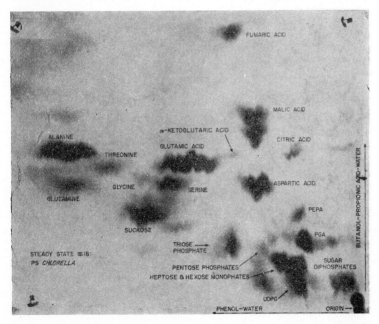

Fig. 8. A typical radiogram of a photosynthetic experiment, showing compounds formed by *Chlorella pyrenoidosa*, after two minutes exposure to $^{14}CO_2$ (courtesy of J. A. BASSHAM[7].

70% of the labeled CO_2 used in the experiments. After 30 seconds the hexoses, glucose and fructose were found and still later sucrose, various amino acids and finally lipid were indicated. All of the carbohydrates were present in the form of esters of phosphoric acid (see Chapter 5).

References p. 45

The CALVIN *cycle*

The evidence that the primary substance formed was PGA has given no indication as yet as to how it was formed and scientists have been looking in vain for a two-carbon atom compound which might become attached to a molecule of CO_2. It was only after the discovery of two more phosphorylated sugars, a five-carbon carbohydrate (ribulose diphosphate) and the very uncommon seven-carbon carbohydrate (sedoheptulose monophosphate) that light began to dawn about the true mechanism involved.

The first step in this mechanism has been shown to be the reaction between ribulose diphosphate (formed later in the cycle), carbon dioxide and water to form two molecules of PGA:

$$
\begin{array}{ll}
CH_2O \cdot PO_3H_2 & \qquad CH_2O \cdot PO_3H_2 \\
| & \qquad | \\
CO & \qquad HCOH \\
| \xrightarrow[+H_2O]{+CO_2} & \qquad | \\
H\,COH & \qquad COOH \\
| & \qquad + \\
HCOH & \qquad COOH \\
| & \qquad | \\
CH_2O \cdot PO_3H_2 & \qquad HCOH \\
\text{ribulose-1:5-} & \qquad | \\
\text{diphosphate} & \qquad CH_2O \cdot PO_3H_2 \\
& \qquad \text{2 molecules of PGA} \\
& \qquad \text{(phosphoglyceric acid)}
\end{array}
$$

As will be explained in detail in the next chapter, all the carbohydrates taking an active part in the metabolic activities of the cell are present in the form of esters of phosphoric acid which brings about a greater reactivity of the sugars. This phosphorylation and transfer of energy is caused by a unique compound, ATP, in conjunction with enzymes called phosphokinases (Chapter 5).

In addition there are a number of other enzymes which aid in catalyzing the transformation of the various sugars taking part in the cycle shown in Fig. 9, p. 42.

As can be seen from this diagram, three molecules of CO_2 combine with three molecules of a pentose (a five-carbon atom carbohydrate), the diphosphate ribulose, to form six molecules of PGA. Out of these six molecules, one enters the hexose pool to polymerize into disaccharides or into polysaccharides.

Another hexose (C_6) molecule, together with an additional C_3-molecule (nine carbon atoms in all) gives two compounds: a pentose (C_5) and a tetrose

(C_4). The tetrose thus created plus an additional C_3-molecule will give a sedoheptulose (C_7) which combines with a fifth molecule of PGA to form two molecules of pentoses, C_5. The three molecules of pentoses so-formed return to the starting point of the cycle to combine again with three molecules of CO_2. At each turn of the cycle, therefore, only one-sixth of the PGA created is actually transformed into hexoses.

The following scheme shows the different intermediate sugars formed and the enzymes taking part in the various steps:

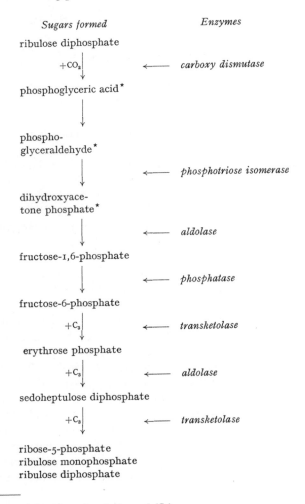

Sugars formed   *Enzymes*

ribulose diphosphate

 $+CO_2$ ⟵ *carboxy dismutase*

phosphoglyceric acid*

phospho-
glyceraldehyde*

    ⟵ *phosphotriose isomerase*

dihydroxyace-
tone phosphate*

    ⟵ *aldolase*

fructose-1,6-phosphate

    ⟵ *phosphatase*

fructose-6-phosphate

 $+C_3$ ⟵ *transketolase*

erythrose phosphate

 $+C_3$ ⟵ *aldolase*

sedoheptulose diphosphate

 $+C_3$ ⟵ *transketolase*

ribose-5-phosphate
ribulose monophosphate
ribulose diphosphate

---

* Members of the triosephosphate pool (C_3).

References p. 45

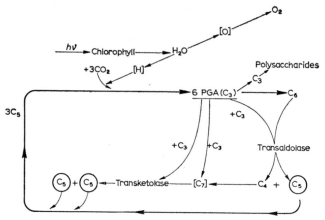

Fig. 9. The Calvin cycle of photosynthesis.

A very similar pathway, only in the opposite direction is the, so-called, *pentose oxidation cycle* (see Chapter 18).

This scheme has actually been proved by using isotopically labeled CO_2 and determining the position of these labeled carbons.

Industrial photosynthesis—"Thought for Food"

Every year green plants, including the algae in the oceans, bind 150 billion tons of carbon with 25 billion tons of hydrogen to produce organic matter and, at the same time, discharge 400 billion tons of oxygen. But perhaps it is not commonly appreciated that 90% of this enormous chemical "manufacture" is carried out under the surface of sea water by microscopic algae, only 10% of it being carried out by higher plants.

The importance of photosynthesis is not only in the creation of organic matter, *viz.*, food, for all living beings upon the earth, but mainly in storing away at least a part of the enormous solar energy. Our sun sends out $9 \cdot 10^{22}$ kcal every second in the form of light energy. This, incidentally, diminishes its weight by 360,000 million tons every day!! Apparently this loss is of no significance if one takes into account the enormous mass of the sun. Of this energy, only a very insignificant part reaches our planet and of that only a trifle is used by the plants, animals and man. Outside the atmosphere light rays which fall perpendicularly upon an area of one square meter bring along 20 kcal of energy every minute. Only about one-tenth of this energy (2 kcal/min) reaches the Earth and man, himself, merely takes advantage of a few crumbs.

Nevertheless, it is a quite remunerative proposition: since, even the poor farmer in China gets a 7-fold return for the energy he puts into growing wheat and 25-fold if he grows rice. In the United States, where the farmer uses machinery and the same solar energy preserved in the form of coal and petroleum, he can get as much as 200 and up to 500 times more energy from his crops than he expends in growing them.

Two crops of corn or potatoes provide 10 million kcal per hectare; raising cattle for milk gives only 1.7 million kcal per hectare, while cattle raised for their meat contribute only 0.25 million kcal; and raising poultry, yields 0.5 kcal per hectare. Calculated in another way: 1 kg of corn, eaten as such, provides us with 3500 kcal (100%); the same kg of corn eaten in the form of milk provided by the cow will give us 600 kcal (17%) and eaten as meat, only 350 kcal (10%). It is obvious that protein feeding is a very expensive proposition; in fact, the greatest part of the world's population is fed today mainly on carbohydrate-rich foods poor in proteins.

Theoretically, it is possible to obtain a much higher yield from the photosynthetic process if one cultivates monocellular algae, which grow much faster than higher plants. Some 17,000 varieties of such microscopic algae are known and a few types, such as *Chlorella* and *Scenedesmus* have been successfully used by scientists in elucidating the intricacies of the photosynthetic process. Such varieties as *Chlorella pyrenoidosa, C. vulgaris* and others have been used in recent years for the so-called "Industrial or Controlled Photosynthesis".

Contrary to other plants, *Chlorella* contains very little cellulose and, by adjusting the growing media, it is possible to develop such algae with a protein content of upto 50% of the total nutrients or with an augmented content of fats, as the case may be. Algae are very efficient in the use of solar energy in comparison with conventional agriculture. While sugar beets, which are the most efficient converters of solar energy, may produce as much as twenty tons of organic matter per acre per year, controlled photosynthesis, using *Chlorella*, can yield up to ten times the peak crops obtained today in agriculture. Considering protein alone, the yield differences are even greater. The soy-bean, the most prolific protein plant, yields up to a ton of protein per acre per year. *Chlorella* can yield ten times as much plant protein. While *Chlorella* protein lacks some essential properties necessary for animal feeding, another algae, *Euglena*, produces a protein more like that produced by animals fed on agricultural crops; however, it can produce 100 times more of it than animals do.

Recently, controlled photosynthesis has been very successfully tried in utilizing sewage as a medium for algae growth, and it is claimed that sewage wastes can be reclaimed and re-used an indefinite number of times and, in so doing, can produce unprecedented quantities of food at costs within the economic reach of most societies.

References p. 45

The possibility of re-using sewage wastes is now being seriously considered by those engaged in outer space travel projects, where the problems of supplying food and oxygen, as well as the disposal of wastes, sewage and carbon dioxide, are very serious. Those concerned regard the creation of such closed systems as the only solution to the problem.

Another important possibility is the utilization of sea water for the growth of algae, thereby conserving fresh water supplies. Several pilot-plants engaged in industrial photosynthesis have been constructed in various countries. One may now visualize large ponds of water, constructed in any desert, containing the required media exposed to sunshine and, instead of plowing, sowing and otherwise preparing the soil, instead of being dependent on the mercy of rain, these ponds will be seeded through a pump with some cells of *Chlorella* or other suitable algae. The algae will not suffer the vicissitudes of weather or disease that afflict agricultural crops; they grow so fast so the hazardous interval between planting and harvesting is short. And when the abundant crop is ready, the algae can be collected by centrifugal separation returning the liquid to another pond and the process started all over again. All this seems very fascinating if it were not for several difficulties which need to be solved by an ingenious chemical engineer:

(1) The growth of *Chlorella* seems to require sterile conditions, otherwise the danger exists that other parasites among the heterotropic organisms, such as protozoa, yeast and molds, will devour them.

(2) In order to obtain high yields, an optimal content of CO_2 is necessary, which is about 5% in the air. To maintain such a proportion in the open is quite impossible at the present time.

(3) Outside a "closed system" industrial photosynthesis will require an ample supply of CO_2 with its source near the ponds. For each kg of dried *Chlorella*, 2 kg of CO_2 and $1/_{12}$ kg of N are required.

(4) The fact that optimal utilization of solar energy (20%) is attained in dispersed light as against 2% to 3% in full sunlight suggests using an intermittent light source, which means using fluorescent lamps or some other method of darkening the ponds.

These and many other difficulties have still to be overcome. However, large-scale experiments continue and, when they finally succeed, they will disprove the old standing Malthusian Theory* that mankind is doomed to perish due to the ever increasing world population and lack of food.

---

* THOMAS ROBERT MALTHUS in 1798.

REFERENCES

[1] S. L. MILLER, *Biochim. et Biophys. Acta*, 23 (1957) 480.
[2] F. T. HAXO AND L. R. BLINKS, *J. Gen. Physiol.*, 33 (1950) 389.
[3] F. F. BLACKMAN, *Ann. Botany*, 19 (1905) 281.
[4] J. FRANCK AND W. E. LOOMIS, *Photosynthesis in Plants*, Iowa State College Press, Ames, 1949.
[5] R. HILL, *Nature*, 139 (1937) 881.
[6] J. A. BASSHAM AND M. CALVIN, *The Path of Carbon in Photosynthisis*, Prentice-hall, London, 1957.
[7] J. A. BASSHAM, *Biochim. Biophys. Acta*, 43 (1960) 447.

SELECTED BIBLIOGRAPHY TO CHAPTER 4

BARLEW, J. S., Algae culture from laboratory to pilot plant, *Carnegie Inst. Wash. Publ. No. 600*, (1953).
BASSHAM, J. A., AND M. CALVIN, *The Path of Carbon in Photosynthesis*, Prentice-Hall, London, 1957.
FRANCK, J., AND W. E. LOOMIS, *Photosynthesis in Plants*, Iowa State College Press, Ames, 1949.
GAFFRON, H., *Research in Photosynthesis*, Interscience Publications, New York, 1957.
HILL, R., AND C. P. WHITTINGHAM, *Photosynthesis*, Methuen and Co., London, 1955,
RABINOWITCH, E. I., *Photosynthesis*, Interscience, New York, 1945, 1951, 1956.
The photochemical apparatus, *Rept. Symp., Brookhaven National Laboratory, Upton, New York, 1958*.

CHAPTER 5

CARBOHYDRATES—MONOSACCHARIDES

Occurrence

It has been shown in Chapter 3 that the first products of photosynthesis are carbohydrates. These compounds, in one form or another, constitute more than one-half of the organic matter upon the Earth: the greatest part of plants is built of carbohydrates while the animal world contains rather limited amounts of them.

Various sugars, starches, cellulose, hemicelluloses, pectins, numerous gums and mucilages are all carbohydrates. The simple sugars, glucose and fructose, are found in honey and various fruits. These are often accompanied by combined sugars, the disaccharides, of which sucrose, for instance, found in sugar beets and in sugar cane, is the most representative example. More complicated carbohydrates are polymers of the simple sugars or of their derivatives and serve as the "building bricks" in plants (such as cellulose, hemicellulose and pectins) or as reserve materials for future use (such as starches) or probably also as waste products, such as the numerous gums produced by plants. Glycogen, produced in the liver, is also a carbohydrate polymer constituting a small energy reserve in animals. All these are only a few examples, but the number of carbohydrates in nature is indeed prodigious.

Classification

The simple carbohydrates, the monosaccharides, are neutral, crystallizable and diffusible substances, readily soluble in water, soluble with difficulty in alcohol, and insoluble in ether. Not all of these sugars are sweet; they cover a wide range of sweetness and some are even bitter.

Monosaccharides may be divided chemically into *polyhydroxyaldehydes* (aldoses) and *polyhydroxyketones* (ketoses). Depending on the number of constituent formaldehyde units (CH_2O) these sugars are classified as:

bioses $(CH_2O)_2$, $C_2H_4O_2$;   *pentoses* $(CH_2O)_5$, $C_5H_{10}O_5$;

trioses $(CH_2O)_3$, $C_3H_6O_3$;   *hexoses* $(CH_2O)_6$, $C_6H_{12}O_6$;

tetroses $(CH_2O)_4$, $C_4H_8O_4$;   and *heptoses* $(CH_2O)_7$, $C_7H_{14}O_7$.

The simplest of the series is glycolaldehyde, a derivative of acetaldehyde, which is a *biose*:

$$CH_3CHO \quad \rightarrow \quad HO \cdot CH_2CHO$$

acetaldehyde   glycolaldehyde

Next in the series come the three-carbon carbohydrates which include two trioses, an aldose and a ketose:

```
        CHO               CH₂OH
         |                  |
       CH·OH              C = O
         |                  |
       CH₂OH              CH₂OH
    glyceraldehyde     dihydroxyacetone
      (aldose)            (ketose)
```

The monosaccharides, which are of primary importance in foods, are hexoses and pentoses.

Hexoses

Of the many hexoses which are possible on a theoretical basis, only five have been found in the free state in the plant kingdom, three of them aldoses (glucose, mannose and galactose) and two ketoses (fructose and sorbose):

```
   CHO         CHO         CHO        CH₂OH       CH₂OH
    |           |           |          |           |
  HCOH        HOCH        HCOH        C = O        C = O
    |           |           |          |           |
  HOCH        HOCH        HOCH        HOCH        HOCH
    |           |           |          |           |
  HCOH        HCOH        HOCH        HCOH        HCOH
    |           |           |          |           |
  HCOH        HCOH        HCOH        HCOH        HOCH
    |           |           |          |           |
  CH₂OH       CH₂OH       CH₂OH       CH₂OH       CH₂OH
 D-glucose   D-mannose   D-galactose  D-fructose  L-sorbose
```

The hydroxyl of carbon atom 3 in all these sugars is oriented in the same direction with regards to the whole molecule (in the above formulas to the left). Mannose is different from glucose in its configuration at carbon atom 2 and is therefore called an epimer of glucose. Sorbose differs from fructose in its configuration at carbon atom 5.

Monosaccharides crystallize with relative difficulty and, therefore, EMIL FISCHER, who truly deserves to be called the father of carbohydrate chemistry, introduced phenylhydrazine $C_6H_5NH \cdot NH_2$ as a reagent which combines easily with the sugars giving beautiful yellow crystals of osazones. This is a most useful means for the characterization of monosaccharides. The following scheme shows the introduction of two molecules of phenylhydrazine from the reaction mixture. Glucose, mannose and fructose give identical osazones because of the similarity of their configurations at carbon atoms 4, 5 and 6. Hydrazones of the aldoses and ketoses are different in their properties.

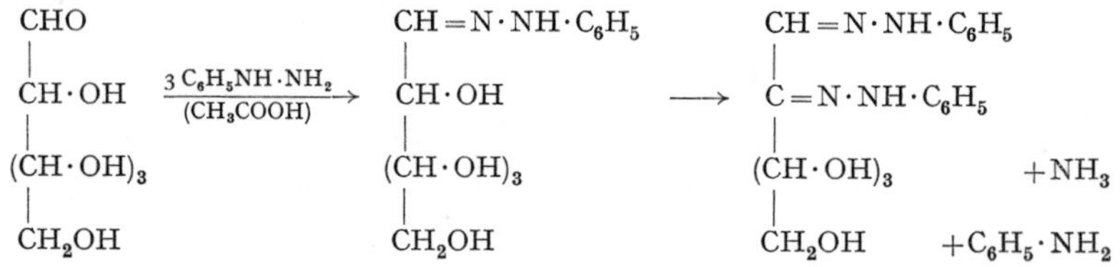

$$
\begin{array}{llll}
\text{CHO} & \text{CH} = \text{N} \cdot \text{NH} \cdot \text{C}_6\text{H}_5 & \text{CH} = \text{N} \cdot \text{NH} \cdot \text{C}_6\text{H}_5 \\
| & | & | \\
\text{CH} \cdot \text{OH} \xrightarrow[\text{(CH}_3\text{COOH)}]{3\,\text{C}_6\text{H}_5\text{NH} \cdot \text{NH}_2} & \text{CH} \cdot \text{OH} \longrightarrow & \text{C} = \text{N} \cdot \text{NH} \cdot \text{C}_6\text{H}_5 \\
| & | & | \\
(\text{CH} \cdot \text{OH})_3 & (\text{CH} \cdot \text{OH})_3 & (\text{CH} \cdot \text{OH})_3 \quad +\text{NH}_3 \\
| & | & | \\
\text{CH}_2\text{OH} & \text{CH}_2\text{OH} & \text{CH}_2\text{OH} \quad +\text{C}_6\text{H}_5 \cdot \text{NH}_2 \\
\text{glucose} & \text{glucose-} & \text{glucose-} \\
& \text{phenylhydrazone} & \text{phenylosazone}
\end{array}
$$

Isomerization

It is evident from the above formula for glucose that it should contain four asymmetric carbon atoms (indicated by asterisks):

$$
\overset{6}{\text{C}}\text{H}_2\text{OH} \cdot \overset{5}{\underset{*}{\text{C}}}\text{HOH} \cdot \overset{4}{\underset{*}{\text{C}}}\text{HOH} \cdot \overset{3}{\underset{*}{\text{C}}}\text{HOH} \cdot \overset{2}{\underset{*}{\text{C}}}\text{HOH} \cdot \overset{1}{\text{C}}\text{HO}
$$

Consequently, the possibility of $2^N = 2^4 = 16$ stereoisomers (8 antipodal pairs) exists. Glucose is only one of these 16 isomers and it should exist in two enantiomorphs, the d- and l-configurations. At this point it is appropriate to mention that in the nomenclature of sugars, it is customary to designate the enantiomorphs by majuscule letters D and L. These *do not* indicate the direction of the optical rotation of the sugars, but the configuration of the hydroxyl on the carbon atom before the last in relation to that of the last one. Glyceric aldehyde is taken as an example:

$$
\begin{array}{ll}
\text{CHO} & \text{CHO} \\
| & | \\
\text{HCOH} & \text{HOCH} \\
| & | \\
\text{CH}_2\text{OH} & \text{CH}_2\text{OH} \\
\text{D-glyceric aldehyde} & \text{L-glyceric aldehyde}
\end{array}
$$

All other sugars are related to these designations of glyceric aldehyde. In order to designate the direction of optical rotations of sugars the signs $(+)$

and (—) are used. Thus, D(+) glucose shows that this particular glucose has the D-configuration and an optical rotation to the right, while D(—) fructose designates that this sugar has the same D-configuration but it is levorotatory.

The above open-chain formula of glucose (as well as of all other monosaccharides) does not, however, tell the whole story. Although hexoses behave in some reactions as if they were aldehydes they differ, however, in many respects from true aldehydes: aldoses reduce Fehling's solution to cuprous oxide as well as an ammoniacal solution of $AgNO_3$ to metallic silver, although fructose, which is, strictly speaking, a ketone, reduces the above solutions as well. Similar discrepancies are seen in the reaction of these sugars with bisulfites: bisulfites do combine with aldoses; however, this addition reaction is quite different from that with all other aldehydes, In addition, Schiff's reagent, which is entirely specific for aldehydes (the formation of a color reaction with fuchsin and SO_2), does not react under normal conditions with the sugars. Finally, although similar to aldehydes, the sugars have no odor as most of the true aldehydes have.

Long ago, these facts raised the suspicion that the structural formulae of the monosaccharides could not be presented as true aldehydes. It was COLLEY, as early as 1870, and later TOLLENS in 1883, who suggested that these sugars have a ring configuration. However, EMIL FISCHER, who did much towards the isolation of the sugars, their synthesis, and the elucidation of their constitution, ignored all these suggestions of the existence of a ring structure in monosaccharides. Yet, in much the same way as PRIESTLEY, who was the greatest opponent of LAVOISIER, discovered oxygen and thereby brought about the downfall of the phlogistone theory, so did FISCHER himself make an important discovery in the field of sugar derivatives which finally established the true structure of monosaccharides. He found that if glucose is heated in a sealed tube with methyl alcohol in the presence of HCl, a crystalline product is obtained, namely, methyl glucoside, $C_6H_{11}O_5 \cdot OCH_3$, with a melting point of 165°C and an optical rotation $[\alpha]_D = +157°$.

Methyl glucoside does not reduce Fehling's solution, does not combine with phenylhydrazine to form a hydrazone or osazones, and on boiling with acid is reconverted into glucose. At the first moment of its being brought into solution, *this glucose* has an optical rotation of $[\alpha]_D = +113°$, which soon begins to decrease, attaining a final polarimetric value of $[\alpha]_D = +52.5°$ after about two hours. At this point it remains constant.

Shortly after this discovery, TANRET (1895) succeeded in crystallizing glucose at the temperature of 98°C, thereby isolating *another form of glucose* which had, immediately after being dissolved, an $[\alpha]_D$ equal to $+19°$ and which increased slowly to $+52.5°$ and thereafter remained constant.

These two forms of glucose are evidently not *enantiomorphs* (since their

References p. 60

original indices of optical rotation are not identical with reversed signs, as the case would be with *d*- and *l*-configurations). The designations of α and β have been given to these forms, *α-glucose* to the first and *β-glucose* to the second.

The phenomenon involving the change of the optical rotation in solution is called *mutarotation* and the interconversion of the two forms α and β can only be explained by the existence of an intermediate open-chain form:

H OH	CHO	HO H
\ /			\ /
C———	HCOH	C———
HCOH	HOCH	HCOH
HOCH	HCOH	HOCH
HCOH O ⇌	HCOH ⇌	HCOH O
HC———	HCOH	HC———
CH₂OH	CH₂OH	CH₂OH
α-D(+) glucose	open-chain	β-D(+) glucose
[α]D = + 113⁰	glucose	[α]D = + 19⁰

Most of the monosaccharides and some of the disaccharides undergo mutarotation. Mutarotation is catalyzed by the addition of H^+ or hydroxyl (OH^-) ions. An enzyme *mutarotase*, present in extracts from the mold *Penicillium notatum* and from some animal tissues (kidney and liver), also catalyzes the mutarotation of glucose.

The final support to the existence of the two forms α and β was given by ARMSTRONG, a disciple of EMIL FISCHER, who found two enzymes, each of which will specifically hydrolyze the different glucosides: α-glycosides by *maltase*; β-glycosides by *emulsin*.

α-methyl D-glucoside   maltase→   α-D-glucose   β-D-glucose   ←emulsin   β-methyl D-glucoside

Structure

The existence of the ring forms in glucose and in other hexoses necessitates the revision of the number of stereoisomers. The ring form makes the first carbon atom asymmetric, therefore, the total number of possible isomers will be $2^5 = 32$. In fact, nearly all these isomers have been found either in nature or have been prepared synthetically.

With the acceptance of the ring structure for monosaccharides the question arose: what is the size of this ring; for, in fact, one can imagine the linkage of carbon atom I with any one of the other carbon atoms. X-ray measurements, however, of the sugars in their crystalline state have shown recently that they exist in two forms only, the six-member ring or the five-member ring similar to pyrane and furane, respectively:

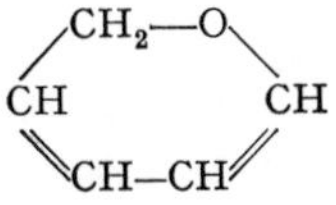

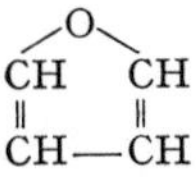

The sugars having a six-member ring are, therefore, named *pyranoses* and their glycosides *pyranosides*, while those having a five-member ring are called *furanoses* and their glycosides *furanosides*. The pyranose form is the more stable of the two and is, therefore, predominately found in nature.

The cyclic structure of the monosaccharides is conveniently depicted by the valuable method suggested by HAWORTH in 1927 and which is now universally accepted. As drawn in the following formulae, the plane of the pyranose ring is shown in perspective to be perpendicular to that of the page on which it is written, with the substituents above or below the plane of the ring:

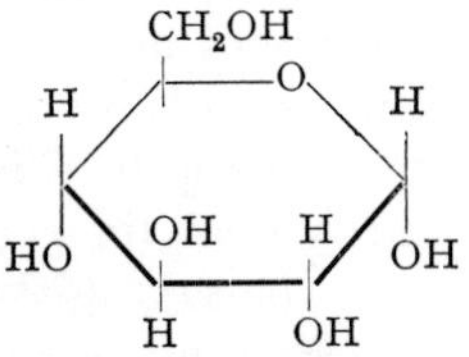

α-D(+) glucopyranose

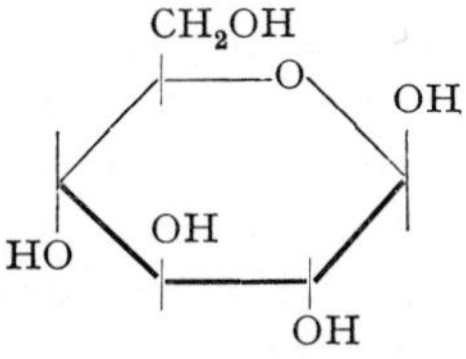

β-D(+) glucopyranose

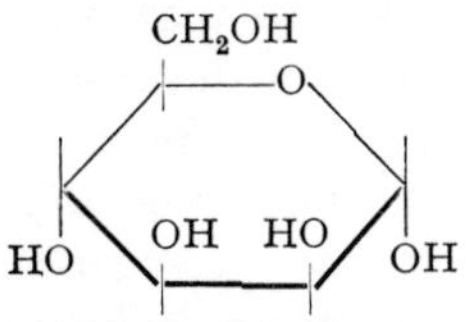

α-D(—) mannopyranose

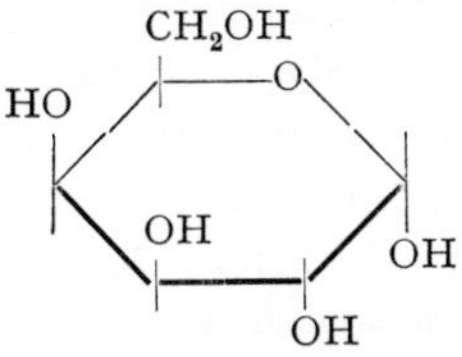

α-D(—) galactopyranose

It is usual to omit the hydrogen atoms when using the HAWORTH method of presentation.

Fructose (or levulose), the so-called "fruit sugar", is a ketose and is found in honey and fruit juices in its pyranose form; however, when in combination with other sugars, such as in the case of sucrose or in polysaccharides, its cyclic form is furanose.

$$
\begin{array}{cc}
\text{CH}_2\text{OH} & \text{CH}_2\text{OH} \\
| & | \\
\text{C}=\text{O} & \text{HOC} \\
| & | \\
\text{HOCH} & \text{HOCH} \\
| & | \\
\text{HCOH} & \text{HCOH} \quad \text{O} \\
| & | \\
\text{HCOH} & \text{HCOH} \\
| & | \\
\text{CH}_2\text{OH} & \text{CH}_2 \\
\text{open-chain form} & \alpha\text{-D}(\text{—}) \text{ fructopyranose}
\end{array}
$$

α-D(—) fructofuranose   β-D(—) fructofuranose

Both the α–β transformation of the sugars and the transformation involving the pyranose and furanose forms, proceed through the open-chain aldehydic state of the sugar which exists in solutions in only very small quantities. These quantities are so small that until recently it was impossible to prove their existence. Today the figures found for the open-chain aldehydic forms in solutions of various sugars at pH 7 and 25°C are (in mole percent): glucose, 0.024%: mannose, 0.064% and galactose, 0.082%, (see ref. 1).

The existence of the acyclic open-chain monosaccharides recently received support from investigations carried out in connection with the structure of their bisulfite addition products[2]. It is well known that when foods are preserved with SO_2 or sulfites these combine slowly with the sugars and that part which is bound loses its preserving ability. The more concentrated the sugars in the foods are, the greater the rate of combination and the greater the amount of bound SO_2. It has been shown that the sugar-SO_2 addition products, the so-called α-hydroxy sulfonates, of glucose, arabinose, galactose and mannose are open-chain compounds, which explains this slow formation.

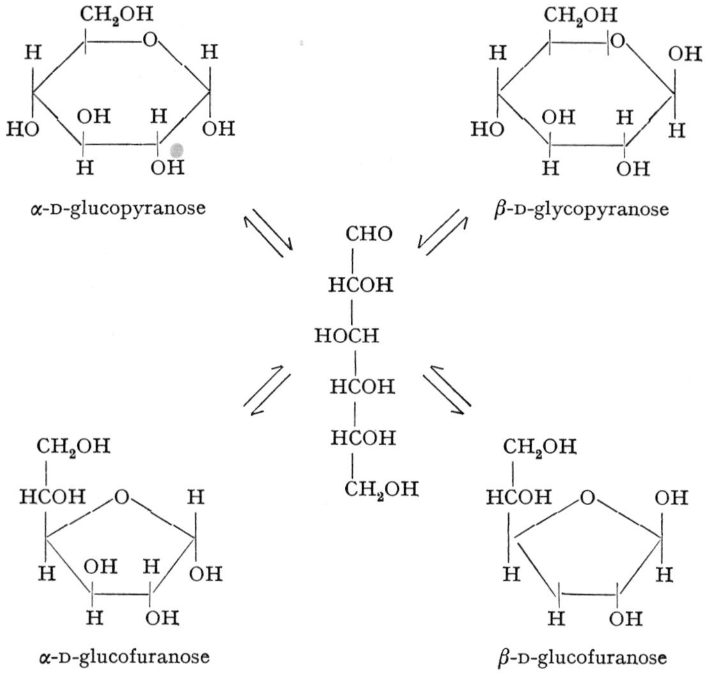

α-D-glucopyranose

β-D-glycopyranose

α-D-glucofuranose

β-D-glucofuranose

When the small quantity of the existing acyclic form of the sugar is bound by SO_2 the equilibrium shown above is disturbed and more of the open-chain form combines with the SO_2 as a true aldehyde.

A very similar state of affairs apparently occurs during non-enzymatic browning in foods when the hexoses combine with amino acids (the MAILLARD reaction). For detailed discussion, see Chapter 20.

Reducing power of sugars

All monosaccharides which possess a free carbonyl group have the ability to reduce Fehling's solution and therefore this solution may be used as an excellent qualitative and quantitative reagent for these sugars. By means of Fehling's solution, which is an alkaline solution of $CuSO_4$ in sodium potassium tartrate buffer, the cupric ion is reduced to the cuprous form and appears as the red cuprous oxide.

In point of fact, the mechanism of this reaction is based on the fact discovered by VON EULER that all sugars with a free carbonyl group are easily transformed, by heating them in alkaline solution, into enediols—strongly reactive compounds oxidizable by oxygen and by other oxidizing agents. Von Euler named the simplest member of this group, hydroxy-glycolaldehyde, *reductone*:

$$\underset{\substack{| \quad |\\ \text{OH} \quad \text{OH}}}{\text{HC}=\!=\!\text{C}\cdot\text{CHO}} \qquad \text{and in general} \qquad \underset{\substack{| \quad |\\ \text{OH} \quad \text{OH}}}{\text{RC}=\!=\!\text{C}\cdot\text{CHO}}$$

hydroxyglycolaldehyde   reductones

These reductones have much in common with the structure of ascorbic acid (vitamin C), as will be seen in Chapter 14. These compounds, having a strong reducing power can reduce ions such as Ag^+, Hg^{2+}, Cu^{2+}, Bi^{3+} or $Fe(CN)^{3-6}$ and by means of this the sugars are oxidized into complicated sugar acids.

There are several modifications of Fehling's method, such as the Bene-dict, Somogyi, Hagedorn–Jensen, or the Willstaetter–Schudel methods, but all of them are based on the same principle. Accordingly, the general scheme can be presented as follows:

$$\underset{\substack{| \quad |\\ \text{OH} \quad \text{OH}\\ \text{reducing sugar}}}{\text{R}\!-\!\text{CH}\cdot\text{CH}\cdot\text{CHO}} \quad \xrightarrow[\text{heat}]{\text{alkali}} \quad \underset{\substack{| \quad |\\ \text{OH} \quad \text{OH}\\ \text{reductones}}}{\text{R}\!-\!\text{C}=\!=\!\text{C}\cdot\text{CHO}}$$

$+Cu^{2+}$ $\Big\downarrow$ (generally copper complexes of tartrates or bitartrates)

$$\text{CuOH} \longleftarrow \text{OH}^- + \text{Cu}^+ + \text{a mixture of sugar acids}$$

The bivalent copper ion Cu^{2+} takes up an electron from the reductone, which is thereby oxidized to a sugar acid, while the reduced monovalent Cu^+ now combines with a hydroxyl ion and, on heating, produces cuprous oxide: $2\,CuOH \rightarrow Cu_2O + H_2O$.

Hexose derivatives

For purposes of research and in some cases of industrial application (as for instance in the manufacture of synthetic vitamin C—see Chapter 14) it is important to bind the free hydroxyl groups of the sugars. There exist several methods for doing this and it is appropriate to mention here at least two such methods:

(a) Acetylation, i.e., esterification of the sugars with acetic acid. α-Glucose pentacetate, for instance, may be obtained by treating α-D-glucose with acetic acid at 0°C in the presence of $ZnCl_2$, while the β-derivative is obtained

when β-glucose is heated with sodium acetate in the presence of acetic anhydride.

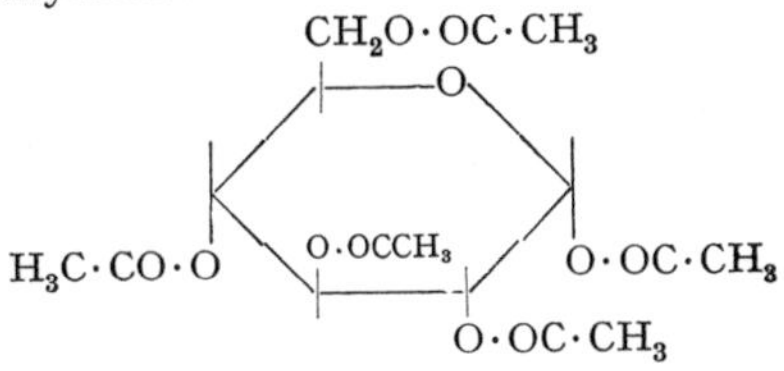

α-glucose pentacetate

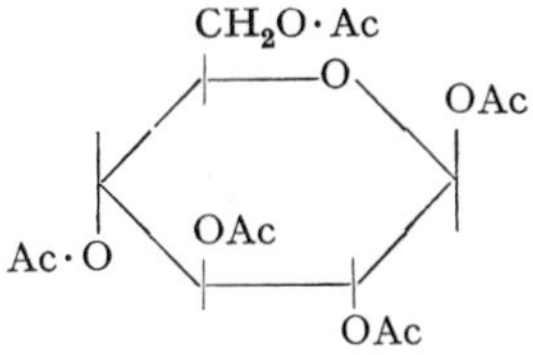

β-glucose pentacetate

(b) *Diisopropylidene derivatives.* A second possibility for binding the free hydroxyl groups of the sugars is by the action of acetone. In this case the acetone generally tends to bind the pair of hydroxyls which find themselves in close proximity and which are on the same side of the plane according to HAWORTH's model—see formulae.

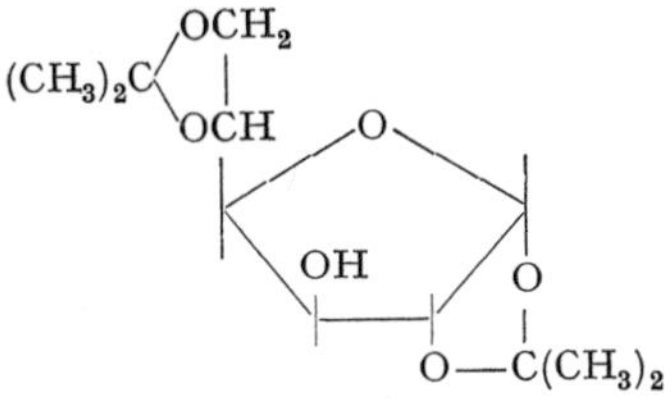

diacetone α-glucofuranose

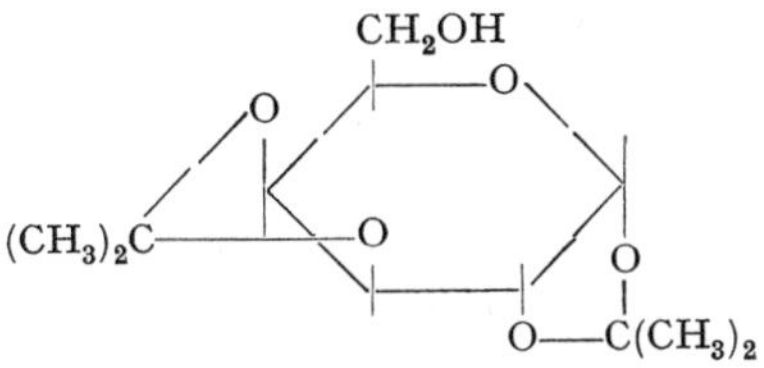

diacetone α-galactopyranose

Pentoses

The next important group of monosaccharides in food technology are the *pentoses.* These are the sugars built up of five-carbon atoms. They are not found in plants in the free state but only as polymers (arabans, xylans) as in the structure of hemicellulose, or they are found occluded in such products as pectins. Ribose is an important constituent of many enzymes as will be discussed later in this chapter. The structures of the most important pentoses are shown here:

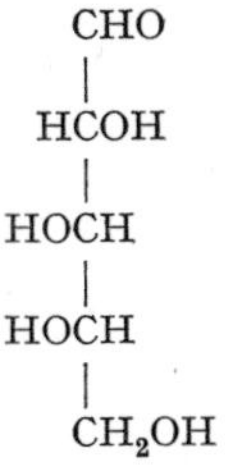

L-arabinose 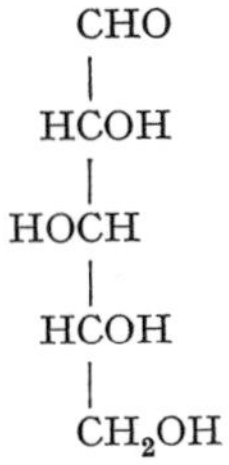   D-xylose 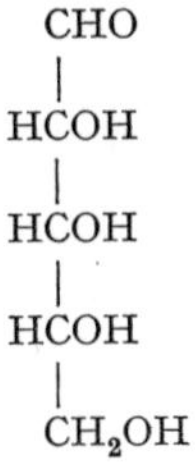   D-ribose 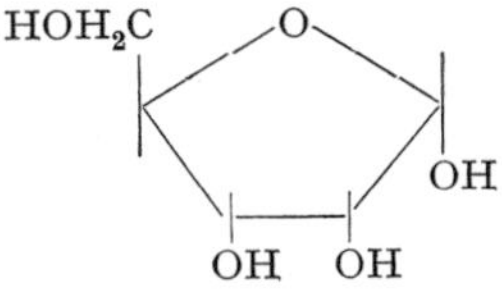   D-ribose
                                               (HAWORTH)

SPOEHR, who carried out important researches in connection with the growth of *chlorella* by photosynthesis, showed that the formation of pentoses during photosynthesis is controlled mainly by the amount of water present and the temperature: low water contents and high temperatures cause an accelerated formation of pentoses and a proportional diminution in hexoses. This phenomenon is observed in various plant materials grown in arid countries.

Pentoses can be easily determined analytically by treating the plant material with a strong acid, such as HCl or H_2SO_4, which causes the conversion of pentoses into furfural through dehydration:

$$
\begin{array}{ccc}
\text{CHOH—CHOH} & & \text{CH—CH} \\
|\qquad\quad | & \xrightarrow{-3H_2O} & \|\quad\ \| \\
\text{CH}_2\quad \text{HCOH}\cdot\text{CHO} & & \text{CH}\quad \text{C}\cdot\text{CHO} \\
\ \ \ \text{OH} & & \ \ \ \text{O} \\
\end{array}
$$

$$\text{pentose} \qquad\qquad\qquad\qquad\qquad \text{furfural}$$

This reaction is being exploited industrially for the conversion of pentose rich waste plant materials such as corn cobs into furfural, the latter being easily polymerized for use in the plastics industry.

The pentoses reduce Fehling's solution, but in contrast to hexoses, they cannot be fermented by yeasts.

The last, fifth, carbon atom of pentose if methylated gives six-member compounds called methyl pentoses. Such compounds might be regarded as hexoses although they are usually accepted as pentose derivatives. One of these is L-rhamnose, a common constituent of some glucosides, such as the anthoxanthins (flavonoids) (see Chapter 15).

$$
\begin{array}{l}
\text{CHO} \\
|\\
\text{HCOH} \\
|\\
\text{HCOH} \qquad\quad \text{L-rhamnose}\\
|\\
\text{HOCH} \\
|\\
\text{CH}\cdot\text{OH} \\
|\\
\text{CH}_3
\end{array}
$$

Transformation of sugars

(a) *Enolization of hexoses—the* LOBRY DE BRUYN *transformation.* From the epimeric hexoses, those which differ from each other only by their configuration at carbon atom 2, can be transformed into each other by heating them in alkaline solution. Thus, when D-glucose is treated accordingly a mixture of three sugars of the following composition is obtained: D-glucose, 65%; D-fructose, 31%; D-mannose, 2.4%.

This transformation is easy to perform in the laboratory and is of importance in connection with non-enzymatic browning of food during processing (see Chapter 20). However, there is no indication whatsoever that it can take place *in vivo*; first, because the plant can hardly have a pH higher than 7 which is required by this reaction and, secondly, because no such equilibrium involving the above proportions has ever been found in plant material, especially so with regards to D-mannose, which has never been found in the free state, being found only as a polysaccharide.

(b) *Phosphorylation of hexoses.* In nature, however, an easy and quick transformation of hexoses at ordinary temperatures takes place by means of an enzyme, *hexokinase*, which imparts to the sugars the energy required for their transformation by means of their phosphorylation.

It will be recalled that chromatograms taken the very first few seconds after the beginning of photosynthesis showed the presence of PGA, the phosphoglyceric acid, the next spot taken containing glucose-1-phosphate.

$$
\begin{array}{ccccc}
\text{CHO} & & \text{CHOH} & & \text{CHO} \\
| & & \| & & | \\
\text{HCOH} & & \text{COH} & & \text{HOCH} \\
| & & | & & | \\
\text{HOCH} & \rightleftharpoons & \text{HOCH} & \rightleftharpoons & \text{HOCH} \\
| & & | & & | \\
\text{HCOH} & & \text{HCOH} & & \text{HCOH} \\
| & & | & & | \\
\text{HCOH} & & \text{HCOH} & & \text{HCOH} \\
| & & | & & | \\
\text{CH}_2\text{OH} & & \text{CH}_2\text{OH} & & \text{CH}_2\text{OH} \\
\text{D-glucose} & & & & \text{D-mannose}
\end{array}
$$

$$
\begin{array}{c}
\text{CH}_2\text{OH} \\
| \\
\text{C}=\text{O} \\
| \\
\text{HOCH} \\
| \\
\text{HCOH} \\
| \\
\text{HCOH} \\
| \\
\text{CH}_2\text{OH} \\
\text{D-fructose}
\end{array}
$$

enolization of hexoses—LOBRY DE BRUYN transformation

References p. 60

All the other sugars appeared in their phosphorylated states. HARDEN AND YOUNG were the first to observe the presence of a phosphorylated sugar during the catabolic process of fermentation: when inorganic phosphate was added to a fermenting glucose solution the phosphate became quickly bound to the glucose and the ester they isolated was found to be a fructose diphosphate. This phosphoric ester of fructose, as well as the other corresponding esters, has been named after various investigators. Here are the formulae of four such hexose esters:

glucopyranose-6-phosphate
(ROBISON ester)

fructofuranose-6-phosphate
(NEUBERG ester)

α-glucopyranose-1-phosphate
(CORI ester)

β-fructofuranose-1,6-diphosphate
(HARDEN–YOUNG ester)

The hexose phosphorylation is catalyzed by the enzyme *hexokinase*, which is found in all higher plants and which has been isolated in its crystalline form from yeast; its behavior has been investigated in particular in potatoes and in the leaves of spinach. In the same way as many other enzymes, hexokinase acts jointly with ATP—adenosine triphosphate. This most important compound is a complicated molecule consisting of adenine (a purine), ribose (a pentose) and three molecules of phosphoric acid:

ATP—adenosine triphosphate

The same compound, but containing only two molecules of phosphoric acid is called ADP, adenosine diphosphate, and containing only one molecule of phosphoric acid, AMP, adenosine monophosphate or adenylic acid.

When *hexokinase* reacts with glucose, ATP transfers one of its molecules of phosphoric acid to the sugar, and thus transforms itself into ADP:

$$\text{glucose} + \text{ATP} \xrightarrow{\textit{hexokinase}} \text{glucose-6-phosphate} + \text{ADP}$$

The equilibrium in this reaction tends strongly to the right since the bond by which the last phosphoric acid molecule is bound to ATP is an energy-rich bond which, on hydrolysis, supplies an energy of 8–12,000 cal per mol. This is the case also with the second phosphoric acid molecule in contrast to that nearest to the ribose, which has an ordinary bond yielding 3,000 cal per mol. The bond connecting phosphoric acid to the glucose is also one of 3,000 cal per mol. The energy-rich bonds in this case are usually denoted by the sign ~ instead of a dash or a dot.

Thus, ATP is an important energy carrier and one of the main energy stores for energy transfer in plant tissues. The very same enzyme has been recently found to take part in the mechanism of accumulation of the sun energy during photosynthesis. This action of transphosphorylation performed by the enzyme *hexokinase* apparently requires the presence of Mg^{2+} ion.

Glucose-6-phosphate, in its turn, can be transformed into glucose-1-phosphate by means of another enzyme, *phosphoglucomutase* and by still another, *phosphoglucoisomerase*, into fructose-6-phosphate. The overall transformations of the phosphorylated hexoses can be represented as follows:

$$\text{glucose} + \text{ATP} \xrightarrow{\textit{hexokinase}} \text{glucose 6-ph} \xrightarrow{\textit{mutase}} \text{glucose-1-ph}$$
$$\big\updownarrow \textit{isomerase}$$
$$\text{fructose-6-ph} + \text{ATP} \xrightarrow{\textit{hexokinase}} \text{fructose-1,6-diphosphate}$$

In other words, such a transformation involves three enzymes and two molecules of ATP. These are the very first steps of the catabolic processes, respiration and fermentation. In a reverse direction, these transformations take place also in the anabolic process of photosynthesis.

Enzyme-catalyzed interconversions of other hexose-monophosphates, such as mannose-6-phosphate and galactose-1-phosphate are also known; however, the enzymes engaged in some of these transformations have not been sufficiently purified and identified except one enzyme (*uridyl transferase*)

References p. 60

involving uridine diphosphate glucose (UDPG) as a cofactor, which converts galactose-1-phosphate to glucose-1-phosphate by the Walden inversion.

uridine diphosphate glucose (UDPG)

REFERENCES

[1] W. W. PIGMAN AND R. M. GOEPP JR., *Chemistry of Carbohydrates*, Academic Press, New York, 1948.
[2] J. B. S. BRAVERMAN, The mechanism of the interaction of SO_2 with certain sugars, *J. Sci. Food Agr.*, 4 (1953) 540; J. B. S. BRAVERMAN AND J. KOPELMAN, Sugar sulfonates and their behavior, *Food Sci.*, 26 (1961) 248.

SELECTED BIBLIOGRAPHY TO CHAPTER 5

See Selected Bibliography to Chapter 8.

CHAPTER 6

FERMENTATION

La vie sans air

Louis Pasteur

The breakdown of simple sugars into alcohol has probably been known since prehistoric times. Ancient Egyptians were well acquainted with the art of fermenting fruit juices into alcoholic beverages and were even able to preserve them from further spoilage in golden jars. One hundred and fifty years ago (in 1810) Gay-Lussac showed that the reaction of alcoholic fermentation can be described as follows:

$$C_6H_{12}O_6 = 2\ C_2H_5OH + 2\ CO_2$$

Fifty years later (1861) Pasteur demonstrated that fermentation caused by living yeast cells is an *anaerobic process*, *i.e.*, does not require the participation of atmospheric oxygen; in other words, that by means of this process yeast organisms are able to draw their required energy from glucose in the absence of oxygen, in his own words: "la vie sans air."

In contrast to the other important catabolic process, respiration, during which glucose undergoes complete breakdown in the presence of oxygen into CO_2 and H_2O, products with very low potential energy, fermentation converts glucose into alcohol which, in itself, still contains quite a large proportion of energy.

The above description of fermentation given by Gay-Lussac describes only the overall reaction but it does not show, however, the true biochemical mechanism. The first most important step towards the clarification of this mechanism was made by the Buchners (1897) who found that fermentation can also be achieved without the presence of living yeast cells. Buchners succeeded in causing the breakdown of glucose into ethanol by using a cell-free extract of the yeast, thereby showing for the first time that such metabolic processes are carried out and catalyzed by ferments or enzymes.

While CO_2 and ethanol are the principal products of alcoholic fermentation, it was soon discovered that a number of other products are present

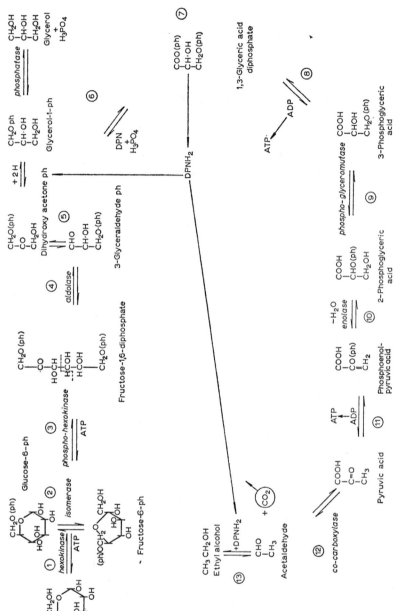

Fig. 10. The Embden–Meyerhof scheme of fermentation.

during this process (although in very small amounts), such as acetaldehyde (CH_3CHO), glycerol ($CH_2OH \cdot CH \cdot OH \cdot CH_2 \cdot OH$), pyruvic acid ($CH_3CO \cdot COOH$), and others. It took quite a long time and involved the participation of a large number of well-known investigators, among them ROBISON, CORI, NEUBERG, HARDEN and YOUNG, before a final scheme was drawn up by MEYERHOF AND EMBDEN, which is now universally accepted.

The EMBDEN–MEYERHOF scheme

According to this scheme (Fig. 10), the first steps (1, 2, 3) in fermentation are the phosphorylation of the hexoses, as described above, by means of the enzyme *hexokinase*, which contains ATP as its prosthetic group. *Hexokinase*, with the aid of two other enzymes, *phospho-glucomutase* and *phospho-glucoisomerase*, brings about the presence of four phosphorylated sugars, glucose-6-phosphate, glucose-1-phosphate, fructose-6-phosphate and, finally, fructose 1,6-diphosphate.

This last phosphorylated hexose has acquired now, due to ATP, the amount of energy required for its fission into two trioses: dihydroxy acetone phosphate and the 3-glyceraldehyde phosphate. This fission (4) is brought about by the enzyme *aldolase* and the two trioses are in equilibrium (5). As long as the fermentation proceeds normally without external interference, this equilibrium tends towards 3-glyceraldehyde phosphate since the latter is being continuously oxidized to 3-phosphoglyceric acid (6, 7). This oxidation is brought about by *dehydrogenase* containing DPN (diphosphopyridin nucleotide) as its prosthetic group. The action of this enzyme will be described later. At this point another molecule of phosphate attaches itself to the glyceric acid only to be transferred back to ADP (8).

The 3-phosphoglyceric acid is now isomerized (9) by the enzyme *phospho-glyceromutase* into 2-phosphoglyceric acid and then, by losing a molecule of water, is converted (10) into phosphopyruvic acid (enol form), which loses its phosphoric acid molecule to ADP, thereby forming a molecule of ATP which re-enters the cycle (11). In the next step, the keto form of pyruvic acid is decarboxylated by the loss of one molecule of CO_2. This step is performed by the enzyme *carboxylase* (12) having as its prosthetic group a phosphorylated thiamine (vitamin B_1).

The product remaining after decarboxylation is obviously acetaldehyde, which is now hydrogenated by the above-mentioned DPN into ethyl alcohol (13). If at this stage any interference occurs, *e.g.* the binding of acetaldehyde with sulfur dioxide, DPN, which will be prevented from delivering the hydrogen to the acetaldehyde, will give it to the second triose formed from fructose-1,6-phosphate at the beginning of the cycle (5), dihydroxy acetone phosphate. This latter will then be reduced to glycerol and the result will be that only one half of the hexose will be converted into acetaldehyde, while the other half will produce glycerol. This type of fermentation, called "NEUBERG's second form of fermentation," has been extensively used industrially in the production of glycerol.

Some yeast enzymes

Enzymes found in the yeast are numerous, and those taking part in alcoholic fermentation can be divided into four categories:

(a) *Phosphorylating enzymes*, the function of which is to attach phosphoric acid groups to the hexoses or to detach them from pyruvic acid or from glycerol. The most important enzyme in this category is *hexokinase* containing the coenzyme ATP, which has been described earlier. Apparently the yeast cell has not created, as yet, enzymes capable of breaking up the fructose molecule into two trioses without it being phosphorylated first. In order to make this possible, appreciable energy is required and this is amply supplied by the energy-rich bonds of ATP.

(b) *Oxidizing–reducing enzymes*. The most important in this category is *acetaldehyde dehydrogenase* containing as its prosthetic group DPN, diphosphopyridine-nucleotide. Although DPN is now the universally accepted name for this prosthetic group, one often finds in the literature the following synonyms for the same compound: *Coenzyme I, Cozymase*. Lately this coenzyme is called more correctly: nicotineamide-adenine-dinucleotide (NAD).

This coenzyme combines, in its structure, nicotinamide, D-ribose, phosphoric acid and adenine, as follows:

DPN (diphosphopyridine-nucleotide)

The purely chemical action of this coenzyme can be represented as follows where R is ribose and R' is the remaining molecule containing phosphoric acid, ribose and adenine (see formula p. 65).

This enzyme plays the main controlling role in the entire alcoholic fermentation cycle.

(c) *The carboxylase enzyme*. The decarboxylation of pyruvic acid to acetaldehyde is catalyzed by the enzyme *carboxylase*, which has as its prosthetic group diphosphorylated thiamine. Thiamine (or vitamin B_1) is known to consist of a pyrimidine nucleus and a thiazol ring, as shown by the structural

DPN (oxidized) DPNH$_2$ (reduced)

formula. The phosphorylated form of thiamine forms the coenzyme of carboxylase, *co-carboxylase*.

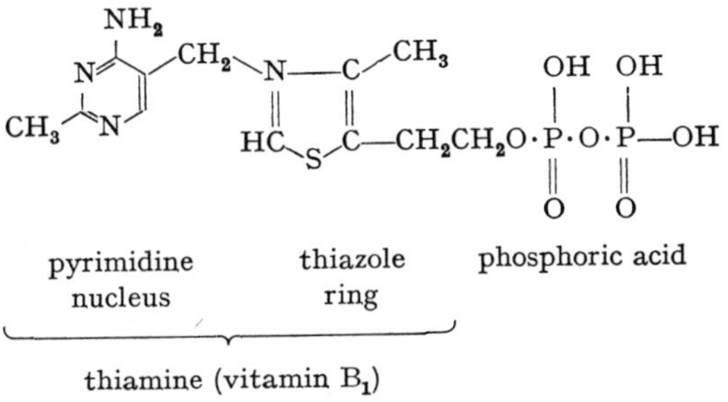

pyrimidine nucleus thiazole ring phosphoric acid

thiamine (vitamin B$_1$)

formula of *co-carboxylase*

The chemical mechanism whereby *co-carboxylase* acts as a cofactor in the enzymatic decarboxylation of pyruvic acid is not yet fully understood. It is probable that thioctic acid, coenzyme A and DPN participate as co-factors. However, it has been established that sulfur dioxide is capable of splitting the thiazole ring from the pyrimidine nucleus, thereby destroying its vitamin potency. One of the reasons why SO$_2$ is an active preservative of foods against fermentation may be the fact that it hinders the enzymatic action of decarboxylation during fermentation.

(d) The last group of enzymes taking part in fermentation deals with reactions of transformation, isomerization, enolization, etc., and includes: *mutases, enolases, isomerases* and *aldolase*. Most of these enzymes have not been isolated in the pure state nor has their structure been elucidated.

The energetics of fermentation

The foregoing remarks show that every molecule of fermented hexose produces two molecules of ethanol and two molecules of carbon dioxide. However, when acetaldehyde is bound by sulfur dioxide or sulfites the net result is only one molecule of acetaldehyde and one molecule of glycerol.

References p. 72

As far as the ADP–ATP system is concerned, two molecules of ATP are used up during the phosphorylation to fructose-1,6-phosphate at the beginning of the process and are thereby converted into ADP. However, four fresh molecules of ATP are formed towards the end of the reaction path.

The total energy loss during the fermentation process is calculated to be about 50.000 cal for each gram molecule of glucose fermented:

$$C_6H_{12}O_6 = 2\ CO_2 + 2\ C_2H_5OH + 50,000\ cal$$

Of this total energy, about half is required by the two molecules of ADP to bind the last energy-rich phosphate in order to form ATP. The rest of the energy is dissipated in the form of heat, for we are well aware that during fermentation a temperature slightly higher than the surroundings is maintained. The optimum temperature for the fermentation process is about $25°C$ and nature seems to be concerned with upholding these conditions.

As mentioned earlier, alcoholic fermentation can proceed also without living yeast cells if "yeast juice" is used instead. Such fermentation is less active and its rate is much slower. The only plausible explanation for this is that, while in yeast juice the enzymes are all distributed at random, they are well-ordered in an organized cell. Although we know very little as yet regarding cell organization, one may surmise that the enzymes in the cell resemble a well-arranged production-line in a factory, each enzyme being ready to attack its specific substrate and transmit it to the other enzyme for the next operation.

Furthermore, fermentation by yeast juice requires a constant addition of inorganic phosphate in order to maintain the level of ATP required for the process. During fermentation with living yeast cells, ADP finds its required phosphate in the right place and at the right moment, as shown in the EMBDEN–MEYERHOF scheme.

Other fermentations

Normally, alcoholic fermentation is at its optimum when the pH of the substrate is about 5. However, when the pH is raised into the alkaline region the course of the yeast fermentation is changed and, under these conditions, glycerol and acetic acid are produced as well as ethyl alcohol and carbon dioxide. In this type of fermentation, acetaldehyde, instead of being reduced to ethanol, undergoes a dismutation in the presence of the enzyme, *aldehyde mutase*, to form alcohol and acetic acid:

$$2\ CH_3CHO + H_2O \longrightarrow C_2H_5OH + CH_3COOH$$

Glycerol, on the other hand, is formed since acetaldehyde is no longer available as an acceptor for $DPNH_2$, which therefore reduces dihydroxy-acetone phosphate to glycerol phosphate. The overall reaction, sometimes called "NEUBERG's third form of fermentation," can be expressed as follows:

$$2\ C_6H_{12}O_6 + H_2O \rightarrow 2\ CO_2 + C_2H_5OH + CH_3COOH + 2\ CH_2OH\cdot CHOH\cdot CH_2OH$$

hexose ethanol acetic acid glycerol

It has been observed that *Zygosaccharomyces acidifaciens*, a yeast often found in decomposed foods, undergoes this type of fermentation.

In addition to alcoholic fermentation, hexoses undergo a number of other fermentations by specific microorganisms, such as:

(a) acetic acid fermentation caused by *Acetobacter* which is made use of in the manufacture of vinegar from wine or from fruit juices;

(b) lactic acid fermentation caused by *Lactobacilli* which is made use of for preserving many vegetables in brine, such as sauerkraut, cucumbers, etc., and in the silage of plants;

(c) acetone–butanol fermentation caused by *Weizman bacillus* which was for some time extensively used industrially for the production of acetone;

(d) citric acid fermentation caused by the fungi *Aspergillus niger*, which is the basis of the mycological method now used exclusively for the production of citric acid;

(e) the fermentation of lactose into lactic acid used in the dairy industry for the production of various types of fermented milk, such as yogurt (by *Lactobacillus bulgaricus*), or buttermilk (by *Streptococcus lactis* or by *L. acidophilus*).

In all these and many other types of fermentation there are individual pathways using their own specific enzymes. There is reason to believe, however, that such processes have many similarities with the EMBDEN–MEYERHOF scheme and some of the enzymes taking part in these processes may even be identical. The whole subject is a part of the science of Industrial Microbiology or Biotechnology[1].

Glycogen, a polysaccharide, is the chief carbohydrate of animal muscle, there being relatively little free glucose in this tissue. During its ordinary metabolism in the muscle, glycolysis, glycogen undergoes breakdown and, if oxygen is lacking, finally forms lactic acid, two moles of L-lactic acid arising from each glucose unit in the polysaccharide. The reaction of this process, which is also anaerobic, is very similar to the EMBDEN–MEYERHOF scheme except for one single step, namely, the last one, in which pyruvic acid catalyzed by a specific enzyme *lactic dehydrogenase*, is converted into L-lactic acid. This particular *dehydrogenase* also contains DPN as its cofactor:

$$CH_3\cdot CO\cdot COOH + DPN\cdot H_2 \rightleftarrows CH_3\cdot CHOH\cdot COOH + DPN$$

pyruvic acid lactic acid

PASTEUR *effect*

As mentioned earlier, the catabolic process of fermentation was discovered by PASTEUR to be an anaerobic process, *i.e.*, proceeding in the absence of atmospheric oxygen. PASTEUR found, however, that when oxygen is introduced into fermenting media, fermentation is arrested, the yeasts beginning to respire and multiply. This phenomenon of anaerobic fermentation inhibition is known now under the title of the PASTEUR *reaction or effect*[2]. This effect does not appear when yeast juice is used instead of living yeast cells. However, it becomes apparent again if oxido-reductive enzymatic systems are added to the substrate. Thus, one can surmise that the PASTEUR effect is caused by some unknown enzyme.

However, in the light of present-day knowledge of the various changes brought about by the PASTEUR effect, it does not appear likely that such an enzyme would be the sole agent affecting the regulatory mechanism.

Numerous other suggestions have been made to explain the PASTEUR effect in yeast, and some of them have been reviewed by NORD AND WEIS[3], but as yet no direct proof has been forthcoming for the existence of a specific enzyme. It may well be that several factors operate simultaneously to produce the PASTEUR phenomenon.

MEYERHOF[4] himself does not exclude the possibility that a hemin-containing enzyme is responsible for the PASTEUR effect. However, since respiration also requires the oxidative steps of fermentation which involve DPN and ATP, at least up to the point of pyruvic acid (see KREBS' cycle, Chapter 18), he believes that the *common sharing* of coenzyme and enzyme systems is the true basis of the connection between fermentation and respiration. Most probably either a phosphorylation step or one involving dehydrogenation which is common to both processes competes for the required enzymes. The determining condition of the PASTEUR effect is, therefore, not the presence of oxygen but the presence of the process of respiration.

This relationship between the fermentation and respiration processes is important also from the point of view of food technology[5].

Bakers yeasts are, in this respect, of particular interest. These yeasts have to produce CO_2 quickly in the dough under anaerobic conditions and, on the other hand, they require oxygen for their growth and multiplication, since it is found to increase their output ten-fold. In fact it is sometimes customary to grow bakers yeasts for a short time under anaerobic conditions so that they may produce some alcohol which will inhibit the growth of all other wild microorganisms present. In the baking industry, therefore, specially adapted yeasts are used, whereas for the production of feed-yeasts, *Torula*, with strong aerobic characteristics, is employed.

Brewers yeasts are usually divided into two types, the "top" and "bottom" yeasts:

(a) "Top yeasts" are very similar to "bakers yeast"; they grow in any substrate, form an abundance of gas which thus brings them to the top of the brewing vats. This type is very common in nature, shows easy spore-forming and serves for baking, wine and beer manufacture since it is easily adaptable to both the aerobic and anaerobic metabolisms. Examples: *Sacch. cerevisiae, Sacch. ellipsoideus.*

(b) "Bottom yeasts" are mostly used as brewers yeast in the manufacture of beer on the Continent in Europe. They are usually found at the bottom of the fermenting vats and they produce gas slowly, especially at the beginning, since their metabolism is mainly anaerobic. Yeasts of this type are not spore-forming and they are not commonly found in nature. Examples: *Sacch. carlsbergensis* and *Sacch. validus.*

There is reason to believe that "bottom yeasts" are a good example of adaptation and that they are nothing else but "top yeasts" which have adapted themselves to anaerobic conditions. It is rather difficult to set up very rigid lines of demarcation between the two types, since it is known, for instance, that if "bottom yeasts" are strongly aerated for several hours they acquire aerobic features.

By-products of alcoholic fermentation

During alcoholic fermentation a number of by-products are formed, such as fusel oil, consisting mainly of iso-amyl alcohol, succinic acid, various esters and sometimes even bitter substances. The sources of all these are not the hexoses but various foreign matter which happen to constitute the particular raw material undergoing fermentation, *e.g.* grapes for wine production, barley for beer, or molasses for alcohol.

Iso-amyl alcohol, for instance, is produced during ethanolic fermentation from leucin, an amino acid.

$$\frac{CH_3}{CH_3}{>}CH \cdot CH_2 \cdot CH(NH_2) \cdot COOH + H_2O \longrightarrow \frac{CH_3}{CH_3}{>}CH \cdot CH_2CH_2OH + CO_2 + NH_3$$

leucin   iso-amyl alcohol

The source of succinic acid, on the other hand, is glutamic acid, this being subjected to oxidative deamination and decarboxylation, see formula p. 70.

The specific flavors of many wines come from the presence of some higher alcohols or esters. Such alcohols are rather toxic and the higher the alcohol the stronger the effect of the wine.

References p. 72

$$
\begin{array}{ccccc}
\text{COOH} & & \text{COOH} & & \\
| & & | & & \\
\text{CH}\cdot\text{NH}_2 & & \text{C}=\text{O} & \text{CHO} & \text{COOH} \\
| & \xrightarrow[-\text{NH}_3]{+\frac{1}{2}\text{O}_2} & | & | & | \\
\text{CH}_2 & & \text{CH}_2 \xrightarrow{-\text{CO}_2} \text{CH}_2 \xrightarrow{+\frac{1}{2}\text{O}_2} \text{CH}_2 \\
| & & | & | & | \\
\text{CH}_2 & & \text{CH}_2 & \text{CH}_2 & \text{CH}_2 \\
| & & | & | & | \\
\text{COOH} & & \text{COOH} & \text{COOH} & \text{COOH} \\
\text{glutamic} & & \alpha\text{-ketoglutaric} & \text{succinic} & \text{succinic} \\
\text{acid} & & \text{acid} & \text{semialdehyde} & \text{acid}
\end{array}
$$

The bitter flavor of beer is partly due to tyrosol, an alcohol produced during fermentation from the amino acid, tyrosine, by the process of deamination and decarboxylation:

$$
\text{HO}\!\!\left\langle\bigcirc\right\rangle\!\!\text{CH}_2\cdot\underset{\underset{\text{NH}_2}{|}}{\text{CH}}\cdot\text{COOH} \longrightarrow \text{HO}\!\!\left\langle\bigcirc\right\rangle\!\!\text{CH}_2\cdot\text{CH}_2\text{OH}
$$

$$\qquad\qquad\text{tyrosine}\qquad\qquad\qquad\qquad\text{tyrosol}$$

Methods of preventing fermentation

One of the major objectives of a food technologist is to preserve foods from spoilage by fermentation. This can be achieved by sterilizing the food in hermetically closed containers, which is normally done by physical methods—application of heat or of radiation in various forms. All these methods destroy the yeasts and other microorganisms and inactivate their enzymatic systems.

In addition, there are a number of chemicals which also have this preserving ability, or rather the ability to prevent fermentation. There are many poisons which stop fermentation, such as heavy metals, cyanides, fluorides, etc., however, it is clear that all these could not be used for preserving foods, since they are poisonous to both man and animals.

Of the chemicals permissible for use in foods, there are a few which can prevent fermentation even if used in very small quantities. The following list gives some of these preserving agents and their applications:

(a) benzoic acid, C_6H_5COOH; its ethyl- and propyl-esters, those of p-hydroxybenzoic acid or their sodium salts (more soluble than the acid)—used in fruit juices or preserves jams and marmalades and many other similar foods to the extent of 0.1 %;

(b) boric acid—used in some countries for the preservation of butter;

(c) propionic acid, $CH_3CH_2\cdot COOH$—used in bread to prevent ropiness;

(d) formic acid, $HCOOH$, and salicylic acid, $C_6H_4\cdot OH\cdot COOH$—both used in some European countries for the preservation of fruit juices and other foods, but not allowed in the United States or in the United Kingdom;

(e) sulfurous acid, SO_2, or sulfites—widely used for food preservation;

(f) sorbic acid, $CH_3CH=CH \cdot CH=CH \cdot COOH$—recently came into use largely to prevent mold formation.

It will be noticed that all these food preservatives are acids, however, their action cannot be explained as being due to their acidic nature. In most cases, they are active only as undissociated molecules. Benzoates are thought to combine with the protoplasm of microorganisms thus preventing their growth and activities, in fact, probably acting as anti-metabolites. Sulfites are strong reducing agents—they combine readily with atmospheric oxygen, thereby excluding any possibility for the micro-organisms to develop and multiply. Since sulfites cause the breakdown of thiamine, which serves in its phosphorylated form as the prosthetic group to the important *carboxylase* enzyme, one might assume some activity of these preservatives in that direction.

An important point to remember with such chemical preservatives is that they all are active only at low pH. With the rise of pH above 4 their activity falls off considerably. Some of these chemicals are found in nature and often constitute quite a large part in the composition of fruits, etc., for instance, benzoic acid is found in plums and especially in cranberries to the extent of 0.2 %. SO_2 is the most convenient of all the chemical food preservatives since, in most cases, it can be easily driven off in acid media by heating or by applying a strong vacuum. Being a strong reducing agent, SO_2 also preserves the vitamin C but destroys vitamin B_1.

Quite recently[6,7] a new preserving agent, a diethyl ester of pyrocarbonic acid, which showed a remarkable capability for arresting fermentation in fruit juices, was put on the market. The quantity to be used depends largely upon the kind of microorganism and varies from 0.05 % for bacteria to 1 pro mille for molds.

This ester is rapidly hydrolyzed in an aqueous medium, giving ethanol and CO_2:

$$C_2H_5-O-\underset{\underset{O}{\|}}{C}-O-\underset{\underset{O}{\|}}{C}-O-C_2H_5 \xrightarrow{+H_2O} 2\ C_2H_5OH + 2\ CO_2$$

It is completely hydrolyzed after 22 hours and has the advantage of leaving only traces of alcohol and carbon dioxide, both quite harmless sub-stances. Apparently the ester combines with some enzymes of the micro-organisms, the remainder being hydrolyzed.

References p. 72

REFERENCES

[1] S. C. PRESCOTT AND C. G. DUNN, *Industrial Microbiology*, 3rd edn., McGraw-Hill Publishing Co., 1951.
[2] L. PASTEUR, *Compt. rend.*, 52 (1861) 1260.
[3] F. F. NORD AND S. WEISS, Fermentation and Respiration, in A. H. COOK, *The Chemistry and Biology of Yeasts*, Academic Press, New York, 1958, p. 357.
[4] O. MEYERHOF, Recent advances in the study of metabolic reactions of Yeast Preparations, *Am. Scientist*, 40 (1952) 482, 517.
[5] M. INGRAM, *An Introduction to the Biology of Yeasts*, Pitman Press, Ltd., London, 1955.
[6] K. HENNIG, Pyrokohlensäure-Diäthylester, ein neues gärhemmendes Mittel, *Deut. Lebensm.-Rundschau*, 55 (1959) 297.
[7] K. MAYER UND H. LÜTHI, Versuche mit Pyrokohlensäure-Diäthylester, einem neuen Getränkekonservierungsmittel, *Mitt. Gebiete Lebensm. u. Hyg.*, 51 (1960) 132.

SELECTED BIBLIOGRAPHY TO CHAPTER 6

See Selected Bibliography to Chapter 8.

CHAPTER 7

CARBOHYDRATES — OLIGOSACCHARIDES

When two or three molecules of monosaccharides (monoses) are joined together they form disaccharides or trisaccharides, respectively. Such combined sugars are given the general name of *oligosaccharides* (oligo = few). These can be formed of either the same or of different monoses. Thus, for instance, maltose is formed of two glucose molecules, while in sucrose one molecule of glucose is bound to one molecule of fructose.

Disaccharides

Disaccharides may be regarded as glycosides in which one molecule plays the role of an aglucone bound to another monose molecule with the elimination of H_2O. In accordance with this definitions, when studying the structure of disaccharides, one has to examine in each case the following points:

(1) *Which monoses constitute a given disaccharide?* This can usually be found by acid hydrolysis and subsequent determination of the resulting constituents: if only one monose is found the indication is that two molecules of the same monose created the disaccharide (as in the case of maltose mentioned above). In the case of sucrose, however, equal quantities of glucose and fructose will be found in the resulting mixture after hydrolysis.

(2) *In what configuration do they appear, α or β?* This can be easily determined according to ARMSTRONG by using the enzymes α- and *β-glucosidases*. If the bond between the two molecules of the disaccharide is an α-bond it will be hydrolyzed by *α-glucosidase (maltase)* which is obtained from germinating barley. If the bond has a β-configuration, the hydrolysis will be catalyzed by *β-glucosidase (emulsin)* found in the seeds of *Rosaceae*.

(3) *Which monose plays the role of the aglucone?*

(4) *At which carbon atom has the bond between the two monoses been formed?* Is it a 1:1 bond or 1:4 or 1:6 bond?

(5) Finally, *what is the size of the rings in both monoses; are they pyranose of furanose?* The latter points are usually elucidated by methylation or acetylation procedures applied to the disaccharide in question followed by hydrolysis to single monoses.

There are only three disaccharides found in nature in the free state: *sucrose* in sugar cane and sugar beet and in many fruits, *lactose* in milk, and *trehalose*, which has been identified as the principal carbohydrate component of the blood of some insects. All other disaccarides are "building stones" in many polysaccharides, such as *maltose,* the product of starch hydrolysis, *cellobiose* —from cellulose, etc.

The structure of the disaccarides is presented here, some examples of the various types being given:

(a) The case when the two monoses are the same, *e.g. maltose:*

maltose: 4-D-α-glucose-α-D-glucopyranoside

When starch is hydrolyzed either by acid or by the enzymes *maltase* or *diastase,* contained in germinating barley, a yield of 80 % of maltose is obtained. This disaccharide is built of two molecules of α-glucose, bound in the position 1:4, *i.e.,* carbon atom 1 of one glucose molecule is bound in a glucosidic bond to carbon atom 4 of the second molecule. It is evident that the carbonyl carbon atom of the second molecule is free, hence the maltose itself can have two stereoisomeric configurations, α and β. Indeed, maltose can undergo mutarotation (from $[\alpha]_D + 130°$ to $[\alpha]_D + 112°$) and is found to be a reducing sugar, *i.e.,* it reduces Fehling's reagent.

(b) *Cellobiose* is also built of two glucose molecules. However, the "gluconic" one is β-glucose and, therefore, the glucosidic bond, although 1:4, is a β-bond:

cellobiose: 4-D-glucose-β-D-glucopyranoside

Cellobiose is the building stone for cellulose, reduces Fehling's solution, and can exist in both α and β configurations. It does not exist in nature in the free state.

(c) The case of two identical monoses, both glucose, both having the β-configuration exists in the disaccharide *gentiobiose.*

gentiobiose: 6-β-D-glucose-β-D-glucopyranoside

This disaccharide is not found in nature in the free state but is a part of the cyanogenic glucoside amygdalin in bitter almonds. It is also a reducing sugar and the bond between the two monoses is 1:6.

(d) To end this series of disaccharides built of glucose alone is the example of *trehalose*, a non-reducing sugar since its glucosidic bond is 1:1. Both glucoses are of the α-configuration. Trehalose is produced by a number of fungi and yeasts and is found in the blood of insects.

trehalose: 1-α-D-glucopyranosyl-α-D-glucopyranoside

As examples of disaccharides built of two different monoses the following are the most important:

(e) Two hexoses, both pyranoses, are the components of *lactose* (milk sugar). Lactose consists of glucose and galactose. It is the principal sugar in cow's milk, reduces Fehling's reagent and is hydrolyzed by emulsin and by the enzyme *lactase*, which is a β-glucosidase; its structural formula is:

lactose: 4-D-glucose-β-D-galactopyranoside

Lactose could, therefore, exist in two configurations, α and β. On oxidation of lactose and subsequent hydrolysis one obtains galactose and glucoronic acid. This indicates that the free carbonyl group is attached to the glucose and not to the galactose.

(f) The most important disaccharide, widely distributed in nature is *sucrose*. In its free state it is found in all photosynthetic plants and constitutes the principal disaccharide in the diet of animals. The current world production of sucrose is approximately 35 million tons per year, one-third of which is extracted from sugar beets and two-thirds from sugar cane.

Sucrose is built from two different monoses, α-glucose and β-fructose, the first a pyranose and the second in its furanose form. The glucosidic bond is 1:2 between the two first carbon atoms. Hence, sucrose has no free carbonyl group and therefore does not reduce Fehling's solutions and does not combine with sulfur dioxide or with amino acids. This fact is of importance in the relation of sucrose to browning (Chapter 20).

Despite the considerable importance of this disaccharide the structural formula of sucrose was established by HAWORTH only in 1927 and its first enzymatic synthesis performed by HASSID in 1944.

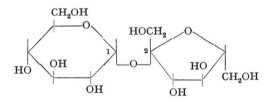

sucrose: 2-D-glucopyranosyl-β-D-fructofuranoside

It is evident that sucrose cannot undergo mutarotation—this is probably the reason why sucrose is easily crystallizable in contrast to many other sugars.

However, sucrose is apt to hydrolyze easily into its components, glucose and fructose, with the aid of weak acids or of the enzyme *invertase*. This phenomenon is called *inversion* and the resulting mixture of the two components—*invert sugar* due to the fact that the positive sign of the optical rotation of sucrose has been now inverted into the negative sign of the optical rotation of the mixture:

$$\text{sucrose} + H_2O \xrightarrow{\text{inversion}} D(+)\text{-glucose} + D(—)\text{-fructose}$$
$$[\alpha]_D = +66.5° \qquad\qquad [\alpha]_D = +52.5° \quad [\alpha]_D = —92°$$
$$\text{mixture: } [\alpha]_D = —20°$$

Honey consists mainly of invert sugar.

Sucrose biosynthesis

HASSID AND DOUDOROFF[1] succeeded in synthesizing sucrose for the first time with the aid of a specific enzyme *sucrose phosphorylase* isolated from the microorganism *Pseudomonas saccharophila* and purified by repeated precipitation with ammonium sulfate. In this synthesis the method of vacuum infiltration and flotation was used: plant tissue was vacuumized and floated in distilled water for 24 hours after which all of its sucrose had disappeared; the tissue was then floated in a 10 % solution of glucose-phosphate in the presence of the enzyme and sucrose was immediately observed to form in increasing quantities:

$$\text{glucose-1-phosphate} + \text{fructose} \rightleftarrows \text{sucrose} + H_3PO_4$$

This reaction proceeds only in the living cell and could not be repeated *in vitro*. The enzyme *sucrose phosphorylase* is apparently very specific and did not work when the above substrate was substituted by fructose 1-phosphate + glucose.

Trisaccharides

Trisaccharides are oligosaccharides comprising three monoses. Only two of them are found in nature in the free state, *raffinose*, in the juice of sugar beet and in cotton seed hulls, and the *gentianose* in gentian roots. Raffinose, on hydrolysis, gives equimolecular quantities of D-glucose, D-fructose and D-galactose; enzymatic hydrolysis with the aid of *emulsin* results in sucrose and galactose; in weak acid and with the aid of the *raffinase* enzyme raffinose is split into the disaccharide, melibiose, and fructose. The structure of raffinose has been established from these reactions as follows:

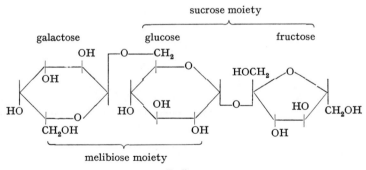

Raffinose

(α-D-galactopyranosyl-(1 → 6)-α-D-glucopyranosyl-(1 → 2)-β-D-fructofuranoside)

In naming trisaccharides and higher oligosaccharides, the nature of each glucosidic bond is denoted as shown in the designation of raffinose.

Maple sap and syrup which have been collected in a sterile condition contain only 0.0001 % of monosaccharides, however, they are found to contain at least five oligosaccharides; one fraction separated by a chromatographic method contained, in addition to sucrose, two trisaccharides: raffinose and glycosyl sucrose.

Sweetness of sugars

Of all the sugars contained in foods, D-fructose is known to be the sweetest. It is usual to compare the degree of sweetness of different sugars to sucrose, to which the number 100 has been assigned; fructose is then 173.3 and glucose only 74.3. It is obvious, therefore, that invert sugar is sweeter than the original sucrose from which it is formed: $(173.3 + 74.3):2 = 123.8$ for invert sugar. In industry a number of sucrose syrups are available, partially or totally inverted, having therefore different degrees of sweetness. These syrups are sold to the industry under the name of "liquid sugar" and can be prepared with a high concentration of solids, since fructose has a very high solubility and glucose does not readily crystallise[2].

TABLE II

DEGREE OF SWEETNESS OF VARIOUS SWEETENERS

Sugar	Degree of sweetness
Sucrose	100
Fructose	173.3
Glucose	74.3
Corn syrup	30
Molasses	74
Honey	97
Sorghum syrup	69
Saccharin	30,000–50,000
Dulcin (Sucrol)	20,000

Use of sugars in the food industry

With its 2,000 or more various types of products, the sweets industry has strict requirements for the sweeteners they use. The following is a list of some of their requirements:

(1) the relative sweetness of the various sugars;
(2) degree of solubility and crystallization;
(3) specific gravity of the syrups;
(4) water contents in dry sugars;

(5) hygroscopicity;
(6) specific flavor;
(7) preservation qualities and proneness toward fermenting;
(8) molecular weight;
(9) osmotic pressure;
(10) point of congelation;
(11) tendency towards browning.

Much depends on the suitable choice of the sugar taking into consideration its physical properties in the final product. For instance, if using sucrose, it is very important to know the possibilities of its inversion in the final product. The quality of the various syrups, prepared by the hydrolysis of starch and other natural polysaccharides, depends very much on the structure of these polysaccharides, *i.e.* whether they are linear or branched, on the size of the molecules, etc. All these qualities open up new possibilities for the manufacturer and modern sweetening materials are indeed tailor-made to the special instructions of the industry.

Sucrose is the most soluble of all sugars and it is quite easy to produce supersaturated solutions, but sucrose is also very easily crystallizable. However, by using invert sugar and various starch syrups, or if the sucrose can be quickly inverted in the product such crystallization, if undesirable, can be prevented. Corn syrups are even better for preventing crystallization, since they do not bring in the factor of hygroscopicity which is a fault of invert sugar.

Glucose is used in order to diminish the solubility of sucrose and also to regulate the relative degree of sweetness. Glucose also causes slower crystallization and in equal concentrations is less viscous.

In fruit juices, which are all more or less acid, sucrose undergoes inversion depending on the pH of the juice, the time, and the storage temperature.

In meat products, sugar is used for its ability to lessen the sharpness of salt and it also prevents discoloration. It is probable that this is due largely to the microorganisms or some enzymatic systems in the meat which are activated by the presence of sugar.

Starch is used in sausage products to prevent loss of humidity and subsequent shrinkage during manufacture, as well as during storage in refrigeration.

Of special interest is the claim of some investigators that meat is improved in flavor if the animals have been fed with some sugar close to their being slaughtered.

One of the causes of browning (Chapter 20) is the so-called MAILLARD, reaction, which consists of the combination of sugars with a free carbonyl group and amino acids. As a result, some very complicated, brown-colored

References p. 80

products, melanoidins, are formed. Hence, by the use of sugars in which this free carbonyl group is absent, browning can be avoided. Sucrose, for instance, will not cause browning in such cases, unless it undergoes inversion. Pure fructose is also inactive in the browning reaction. Glucose, on the other hand is very active.

REFERENCES

[1] W. F. HASSID AND M. DOUDOROFF, *Advances in Enzymol.*, 10 (1950) 123.
[2] P. R. DAVIS AND R. N. PRINCE, Liquid sugar in the food industry, in Use of sugars and other carbohydrates in the food industry, *Advances in Chem., Ser. No.* 12 (1955).

SELECTED BIBLIOGRAPHY TO CHAPTER 7

See Selected Bibliography to Chapter 8.

POLYSACCHARIDES

Food for thought

Classification

Unlike the sugars (mono- and disaccharides) the polysaccharides are not sweet. They are polymers of the simple monoses, hexoses or pentoses joined by glucosidic bonds, and occur in nature in many different variations. Like many other macromolecules, they are mostly insoluble in water or in the usual solvents and, when soluble to any degree, form colloidal suspensions. The polysaccharides may form long chains of polymers, as in the case of cellulose, or may be branched in two or even three dimensions, as in starches and pectins. In most cases these polymers can be hydrolyzed to their monomers, *i.e.*, by introducing a molecule of water at the position of the glucosidic bond.

Those polysaccharides which give, on hydrolysis, only one monomer are called *homopolysaccharides*. These comprise cellulose, starch, galactan, mannan, araban, xylan, levan, and dextran. Polysaccharides which are resolved by hydrolysis into two or more monomers are named *heteropolysaccharides* and comprise pectins, hemicelluloses, many mucilages, and resins.

Some authors classify the polysaccharides in three broad groups, according to their functions:

(a) the so-called "skeletal" polysaccharides which serve as rigid mechanical structures in plants (such as cellulose, hemicellulose, etc.);

(b) the "nutrient" polysaccharides which act as metabolic reserves (such as starch, glycogen);

(c) polysaccharides which have been regarded up-to-now as waste materials (*e.g.* those derived from bacteria and fungi).

In studying the composition of polysaccharides the term DP—*average degree of polymerization*—is often used. This is the average number of monomers present in a given polysaccharide. This can be determined according to the following formulae (where w = weight of a single component):

$$\text{number average} = \frac{\Sigma w}{\Sigma(w/\text{DP})}$$

$$\text{weight average} = \frac{\Sigma(w \cdot \text{DP})}{\Sigma w}$$

If the polymers were strictly homogeneous, the above averages would be identical. The larger the heterogeneity the smaller will be the value of the number average, which tends to represent the smaller units, whereas the *weight average* tends to express mainly the larger units, and its value, therefore, will be larger.

The molecular weights of most of the polysaccharides are usually determined by measuring their viscosity or by means of ultracentrifuging. Modern X-ray spectroscopy has confirmed that the majority of polysaccharides (with the exception of glycogen) are of a crystalline nature.

Cellulose

The fabrics or the structural materials of the entire plant world consist largely of cellulose. In quantity, therefore, cellulose occupies the first place in nature among all organic substances: it is estimated that half of the carbon dioxide in the atmosphere is fixed by the cellulose of the vegetable kingdom.

Cellulose is insoluble except in Schweitzer's reagent (ammoniacal solution of copper hydroxide) and is relatively resistant to hydrolysis by dilute acids. On complete acid hydrolysis, cellulose yields over 95% glucose; if previously acetylated and subsequently carefully hydrolyzed, however, cellulose yields a disaccharide, cellobiose. This proves that the monomer in cellulose is glucose-bound in a β-glucosidic bond at the 1:4 position.

According to HAWORTH and other investigators, the cellulose molecule is composed of a long chain of about 50 to 100 cellobiose units. About 50 of these chains are arranged in a bundle, called a *micelle*. A cellulose micelle is about 50 Å thick and 500 to 1,000 Å long. Because of its importance in the manufacture of paper, textiles, explosives, paints, etc., cellulose is the most widely studied polysaccharide[1]; only a brief description is presented here, however (see formula p. 84).

Molecular weights of cellulose from different sources, have been determined by the ultracentrifuge method; the values obtained range from 100,000 to 2,000,000. Apparently the length of the chain varies in different plants. The purest cellulose in nature has been isolated from the hair of the cotton linters. The cellulose from flax and that from ramie originate in their stems. Sisal and Manila hemp, used in the manufacture of ropes, contain the so-called leaf cellulose. X-ray diffraction methods showed the cellulose to consist of partly crystalline and partly amorphous areas. In the cellulose crystal the cellulose is arranged in long bundles, which gives the fibres extra strength; the molecules are close together and are probably held by hydrogen bonds between the oxygen atoms.

The free hydroxyls in positions 2, 3 and 6 are accessible to esterification, such as acetification or nitration. Such cellulose esters are soluble and are good solvents extensively used in industry. In the presence of CS_2 and NaOH, it is possible to perform a partial xanthation (cellulose xanthate) and from it to regenerate the cellulose in the form of viscose rayon (manufacture of cellophane used for food packaging). The DP (degree of polymerization) of cellulose may be about 100 in small disintegrated units and as much as 2,000 in natural samples.

Man and carnivorous animals are unable to digest cellulose since they lack the necessary enzymes for its breakdown in their intestines. However, many microorganisms and protozoa are able to break it down. The fact that ruminants are able to digest cellulose is explained by the presence in their intestines of these microorganisms.

In higher plants, cellulose is accompanied by *lignin* which is a non-carbohydrate polymer, the structure of which has not yet been completely elucidated. Lignin represents some 15 to 30 % of natural cellulose.

Another polysaccharide associated with cellulose in wood is *xylan*, a polymer of the pentose D-xylose. This latter is bound in 1:4 β-glycosidic bonds joined in chains of 20 to 40 units.

Starches

Starch is the most important polysaccharide carbohydrate and is distributed widely in nature as a reserve material in almost every part of all plants. It contributes more calories to the normal diet of human beings than any other single substance. Total acid hydrolysis, or enzyme hydrolysis results in the quantitative conversion of starch to glucose. However, the final elucidation of the structure was solved comparatively recently.

Starch from different sources consists of granules of various shapes and sizes and it is possible, by means of an ordinary microscopic examination, to determine the source of a given starch. Generally, all starches contain two types of molecular structure:

amylose, which is a long straight chain of glucose units and which reacts with iodine to give a blue coloration, and

amylopectin, which is a branched molecule consisting of a number of amyloses and which reacts with iodine to give a reddish color. (Incidentally, amylopectin bears no relation to the pectins which are discussed in the next chapter.)

The action of iodine on starches has been shown to be solely an optical effect and not a chemical change. If heated, a starch solution containing a drop of iodine, will lose its blue color, it returning on cooling.

Ordinary corn starch contains only 25 % amylose, the majority of the remainder being amylopectin. Today, however, new varieties of corn have been developed which contain in their starch up to 65 % amylose. Wrinkled

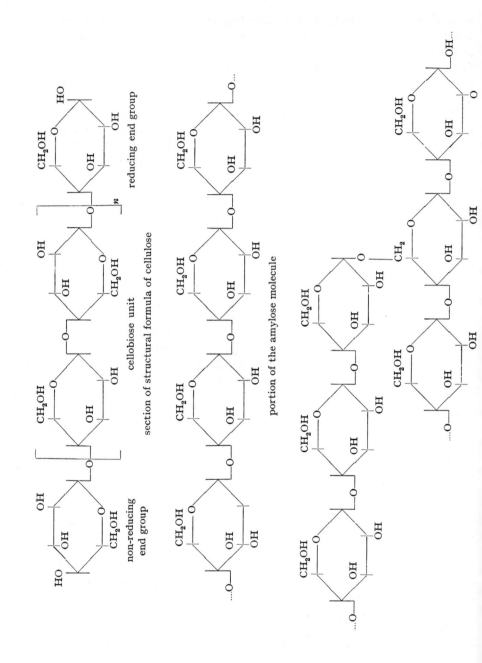

pea and rice *Oriza glutinosa* contain in their starch as much as 70%
amylose.

The great differences in the various starches depend on:

(a) the relative proportion of the two fractions, amylose and amylopectin;

(b) the degree of polymerization, of the amylose and the homogeneity of
the chain units;

(c) the branching of the amylopectin fraction.

As in cellulose, the molecular structure of amylose is a straight chain of
glucose monomers connected in an α-glucosidic bond at the 1:4 carbon
atoms (the so-called maltose bond). The DP of amylose is, however, much
smaller than that of cellulose.

It has been found that amylose has a helical structure and when reacted with iodine, the iodine molecules take up a position inside the helix
(Fig. 11).

Amylopectin is built up of a number of amylose units connected to each
other by a 1:6 bond (see formulas p. 84).

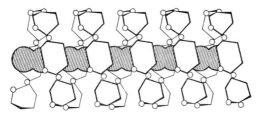

Fig. 11. Helical model of amylose chain in which iodine molecules find their place
inside the helix.

According to HAWORTH, amylopectin should be represented as in the
following graph, in which each line represents an amylose with some 20 to
30 glucose molecules, each amylopectin molecule containing about 40 such
amylose units:

It is thought that amylopectin also has a helical structure.

In the structure of amylopectin it is possible that the free hydroxyls at
carbon atoms 2 and 3 may also be involved in some cross-linkages. In fact,
evidence for the presence of some α-1:3-glucosidic bonds exists since the
isolation of 3-α-D-glucopyranosyl-D-glucose (nigerose) from partial hydrolysates of amylopectin[2].

Both amylopectin, the branched fraction of starch, and glycogen, its
counterpact in animals, are composed of the same monomer, glucose, held
together by α-1:4-glucosidic bonds in the main chains and branched at

References p. 92/93

α-1:6-glucosidic linkages. The two substances differ structurally only in the ratio of α-1:6-links to α-1:4, the ratio lying between $1/_{18}$ and $1/_{27}$ for amylopectin from various sources and $1/_{10}$ and $1/_{18}$ for glycogen.

Three models have been proposed for amylopectin and glycogen: the HAWORTH model shown here, which consists of a number of amylose

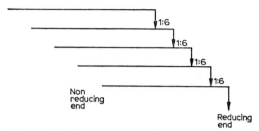

Fig. 12. The Haworth model of amylopectin.

chains, each one attached to the next amylose at the branching points by α-1:6-links, so that each chain has only one branching point; the STAUDINGER model, consisting of a long chain of amylose with side chains attached to the main chain at branching points by α-1:6 bonds; and the MEYER model consisting of a combination of the two, so that each chain may branch further whether its origin be a 1:4 or 1:6 bond at the main stem (see Fig. 13). BECKMAN[3] suggests a statistical method for the characterization of the branching of amylopectin and glycogen and comes to the conclusion that their structure lies about half-way between the HAWORTH and the MEYER models.

Starch enzymes

In order to make the polysaccharides, such as starch, available for metabolic transformations, they must be broken up into smaller units, *i.e.*,

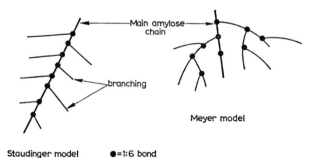

Fig. 13. The Staudinger model and the Meyer model of amylopectin.

their glucosidic linkages must be split. A number of enzymes are known to catalyze the breakdown of starches and some other enzymes are capable of catalyzing their biosynthesis.

α-Amylase is a specific enzyme, acting only at the 1:4 bond which will detach large molecules of oligosaccharides from starch. In industry such mixtures obtained by the enzymatic or acid hydrolysis are called *dextrins* or starch syrups (also corn syrups).

Another enzyme, *β-amylase*, attacks the amylose molecule at its non-reducing end, splitting off molecules of maltose at the 1:4 positions, continuing to do so until it arrives at the branching point of the 1:6 bond, where its activity is arrested.

Maltose molecules created in this way by *β-amylase* can now be attacked by the enzyme *maltase* (or *α-glucosidase*) and converted into single glucose molecules. The above shows the absolute specificity of these enzymes.

Another enzyme, *phosphorylase*, which is capable of detaching single molecules of glucose from the amylose and of phosphorylating them, has been isolated from potatoes and also from pea seeds. This enzymatic cleavage of the amylose molecule to glucose-1-phosphate is called "phosphorolysis". The salient difference between the cleavage reactions catalyzed by *amylases* and *phosphorylases* is that the former introduce a molecule of water into the broken glucosidic link, while during phosphorolysis a molecule of phosphoric acid is introduced instead.

Phosphorylase catalyzes the degradation of only a part of the amylopectin molecule in the presence of phosphate ion to form glucose-1-phosphate and a residual high molecular weight "limit dextrin," which is resistant to further action of this enzyme. The mechanism established for this reaction consists of the splitting off of glucose units as glucose-1-phosphate, beginning at the terminal non-reducing end of the chain and stopping near the α-1:6-link of the branching point. HESTRIN[4] has estimated that approximately six glucose units remain at each outer branching point of the limit dextrin after the action of the *phosphorylase*. These residual glucose units so formed may be degraded further by the enzyme *β-amylase* which, however, will also not proceed beyond the 1:6 branching point.

Recently a new enzyme, *α-amyloglucosidase*, has been discovered[5] which will act *only* on the limit dextrins left after the degradation of amylopectin by *phosphorylase*, the only substance split off in this case being glucose. By treating various samples of amylopectin with the two enzymes, *phosphorylase* and *α-amyloglucosidase*, simultaneously, it was possible to determine both glucose-1-phosphate and free glucose in the reaction mixture. Assuming that each glucose molecule arose from a branch pointing and each glucose-1-phosphate molecule from the amylose chain, the ratio of the two quantities

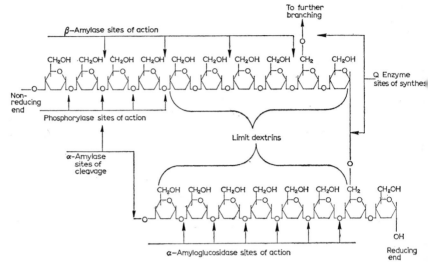

Fig. 14. Sites of enzymatic action of various starch enzymes on a molecule
of amylopectin.

would be the fraction of branching units in the amylopectin molecule and
should be equal to the fraction of end groups. This should give a measure
of the extent of branching in amylopectin.

To summarize the above, Fig. 14 shows schematically the sites of action of
the various starch enzymes on a structural model of a portion of amylopectin.

The potato *phosphorylase-P*-enzyme described above is also capable of performing the synthesis of a straight-chain amylose from glucose-1-phosphate
since the above phosphorylating reaction is reversible:

$$n\,(\text{D-glucopyranose-1-phosphate}) \;\rightleftarrows\; \text{amylose} + n\,H_3PO_4$$

A priming substance, in the form of a small glucose polymer must, however,
be present to start the reaction.

In addition to the above, yet another enzyme has been isolated from
potatoes which is capable of branching amyloses of 20 to 24 glucose units
into amylopectin. This enzyme has been given the name *Q enzyme*. Both
products of the synthesis, amylose and amylopectin, obtained with the aid
of *phosphorylase* and *Q enzyme*, give the appropriate colorations with iodine
and undergo the normal hydrolysis with α- and *β-amylases*.

Mixtures of *amylases* and *maltase* enzymes are widely used in industry, for instance, in beer brewing: the cereals from which beer is brewed are first subjected to the action of these enzymes which are usually obtained from malt. Malt is prepared by germinating barley during which an abundant quantity of these enzymes is formed. After the conversion of the starch to glucose the substrate is now ready for fermentation by the yeast.

The baking industry also makes use of starch enzymes. Very often the quantity of amylose in flour is not sufficient for optimal baking. This defect can be corrected by the addition of small quantities of malted barley flour or malted wheat flour, which contain the necessary *amylase* enzymes, to the dough or to the flour itself. Today, enzymatic preparations of specific *amylases* prepared from fungi can be obtained commercially (see Chapter 12).

Another nutrient reserve polysaccharide found in Compositae and in the Jerusalem artichoke is *inulin*, which represents a linear array of fructo-furanose units linked together by $\beta(2:1)$-glycosidic bonds, so-called fructans.

Manufacture of starch

Industrially, starch is produced either from root plants (such as potatoes or sweet potatoes) or from cereals (wheat, corn, rice, etc.). About 16 to 22% starch can usually be obtained from potatoes. By genetic improvement of certain varieties it has been possible to obtain a yield of 25 to 40%. The main manufacturing steps comprise:

(1) thorough washing to remove earth and impurities;

(2) complete disintegration to open all cells;

(3) washing out the starch granules and separating them from the pulp upon vibrating screens;

(4) addition of SO_2 to prevent browning caused by the enzyme *tyrosinase*, which oxidizes the amino acid tyrosin into 3:4 dihydroxyphenyl alanine and finally into brown melanoidin compounds (see Chapter 19);

(5) "tabling"—separation of the soluble impurities from the starch milk by passing it through long channels in which the starch settles. This step can also be achieved by centrifugation;

(6) washing, bleaching with SO_2 and permanganate;

(7) drying with warm air at 30° to 40°C.

In manufacturing starch from cereals the above steps must be preceded by removal of the proteins before the precipitation of the starch. Consequently, corn grains, for instance, are steeped in water containing 0.3% SO_2 for 30 to 40 hours in order to soften them. They are then subjected to wet milling in order to remove the germ by floatation. Subsequent steps for the extraction of starch are similar to those used for root materials. Removal of proteins from wheat is done by working the dough and separating the gluten mechanically. In this so-called Alsace process, one gets 500 kg of first-grade starch from a ton of flour and an additional 200 kg of second-grade starch.

Synthetic and other polysaccharides

Recently it has been found that specific microorganisms are able to synthesize polysaccharides from glucose and fructose. Polysaccharides prepared in this way from glucose by means of bacterial cells belonging to the *Leuconostoc* group are called *dextrans* and are used as substitutes for blood plasma to increase blood volume in patients who have lost a lot of blood from an injury or surgery. A similar polymer from fructose (*Levan*) has been prepared by microbial synthesis involving the use of *Bacillus subtilis* and *Bacillus mesentericus*.

Chitin is an important polysaccharide which constitutes the major structural part of the body of invertebrates. It is found in large quantity in the shells of lobsters and crabs and has the following structural formula:

partial formula of chitin

According to this formula, chitin consists of N-acetyl-D-glucosamine joined to one another by a β-1:4-glucosidic bond.

Sugar acids and uronides

Mention should be made of some sugar acids, especially uronic acids, before beginning the next chapter on pectins.

A number of sugar acids are known which result from the oxidation of the carbonyl group of aldoses. The most familiar are: D-gluconic acid, which has the carbonyl at carbon atom 1; D-saccharic acid, in which both C_1 and C_6 are carboxyl groups; and sorbic acid, which has been recently introduced as a mold preventive in many food products.

```
   COOH              COOH             COOH
    |                 |                |
   HCOH              HCOH             CH
    |                 |               ||
   HOCH              HOCH             CH
    |                 |                |
   HCOH              HCOH             CH
    |                 |               ||
   HCOH              HCOH             CH
    |                 |                |
   CH₂OH             COOH             CH₃
```

D-gluconic acid   D-saccharic acid   sorbic acid

Hexoses in which C_6 alone is oxidized into a carboxyl group represent an important group of uronic acids, such as glucuronic, galacturonic, mannuronic acids, etc.

```
   CHO               CHO              CHO
    |                 |                |
   HCOH              HCOH             HOCH
    |                 |                |
   HOCH              HOCH             HOCH
    |                 |                |
   HCOH              HOCH             HCOH
    |                 |                |
   HCOH              HCOH             HCOH
    |                 |                |
   COOH              COOH             COOH
```

D-glucuronic acid   D-galacturonic acid   D-mannuronic acid

Uronic acids form a number of polymers, of which pectins, which are built of units of galacturonic acid, will be discussed in detail in the next chapter.

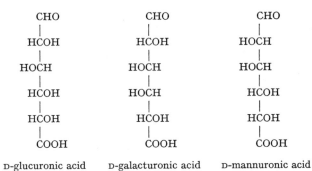

β-D-mannuronic acid is the monomer of *alginic acid*, which is a poly-mannuronic acid and possesses the important property of forming gels.

References p. 92/93

Alginic acid and its salts are prepared from sea algae. It is widely used in food products.

Hemicelluloses

Under this generic name we designate a large number of complex polymers comprising polyuronic acids in combination with xyloses, glucose, mannose and arabinose.

Hemicelluloses are present in fibrous and woody plant tissues, where they are combined with cellulose and lignin to form the cell walls. The acidic properties of hemicelluloses arise from the presence of D-glucuronic acid. Most gums and mucilages belong to this class of compounds. However, due to their complexity, very little is known at the present time about their correct structure.

The plant gums, such as cherry gum, gum arabic and gum tragacanth, widely used in some food products, are neutral salts of complex polyuronic acids, mainly D-glucuronic in combination with hexoses and pentoses. Plants produce such gums when they are injured, most probably as a protective mechanism.

The mucilages, such as agar-agar, the seaweed mucilage, well known for its property of forming gels and widely used as a bacterial culture medium and also in many foods, are widely distributed in plants and form viscous, colloidal solutions in water.

REFERENCES

[1] W. HAYNES, *Cellulose: The Chemical that Grows*, Doubleday and Co., 1953.
[2] M. L. WOLFROM AND A. THOMPSON, *J. Am. Chem. Soc.*, 78 (1956) 4116.
[3] C. O. BECKMAN, *Ann. N.Y. Acad. Sci.*, 57 (1953) 384.
  S. HESTRIN, *J. Biol. Chem.*, 179 (1949) 943.
  G. T. CORI AND J. LARNER, *Federation Proc.*, 9 (1950) 163; *J. Biol. Chem.*, 188 (1951) 17; *J. Biol. Chem.*, 199 (1952) 631.

SELECTED BIBLIOGRAPHY TO CHAPTERS 5, 6, 7 AND 8

Use of sugars and other carbohydrates in food industry, *Advances in Chem., Ser. No. 12* (1955).
BATES, F. J. *et al.*, *Polarimetry, Saccharimetry and the Sugars*, U. S. Government Printing Office, Washington, D.C., 1942.
FRENCH, D., The Raffinose Family of Oligosaccharides, *Advances in Carbohydrate Chem.*, 9 (1954) 149.
PERCIVAL, E. G. V. *Structural Carbohydrate Chemistry*, F. Muller, London, 1950.
PIGMAN, W. W., *The Carbohydrates, Chemistry, Biochemistry, Physiology*, Academic Press, New York, 1957.
PIGMAN, W. W. AND R. M. GOEPP, *Chemistry of Carbohydrates*, Academic Press, New York, 1948.

PRESCOTT, S. C., AND C. G. DUNN, *Industrial Microbiology*, 3rd edn., McGraw-Hill, New York, 1959.

RADLEY, J. A., *Starch and its Derivatives*, Chapman and Hall, London, 1943.

ROMAN, W. *Yeasts*, Academic Press, New York, 1957.

TAUBER, H. *The Chemistry and Technology of Enzymes*, J. Wiley and Sons, New York, 1949.

CHAPTER 9

PECTIC SUBSTANCES

Occurrence

A very important group of substances known in food technology as *pectins* belong to the second group of polysaccharides, the heteropolysaccharides. Pectin was first discovered by BRACANNOT in 1825. It is, in fact, only a generic name embodying a group of closely related substances—the pectic substances. These fill the intercellular spaces, the *middle lamella*, of plant tissues. In young tissues, especially in fruits, pectins are often formed in such large amounts that they form wide channels, pushing apart the cells (Fig. 15).

Fig. 15. Diagrammatic drawing of pectin in channels as seen under the microscope.

Being a colloid *par excellence*, pectin has the property of imbibing large quantities of water. Because of this capacity, pectic substances apparently play a important role in the early stages of development of plant tissues when the cells still lie apart and at a comparatively great distance from the water-conducting vessels. The pectic substances quickly absorb water and transfer it among the cells more easily than could be effected by osmosis in the cells themselves.

As long as pectic substances are in the outer cell walls in the region of middle lamella in the plant, they are thought to be closely associated with cellulose. In this form, as a precursor of pectin proper, the substance is called *protopectin* (or pectose). Protopectin is insoluble in water and, according to BRANFOOT (CARRÉ)[1], can be observed microscopically in the plant tissue using ruthenium red as a stain. SUCHARIPA (RIPA)[2] claims to have isolated pure protopectin from lemon albedo by dissolving the adhering cellulose in Schweizer's reagent and treating the resulting copper complex with acetic acid. This, however, has not been confirmed by later investigators. It is suggested that protopectin is either an hydride of pectin or that it is formed by the union of pectin and cellulose with the elimination of some molecules of water.

When pectin-rich plant materials, apple pomace or citrus peels, are heated with acidified water, the protopectin is liberated, probably from the adhering cellulose, and is hydrolyzed into pectin, which is readily soluble in water. The same transformation or hydrolysis of the protopectin takes place in plant tissues during ripening of the fruits apparently with the aid of an unknown enzyme to which the name *protopectinase* has been assigned. As the ripening of the fruit proceeds, more and more of the insoluble protopectin is converted into soluble pectin[3].

Pectin is readily precipitated from aqueous solutions by alcohol or acetone as a suspended jelly, which will in turn again dissolve in water. This coagulation can also be brought about by the action of a mixture of certain salts, such as aluminum sulfate in conjunction with ammonium hydroxide, whereby aluminum hydroxide is formed, the colloidal particles of which carry an electric charge of opposite sign to that of pectin (pectin is a negatively charged colloid).

Structure

Pectin is, therefore, a reversible colloid of the lyophilic type; its solutions rotate polarized light to the right. Crude pectin contains a number of impurities, such as hemicelluloses, pentosans (araban), galactosans and other compounds, but can be purified by repeated precipitation and redissolution.

According to SCHNEIDER *et al.*[4], pectin is now regarded as a long chain of polygalacturonic acid molecules with the carboxyl groups partially esterified with methyl alcohol.

Pectins derived from different sources vary widely in their jelly forming properties due to the different lenghts of their polygalacturonic acid chains and to the different degree of esterification of their carboxyl groups with methyl alcohol. These also vary greatly for the different methods of extraction employed. There are probably no two pectin preparations which are identical as far as their structure and length of molecule is concerned.

Pectins may undergo hydrolysis by acid or alkali or by the action of suitable enzymes. The first step in such hydrolyses is the removal of a varying number of methoxyl groups leaving ultimately a water-insoluble polygalacturonic acid, called *pectic acid*, completely free of methoxyl groups. The many intermediate components, still possessing a varying number of methoxyl groups, give rise to a large number of *pectinic acids*. This is the

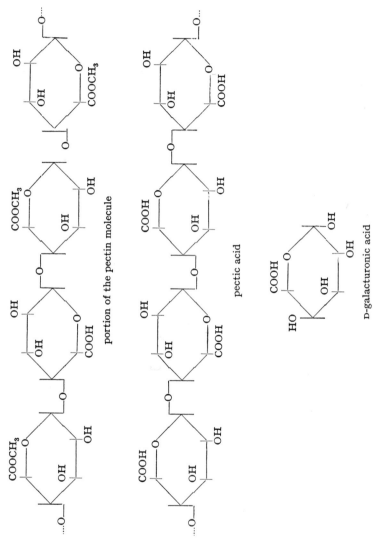

portion of the pectin molecule

pectic acid

D-galacturonic acid

main reason why *pectin* can be regarded only as a generic name covering a wide range of pectinic acids differing only in their degree of esterification. Fully esterified pectic acid has never been found in nature; however, it may be synthesized for research purposes. Complete hydrolysis of pectic acid (polygalacturonic acid) results in the formation of single D-galacturonic acid units.

Pectolytic enzymes

A number of enzymes have been found to catalyze the various stages of pectin breakdown:

Pectin esterase (PE), which catalyzes the removal of the methoxyl groups from the pectin molecule. (Synonyms: *pectase, pectinmethoxylase, pectin methyl esterase*).

This enzyme is not always present in fruits rich in pectin. While tomatoes and all citrus fruits contain PE in abundance, it has not been found in beets, carrots, and is found in only a few varieties of apples. Most fungi contain appreciable amounts of PE. So far, *pectic esterase*, has not been found in yeasts.

The optimum activity of *pectin esterase* occurs at pH 7.5 and the enzyme is found to be quite specific: it apparently requires at least one galacturonic unit free of a methoxyl group in order to attack an esterified unit, as shown by the following scheme. With the diminution of the number of such molecular arrangements the PE activity will decrease.

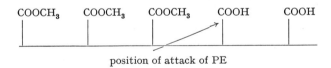

position of attack of PE

It has been recently demonstrated that in some cases PE is associated with solid particles of the cell wall. Such an association has been found by BONNER[5] and his coworkers in orange juice where PE is a structure-bound insoluble enzyme. Such deesterified cell walls have been shown to have a strong affinity for PE: approximately 5 mg of this enzyme can be bound by 1 mg of pectic material in the cell wall. The activity of this bound enzyme acting on cell wall pectin has been compared with that of the soluble enzyme acting on soluble pectin. Both have optima at pH 7.5. However, while the bound enzyme is inactive at pH 4.5 and below, the soluble PE is still active in this pH region.

Polygalacturonase (PG), which catalyzes the glycosidic hydrolysis of polygalacturonic acid (pectic acid) into single D-galacturonic acid units. (Synonyms: *pectinase, pectolase, polygalacturonidase*.)

The optimal activity of this enzyme occurs at pH 3.5–4.2 and its position of attack is considered to be at a point between two carboxyl groups[6]:

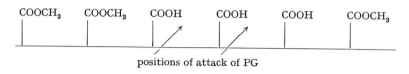

positions of attack of PG

PG is inactive toward the fully methylated polymer, however, in the presence of PE, which is capable of demethylating the pectin, *polygalacturonase* can split all the links of the chain and produce free D-galacturonic acid.

In recent years, various investigators have demonstrated the complex nature of pectic enzymes. For some time it has been suggested that another intermediary enzyme exists, to which the name, *pectin depolymerase*, has been assigned, and which is capable of splitting the pectin molecule into smaller units although not to galacturonic acid. Such an enzyme has been suggested to exist in tomatoes and in yeasts. It splits only about 11 % of the glucosidic bonds in pectic acid and is very resistant to heat: even after being heated to 100°C for 15 minutes it is still active to the extent of 15 %. The optimum pH is considered to occur at 3.4–4.0 at a temperature of 55 to 60°C.

Another enzyme, *polymethylgalacturonase*, has been found which also splits the glucosidic linkage, but in contrast to PG, it is capable of acting on the completely esterified polymer[7].

PHAFF AND DEMAIN[8] have suggested recently a system of nomenclature for the glucosidic enzymes involved: the use of the prefixes *endo-* and *exo-* to designate the preferred mode of attack, random *versus* terminal, and the terms *polymethylgalacturonase* and PG (*polygalacturonase*) to indicate whether the enzyme prefers pectin or pectic acid as its substrate. According to these investigators, with the exception of enzymes preferentially attacking pectins with a high degree of esterification, there are two well-established pectic enzymes which attack polygalacturonic acid:

endo-polygalacturonase of yeast, which is a single enzyme, hydrolyzes pectic acid at random to a mixture of galacturonic and digalacturonic acids,

exo-polygalacturonase, a component of the pectic enzyme complex of certain fungi, removes single galacturonic acid units from the end of a pectic acid polymer, ultimately hydrolyzing it completely to galacturonic acid.

In this system, pectin and pectic acid *depolymerases* are simply types of *polymethylgalacturonase* and PG. As an example, the PG of tomato fruit can be cited, which has been found[9] to contain at least two *polygalacturonase* components, but their separation or differential inactivation has not yet been accomplished.

As far as *protopectinase* is concerned, it is now doubtful whether a special enzyme, the so-called *"protopectinase"* exists or is altogether necessary: apparently a mixture of PE and PG are sufficient for the hydrolysis of protopectin into pectinic acids.

The following scheme summarizes the interrelation of the various pectic substances:

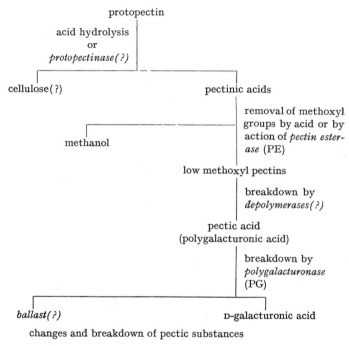

changes and breakdown of pectic substances

Almost all fungi contain the full spectrum of pectolytic enzymes. This can be easily observed in different natural phenomena when the plant tissue is entirely disintegrated and falls apart, *e.g.*, when some molds attack it; a fruit attacked by *Penicillium glaucum,* for instance, will ultimately become a powder since the pectin which has held together the fruit cells has been converted by the enzymes of the fungi into pectic acid which has no more binding power. A similar phenomenon can be observed during the retting process of flax or the fermentation of tobacco leaves and of coffee beans.

Yeast, on the other hand, contains only the *polygalacturonase* enzymes.

Industrial preparations of complex pectolytic enzymes are manufactured from fungi and sold under the trade-names "Pectinol" and "Mylase".

Pectin as a jellifying agent

The most important use of pectin in food is based on its ability to form gels and it is, therefore, widely used in the manufacture of jams, jellies, marmalades, and preserves. In order that a pectin may form a gel, a dehydrating agent must be present: alcohol or acetone are typical dehydrating agents used in the extraction of pectin and during its manufacture. In the production of jams and jellies, it is the sugar that plays this dehydrating role. Although the actual mechanism of gel formation has not as yet been properly elucidated, some conditions for optimal gelification have been established. It is now accepted that in forming a good jelly suitable pectin–acid–sugar ratio should be maintained. The practical results of numerous researches in this field show that it is best to adjust the amount of pectin and the acidity in such a manner as to save sugar.

An increase in acidity from 0.1 to 1.7 % results in a saving of nearly 20 % sugar. The same is true of pectin: within certain limits (0.5–1.5 % pectin content) the higher the percentage of pectin in the fruit pulp or juice the lower the amount of sugar required to form a jelly.

Comprehensive investigations made by TARR[10] have shown that there is no direct relation between total acidity and jelly formation, only a strict limit of pH values should be maintained. This definite limit of hydrogen-ion concentration is found by TARR to be at a pH value of 3.46, when a soft, delicate jelly is given. Jelly increases in stability at lower pH values (down to 3.1–3.2); at still lower pH values, *syneresis* occurs, *i.e.*, the jelly exudes liquid on standing.

As far as pectin is concerned, some fruits rich in pectin, such as apples, quinces and citrus fruits, have excellent jellying power of their own. To jams made of other fruits poor in pectin, such as strawberries and many other berries, commercial pectin has to be added. The number of methoxyl groups present in a pectic substance apparently plays an important role in the capacity of a given pectin to form a good jelly. A fully esterified pectinic acid (not found in nature) should contain, theoretically, 16 % methoxyl groups. Naturally obtained pectins contain from 9.5 to 11 % methoxyl groups and, if deesterified to the extent of about 8 % ester, it will give pectinic acids best suitable for preparing jellies.

Because the degree of methylation is not the only measure of the jellifying property of the pectins and because such other qualities as the size of the molecule, etc., are rather complicated to be determined in industrial usage, commercial pectins are evaluated by *"pectin grades"* and are expressed as the number of parts of sugar that one part of pectin will gel to an accepted firmness under standard conditions. These standards are accepted to be a pH of between 3.2 to 3.5, 65 to 70 % sugar and pectin in the limits 0.2 to 1.5 %. In commerce, pectins of 100 grade up to 500 grade are marketed, They also differ by their "setting time": a "rapid set" begins at about 85°C while a "slow set" forms a jelly below 55°C. The rapid set is used in the manufacture of preserves in order to prevent whole fruit or chunks settling to the bottom or rising to the top of the jar instead of being evenly distributed throughout the jam.

Theories of gel formation

Pectins, as well as many other polysaccharides such as alginic acid, belong to the group of chemicals to which the general name of polyelectrolytes has been assigned. These compounds are known to increase considerably the viscosity of a solution when present in an ionized state.

Alginic acid or pectic acid, for instance, should, when ionized by the addition of NaOH, be represented as follows:

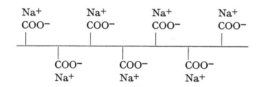

When in an ionized state such molecules have a much higher viscosity and, therefore, an apparently higher molecular weight. This inconsistency is explained by the fact that while being in an unionized state the monomers may rotate freely around their glucosidic bond, and most probably such long chains create bundles of some kind with the aid of hydrogen bonds. Whereas, when ionization occurs, each of the carboxyl ions will push away its neighboring carboxyl ion (being of equal charge) and so the long molecule chain will gradually become straightened out. The mechanical implication of this phenomenon is an increase of viscosity*. By reversing the process, i.e., neutralizing the alkali with acid thus causing deionization of the solute, the viscosity decreases, the long chains forming bundles again. KATCHALSKY et al.[11] used this phenomenon in creating a model of strings of polymetacrylic acid suitably cross-linked to form a strong rope:

---

* Compare the amount of friction created between two perfectly polished sheets when a long, thin string is placed between the sheets with that caused by the same string when it is twisted (see Chapter 10).

$$CH_2 = \overset{\overset{\displaystyle CH_3}{|}}{\underset{\underset{\displaystyle COOH}{|}}{CH}}$$

metacrylic acid

$$-CH_2-\overset{\overset{\displaystyle CH_3}{|}}{\underset{\underset{\displaystyle COO^-}{|}}{C}}-CH_2-\overset{\overset{\displaystyle CH_3}{|}}{\underset{\underset{\displaystyle COO^-}{|}}{C}}-CH_2-\overset{\overset{\displaystyle CH_3}{|}}{\underset{\underset{\displaystyle COO^-}{|}}{C}}-CH_2-$$

polymetacrylic acid

When submerged in a suitable alkali solution, this model will become elongated and subsequently shorten on acidification, thereby transferring chemical energy directly into mechanical energy without passing through a combustion cycle. These effects have been given the name *mechanochemistry*. It is of interest to note that all such work performed by animals or plants, muscle work, movement of fluids, building of cells, etc., can be related to similar phenomena or mechanochemistry.

Returning to pectins, when an alkali is added to a slurry of apple or citrus peel, a very viscous solution is soon obtained. If this reaction is allowed to proceed until the pH has attained 7 and then stopped by acidification to pH 3 to 4, partially deesterified pectins extracted by this method form very viscous solutions which are useful wherever water-soluble, oil-repelling films are desired[12].

Totally or partially deesterified pectins can also form gels even without, or with very little, sugar. However, in such cases some divalent ions must be present, in the form of calcium salts, for instance. Ca^{2+} apparently binds the free carboxyl into a pattern which favors the gel formation. Such partially demethoxylated pectins are called *low-methoxyl pectins* and are now widely used for the production of low-caloried jellies or other food products where little or no sugar is used.

To summarize, the special gel systems obtained with pectins of various degrees of methoxylation are as follows:

(a) *Completely methoxylated* polygalacturonic acid will form gels with sugar alone. Here the gelation is caused solely by the dehydrating effect of the sugar.

(b) *Rapid-set pectins* are pectins with a degree of methoxylation of 70 % and higher. They will form gels on addition of acid and sugar at a pH optimum of 3.0 to 3.4 at relatively high temperatures. The gel strength of such gels is largely dependent upon the molecular weight and is not influenced by the degree of methoxylation. The higher the molecular weight the stronger is the gel.

(c) *Slow-set pectins* are those with a degree of methoxylation of 50–70 % They will form gels on addition of sugar and more acid at a pH optimum of 2.8–3.2 and at lower temperatures. The amount of acid required is approximately proportional to the number of free carboxyl groups[13].

(d) *Low-methoxyl pectins* are pections with a degree of methoxylation under 50 %. They do not form jellies with sugar and acid but will gel in the presence of calcium ions and other polyvalent cations. The amount of pectin required for the formation of such gels decreases with the degree of methoxylation. The strengths of such ionic-bonded gels are strongly dependent upon the degree of esterification and are only little affected by the molecular weight of the pectins.

While some explanations for gel formation can be found for totally or partially deesterified pectins especially when ionized, the cause of gel formation in esterified pectinic acids in acid milieu has not been elucidated up-to-now. SOLMS AND DEUEL[14] suggest that the specific spatial configuration attained by the free hydroxyl groups in a normally esterified pectin are the real cause of its gel-forming property. They ascribe this to the intramolecular hydrogen bridges created between these secondary hydroxyl groups bound to carbon atoms 2 and 3 of each galacturonic acid monomer.

To conclude this section on gel formation, it is interesting to note that a perfect jam or jelly should also be able to be made without cooking the fruit juice: if a product containing the right proportions of sugar, acid and pectin were mixed at a room temperature of 25°C, it should slowly set to a strong gel. At a much lower temperature, such gel formation would be very slow and inadequate, probably due to the slower Brownian movement or to a more helical configuration of the pectin molecules.

Coagulation and cloud stability

Since pectic substances are so widely distributed throughout the plant kingdom, food technologists are often confronted with two conflicting problems. On one hand, it is frequently important to remove pectic substances in order to clarify the products such as wines, for instance, where it is desired to obtain a clear liquid. On the other hand, it is sometimes desired to keep the insoluble particles in suspension and to obtain a permanent cloud stability, as in the case of natural fruit juices.

Products containing pectins, or other polysaccharides, are usually difficult to filter. Moreover, products such as wines or vinegars may often attain undesirable precipitates and cloudiness due to certain microorganisms. Mucilages, ropiness of wines, etc., may, for instance, be caused by *Streptococcus mucilaginosus*, Var. Vini, Lüthi. In such cases, filtration alone is very tedious and often useless.

It has been found[15] that such precipitates are very complex polyelectrolytes containing glucans, glucomannans, and other polysaccharides consisting of galactose, mannose, arabinose and galacturonic acid. DEUEL and his coworkers took advantage of the fact that such colloids with a negative charge will create insoluble complexes with other soluble polyelectrolytes of opposite charge and will then precipitate easily. It is suggested, therefore, that such cloudy wines or juices should be treated with a synthetic polymer of positive charge, such as polyethylene imine:

$$-CH_2-CH_2-\overset{+}{N}H_2-CH_2-CH_2-\overset{+}{N}H_2-CH_2-CH_2-\overset{+}{N}H_2-CH_2-$$

This substance will then precipitate the colloids present according to the following scheme:

pectinate$^-$ Na$^+$ + polyethylene imine$^+$ Cl$^-$ $\rightleftarrows$

$\rightleftarrows$ pectinate$^-$ polyethylene imine$^+$ + NaCl

The precipitate thus formed will soon settle, carrying with it all suspended matter as well as tannins, which may be adsorbed upon large molecules of this kind.

Other methods for attaining similar effects consist of treating cloudy liquids with commercial preparations of pectolytic enzymes, such as "Pectinol". These enzymic preparations containing PE and PG will soon deesterify the pectic substances which will thus be converted into insoluble pectic acid and can then be removed by filtration (see Chapter 12).

When, however, the opposite is required, i.e., a permanent cloud stability, it is then necessary to prevent, as far as possible, the deesterification of the pectin. In natural juices the pulp is kept in suspension by the fact that the soluble pectin, being a colloid, helps to keep the small fruit particles afloat. This will continue only as long as the pectin remains unaltered. Soon, however, the pectin will begin to deesterify through the action of the pectolytic enzymes naturally present in the juices. It is imperative, therefore, to inactivate the pectolytic enzymes as quickly as possible. Such inactivation is achieved by heating the juices for a short time at a comparatively high temperature. High-temperature–short-time (HTST) pasteurization is often sufficient to inactivate pectolytic enzymes and to achieve permanent cloud stability[16]. In other cases, such as tomato juice and purée, the pectolytic enzymes act so quickly that precautions should be taken at the very outset, before the crushing of the plant tissue and the extraction of the juice, for even momentary action of the pectolytic enzymes present will destroy the desirable properties of the pectin. "Hot-break" methods of extraction are used in such cases.

Use of pectins in food

As already mentioned, the main use of pectin is in the manufacture of jams, jellies, marmalades and fruit preserves of all kinds, especially when fruits of naturally poor pectin content are used. Dry pectin is used in the preparation of synthetic powders for home-made jellies and in a number of sweets. In the natural juice products, pectin can be used for strengthening the permanent cloud stability, for raising the viscosity of tomato products and for similar purposes.

When canning fruits which are somewhat over-ripe, their texture may be too soft because of the degradation of the natural pectic substances having advanced too far. In such cases use is often made of calcium salts, which will create Ca-pectate in the cells of the fruit and thereby strengthen the texture. For the same reason, pectin is used as a stabilizer in ice cream production.

Second only to its ability to form gels is the very important property of pectin to act as an emulsifier. Pectin makes very good emulsions with edible oils for the production of mayonnaise, and also with essential oils when used in the manufacture of various flavors.

Good use is made of pectins in medicine as cleansers for the intestines, for treating wounds and in blood transfusions for raising the blood volume. Some use of pectin is also made in industry for steel hardening, etc. For a comprehensive description of such uses, together with a discussion of problems relating to pectic substances and their enzymes, the reader is referred to the classical treatise on this subject by KERTESZ[17].

Industrial manufacture of pectins

Commercial pectins are manufactured in two main forms: "liquid pectins", which represent more or less concentrated solutions of pectin extracted from waste plant materials, such as apples or citrus peels, and "dry pectin powders". In commercial practice the resulting products are not pure substances; their degree of purity, or rather their evaluation, depends largely on the methods of manufacture, the molecular size of the pectic substances, the degree of esterification and the amount of accompanying ballast material present in the final product.

The amount of pectin in the raw material greatly varies for different varieties. Thus, for instance, among citrus fruits the most pectin-rich varieties are grapefruit, lemon and pomelo. Secondly, it has been shown that unripe fruit is richer in pectin than fully ripe apples or citrus because, as the season advances, the quantity of effective pectin in the fruit diminishes.

The manufacturing procedures comprise the following main steps:

(1) preparation of material;
(2) removal of ballast;
(3) acid hydrolysis of protopectin and dissolution of pectin;
(4) precipitation;
(5) purification and drying.

Detailed methods of pectin manufacture have been described by BRAVER-MAN[18]. These are mainly based on two procedures: the precipitation of pectins by alcohols or acetone or by making use of the fact that some mineral salts, such as aluminum hydroxyde, carry in their colloidal state an electric charge with opposite sign to the negatively charged pectinic acids and are, therefore, able to coagulate the pectin from its aqueous solutions. In this method ammonia is added to the filtered aqueous extract of pectin to bring its pH to 4 and then sulfate of alumina added:

$$Al_2(SO_4)_3 + NH_4OH \longrightarrow Al(OH)_3 + (NH_4)_2SO_4$$

When the precipitation of pectin has been completed, the free liquid is drained off in false-bottom tanks and, aided by agitators, the precipitated gel is collected, pressed between cloth and treated with acidified alcohol–water solutions in order to remove excess $Al(OH)_3$. Repeated washings with acidified isobutyl alcohol and finally with water-free alcohol give a more or less pure gel which is pressed, dried and ground, while the alcohol is regenerated by distillation. The grade of pectin obtained in this process is about 300.

A number of processes using ion exchange and others have been patented in many countries.

Pectins in alcoholic fermentation

When ethanol is produced from waste plant materials containing pectins, care must be taken that the pectins are not deesterified before or during fermentation, otherwise there is a danger of methanol being present in the final product. Such instances may occur when the plant material is limed before fermentation, as the case may be during the extraction of citrus-peel juice, for instance. Similar difficulties may arise during the manufacture of fermented apple cider. If the fruit or other plant material becomes contaminated with mold (a rich source of PE) the amount of methanol formed may be fairly high[19].

REFERENCES

[1] M. H. BRANFOOT (CARRÉ), A critical and historical study of the pectic substances of plants, *Dept. Sci. Ind. Research, Brit. Food Invest.*, Special Report, No. 33 (1929) H.M.S.O., London.

[2] R. RIPA, *Die Pektinstoffe*, Serger and Hempel, Braunschweig, 1937.

[3] C. W. WOODMANSEE, *et al.*, Chemical changes associated with the ripening of apples and tomatoes, *Food Research*, 24 (1959) 503.

[4] G. G. SCHNEIDER AND H. BOCK, Über die Konstitution der Pektinstoffe, *Ber. deut. chem. Ges.*, 70B (1937) 1617.

[5] E. F. JANSEN, R. JANG AND J. BONNER, Orange pectinesterase binding and activity, *J. Am. Chem. Soc.*, 68 (1946) 1475.

[6] H. DEUEL AND E. STUTZ, Pectic substances and pectic enzymes, *Advances in Enzymol.*, 20 (1958) 341.

[7] C. E. NEUBECK, Pectic enzymes in fruit juice technology, *J. Assoc. Offic. Agr. Chemists*, 42 (1959) 374.

[8] H. J. PHAFF AND A. L. DEMAIN, The unienzymatic nature of yeast polygalacturenose, *J. Biol. Chem.*, 218 (1956) 875; also in *Wallerstein Labs. Communs.*, 20 (1957) 119.

[9] D. S. PATEL AND H. J. PHAFF, Properties of purified tomato polygalacturonase, *Food Research*, 25 (1960) 37.

[10] L. W. TARR, A study of the factors affecting the jellying of fruits, *Univ. Delaware Agr. Exptl. Sta. Bull.*, 133 (1923) 14.

[11] A. KATCHALSKY AND H. EISENBERG, *Nature*, 166 (1950) 267.

[12] H. S. OWENS, R. M. MCCREADY AND W. D. MACLAY, Enzymic preparation and extraction of pectinic acids, *J. Ind. Eng. Chem.*, 36 (1944) 936.

[13] J. SOLMS, Some structural aspects of the gel formation of pectins and related poly-saccharides, in Physical functions of hydrocolloids, *Advances in Chem. Ser. No. 25*, 1960.

[14] J. SOLMS AND H. DEUEL, *Helv. Chim. Acta*, 34 (1951) 2242.

[15] H. DEUEL, J. SOLMS AND A. DENZLER, *Helv. Chim. Acta*, 36 (1953) 1671.

[16] W. PILNIK AND G. ROTHSCHILD, Trübstabilität und Pektinesterase-Restaktivität in pasteurisierten Orangenkonzentrat, *Die Fruchtsaft-Industrie*, 5 (1960) 131.

[17] Z. I. KERTESZ, *The Pectic Substances*, Interscience, New York, 1951.

[18] J. B. S. BRAVERMAN, *Citrus Products—Chemical Composition and Chemical Technology*, Interscience, New York, 1949.

[19] J. B. S. BRAVERMAN AND A. LIPSHITZ, Pectin hydrolysis in certain fruit during alcoholic fermentation, *Food Technol.*, 11 (1957) 356.

SELECTED BIBLIOGRAPHY TO CHAPTER 9

DEUEL, H., J. SOLMS AND H. ALTERMATT, *Die Pektinstoffe und ihre Eigenschaften*, Naturforsch. Ges., Zurich, 1953.

DEUEL, H. AND E. STUTZ, Pectic substances and pectic enzymes, *Advances in Enzymol.* 20 (1958) 341.

HINTON, C. L., Fruit pectins, their chemical behavior and jellying properties, *Dept. Sci. Ind. Research, Brit. Food Invest.*, Special Report, No. 48 (1948) H.M.S.O., London.

KERTESZ, Z. I., *The Pectic Substances*, Interscience, New York, 1951.

PHAFF, H. J., AND M. A. JOSLYN, The newer knowledge of pectin enzymes, *Wallerstein Labs. Communs.*, 10 (1947) 133.

PILNIK, W., Cloud stability of citrus concentrates, *Intern. Fruit. Juice Union, Symposium, Bristol* (1958) .

RIPA, R., *Die Pektinstoffe*, Serger and Hempel, Braunschweig, 1937.

CHAPTER 10

THE COLLOIDAL STATE

Natura enim simplex est

NEWTON, 1687

Dispersed systems

At this stage, after having dealt with polysaccharides and before indulging in the study of proteins, both of these belonging to the class of macromolecules, it would be appropriate to dwell for a short time on the nature of the colloidal state.

One hundred years ago THOMAS GRAHAM (1860) showed that while simple crystalline compounds, such as sugars or salts, will readily diffuse through a "semi-permeable membrane," *i.e.* parchment, proteins or other similar macromolecules will not do so. GRAHAM divided, therefore, all materials into two distinct classes: the *crystalloids*—those which diffuse and the *colloids* (from the Greek word *colla* for glue)—the non-diffusible substances. In practice, this operation, known as *dialysis*, is often used for removing certain salts from proteins in solution, and as will be seen, to separate certain prosthetic groups attached to the protein in the enzymes.

However, GRAHAM himself ascribed this differentiation to the size of the molecules: by choosing membranes of suitable porosity even proteins of moderate size (upto molecular weight of 4,500) may pass through. Today, we do not strictly distinguish between crystalloids and colloids, but, instead, between the state of dispersion in which the substance occurs.

A *colloidal state* is considered to be a state in which particles of one phase of a size of between 0.1 μ and 1 mμ (or 10 to 10,000 times larger than a single atom) are dispersed in another phase, there being no difference between whether these particles are crystalline, or amorphous, or droplets of a liquid, or gas bubbles.

Any substance can, therefore, appear in the colloidal state. In fact, most of the foods of both man and animal (all proteins, most carbohydrates and lipids), everything which we wear (wool, silk, linen, cotton, etc.), and even some of the materials of which our dwellings are built, are all substances that are usually found in the colloidal state; namely, they form dispersed systems. The Table III gives such two-phase systems, with appropriate examples of food products.

A *sol* is a state which normally looks like a solution. Liquids and solutions, however, lack rigidity. On the other hand, a *gel* is a state possessing a certain degree of rigidity. A *paste* is a state in which more solids are present than in a gel, such as tomato puree, comminuted orange, etc.

Every substance can ultimately be present in a colloidal state: it merely depends on the size of its particles and the conditions of dispersion. One can disperse, for instance, crystals of NaCl and bring them into the colloidal-

TABLE III

Dispersed particles	Dispersion medium	Type of colloid	Examples
gas	liquid	foam	the froth on beer, the scum formed during fermentation
liquid	liquid	emulsion	milk, mayonnaise, cream
solid	liquid		gels, jellies, pastes, starch solutions
liquid	solid	solid sols	butter, margarine, chocolate
solid	solid	solid sols	candy

state in an organic non-polar solvent. On the other hand, substances such as certain proteins, usually considered to be colloids, have been shown, by means of X-ray diffraction methods, to be at least of a partly crystalline nature.

There are, however, quite marked differences between various colloidal dispersions. Consider, for example, two such systems as starch in water, on the one hand, and olive oil in water, on the other. The first suspension is easy to prepare and equally easy to retain in this state. The other is difficult to prepare, for it requires emulsification and homogenization, and, furthermore, it is difficult to keep it in this state of dispersion for any length of time. The first, therefore, belongs to the general type known as *emulsoids*, in which a certain amount of interaction between the starch and water occurs. The second type is called *suspensoid*. Accordingly, if one takes into consideration the media in which the starch and the oil are dispersed, they may also be classified as *lyophilic* or *lyophobic*, respectively. When water is the dispersion medium they are also called *hydrophilic* or *hydrophobic*.

The state of suspension of solid particles in a liquid medium depends primarily on the following factors:

(a) the size of the particles, their surface area, and their proximity;
(b) the Brownian movement;
(c) the electrostatic charges of the particles;

References p. 118

(d) the physical properties of the suspending medium;
(e) the presence of adsorbed gases, liquids or solids.
Let us consider each of these factors separately.

The size of the particles has been previously mentioned in the definition of the colloidal state. The classical researches of BURTON made on colloidal particles of gold in water showed that:

if their diameter equals 200 μ , they travel 1 cm in 0.05 sec;

if their diameter equals 2 μ , they travel 1 cm in 500 sec;

if their diameter equals 20 mμ, they travel 1 cm in 58 days.

But even so, these very small particles would precipitate at some time if it were not for the Brownian movement. The molecules of the suspension medium are in constant thermal movement which is transmitted to the particles of the suspended material. Comparing the Brownian movement with the movement due to gravitational force in the same gold particles, it has been found that when their diameter is 1 μ the two forces are of the same order of magnitude so that complete precipitation is practically impossible, as shown in Table IV.

TABLE IV

Diameter of particle (mμ)	Distance traveled in 1 sec	
	Brownian movement (mμ)	Gravitation (mμ)
100	10,000	67.6
1,000	3,162	6,760
10,000	1,000	676,000

The Brownian movement, however, brings the single particles closer to each other and ultimately they agglomerate to form larger aggregates due to various attractive forces, such as Van der Waals' forces. As a result of the formation of larger particles, precipitation due to gravity will now take place more quickly while the Brownian movement will diminish.

The third force playing an important part in a dispersed system is surface tension. It is important to realize that with such small bodies as colloidal particles, the sum of their total surface area is enormously large. As is well known, the surface tension aims constantly to diminish the surface area and, therefore, directly opposes the dispersion of the particles. Which then are the forces which oppose the surface tension?

In the first place, one should take into consideration the electrostatic forces between uniformly charged particles which tend to repel each other. Such particles can have obtained their charge either through their own electrolytic dissociation or through adsorption of other ions. Secondly, dispersed colloidal particles, whether solid, liquid or gaseous, are encircled by films of the medium in which they are dispersed. This phenomenon is generally known as *solvation,* or *hydration,* when the dispersing medium is water. These films of water adsorbed on the surface of hydrophilic colloids may be relatively thick. In the case of proteins, for instance, it has been observed that the amount of water which is so tightly bound to the protein molecule that it moves with it in gravitational or electric fields, can be as much as 4 g of water per 10 g of protein. The stability of hydrophilic sols is largely due to this type of hydration. It has been suggested that the energy of solvation compensates for the large increase in surface energy resulting from the small size of the dispersed particles, thus giving the system stability against agglomeration.

In general, hydrophobic colloids are stabilized by their own electrostatic charges, while hydrophilic colloids are stabilized by hydration. The colloidal particles are coated in this case by films in which the water dipoles orient themselves round the colloidal particle. This latter becomes then almost free from interfacial tension and the suspension should ordinary remain quite stable.

It often happens that a hydrophilic colloid suddenly loses its stability. The originally stable dispersion becomes unstable, and the particles agglomerate causing coagulation, or flocculation. These changes may be due either to the addition of an agent which competes for the solvent, thus causing *desolvation,* or *dehydration,* or to changes in the colloidal particles themselves. Destabilization due to desolvation is often reversible, but the changes in the particles themselves are usually irreversible. Such is the case, for instance, in the coagulation of protein sols due to the denaturation of proteins. The denaturation of proteins, which will be discussed later, causes major changes in the structure of the protein molecules and results in the irreversible coagulation of many food systems, such as egg white or milk proteins. On the other hand, small additions of colloidal substances, such as gelatin, often prevent separation of the dispersed system. These substances are called *protective colloids.*

They form primarily a thin film around the original colloidal particle which may, in addition, be surrounded by an additional film of water. Such protective colloids act as good stabilizers for the dispersed system and often protect it from the adverse influence of heat, cold or the addition of electrolytes.

References p. 118

Food industry's use of colloids

Let us see now how the above-mentioned principles can be applied in the food industry, in dispersions, in emulsions and in foams.

It appears from the above that a given phase is colloidal when it is sufficiently finely divided and that colloidal chemistry is the chemistry of grains, drops, bubbles, filaments and films, because in each of these cases at least one dimension of a phase is extremely small. Consequently, in order to create a suspension of a solid food, the solid must undergo fine disintegration in a colloidal mill and, in the case of emulsions, in a suitable homogenizer.

The next consideration is the stabilization of such preparations. Very often it is necessary to control the structure of the product in order to achieve smoothness, more body, better chewiness or a more desirable texture. This is usually done by the addition of some edible *hydrocolloid* having gelling properties, thereby helping in the suspension of the solids. These additives, some of which are described more fully below, also have the properties of increasing viscosity, binding and holding moisture, affecting interfacial tension and, since they are mostly charged polymers, affecting the electrostatic charges of the suspended particles.

Not all the stabilizers fulfill all these requirements; it is therefore customary to mix several of the hydrocolloids. A short description of the most important stabilizers in use is given below:

Pectic substances and their uses in the food industry have already been discussed in the preceding chapter.

Sodium alginate (*algin*) is the sodium salt of polymannuronic (alginic) acid (see Chapter 8). It is extracted from algae and is most widely used for ice cream and frozen desserts stabilization; it has also shown exceptional foam stabilization properties in beverages. While algin can not be used as a stabilizer in acidic solutions, its propylene glycol derivative has achieved considerable importance in this direction.

Karaya gum[1] is the dried exudation of the *Sterculia urens* tree grown in India. While its structure has not yet been elucidated, it is considered to be an acetylated polysaccharide of high molecular weight. Of all the hydrocolloids, Karaya gum is the least soluble, but, when finely ground, it readily absorbs water. Karaya is used as a stabilizer in French dressings, in ice popicles and sherbets where it prevents syneresis as well as the formation of large ice crystals. In order to prevent water separation and to increase the ease of spreading, Karaya is also used in the manufacture of cheese spreads. In addition, this gum imparts a smooth appearance to ground meat products which require an efficient water-holding capacity on one hand and low adhesiveness on the other hand.

Gum tragacanth[2] is a water-soluble exudate obtained from *Astragalus gummifer* and forms a thick viscous liquid. Tragacanth gum has been shown to have a complex structure containing D-galacturonic acid as a main chain to which several pentoses (L-fucopyranose, D-xylopyranose, D-galactose and L-arabinose) are linked in glycosidic bonds. Its ability to swell in water to form gels of high water content makes it very useful as a stabilizer in puddings, salad dressings, mayonnaise and ice cream manufacture.

Both *locust bean gum*[3,4] and *guar gum* are produced from the plant family *Leguminose*: the former from the seed endosperms of the carob tree, *Ceratonia siliqua* L., which grows in Mediterranean countries, and the latter from the guar, a legume resembling the soy-bean plant. Both gums are galacto-mannans, *i.e.*, long 1:4 chains of polymannans to which single galactose units are attached through 1:6-glycosidic bonds:

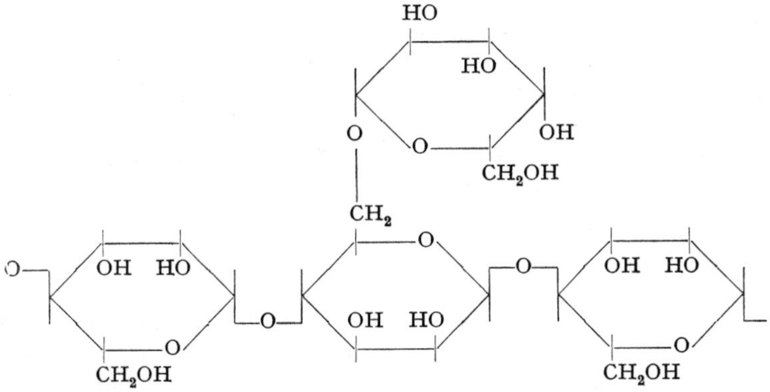

These gums swell in cold solutions and require no heat to complete their hydration. Because of their strong hydrophilic character they are excellent additives in salad dressings, ice cream mixes and bakery products. They are also used in the paper and textile industries.

Carageenins[5] or *Irish moss extract* is a water-soluble extract from the Red Sea plant, *Chondrus crispus*. This compound consists of a complex polysaccharide composed principally of D-galactopyranose and some L-galactose, 2-ketoglu-conic acid and non-reducing sugar units. Each monomer is an ester of H_2SO_4:

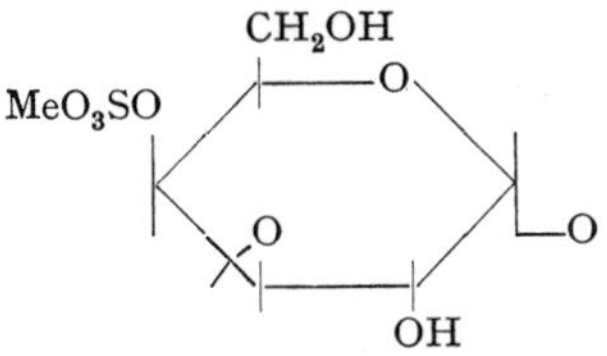

The galactose units are linked at positions 1 and 3, while carbon atom 4 is sulfated. Carrageenin is a negatively charged polymer which reacts with positively charged protein molecules causing a rapid increase in their viscosity. It sets into gels and stabilizes emulsions and suspensions.

Of other stabilizers mention should be made of *gelatin*, a protein, which was probably the first to be used for such purpose; however, its use is now decreasing; *agar-agar*, a complex polysaccharide, and finally *carboxymethyl cellulose* (CMC), which has excellent water-binding properties and which will also stand up to high-temperature–short-time pasteurization.

Solid dispersions

When solid in liquid dispersion are desired, the next step after the reduction of the aggregates to an acceptable minimum size, is the *wetting* of the particle surfaces. For wetting to occur, the adhesive forces between the dispersing medium and the solid particles must exceed the cohesive forces in the liquid itself. When true wetting occurs, the solid particle no longer displays its own surface phenomena, in fact, its surface assumes the properties of the materials adsorbed.

Many of the colloids encountered in food dispersions possess a sufficiently large number of hydrophilic groups to allow *wetting* and *hydration*. The presence of this water layer tightly bound to the solid particles greatly impedes particle aggregation and contributes to the stability of such dispersions.

When the dispersed solid itself is not readily hydrated, use can be made of a variety of surface-active agents. The introduction of *surfactants* such as mono- and diglycerides, polyethylene derivatives, pectins, alginates, gums, gelatin, lecithin, etc., which lower the interfacial tension, often help to deflocculate the agglomerates, facilitate the wetting of the solid particles and displace the gases which may be adsorbed on the solid surface. Upon the addition of surfactants the gas film is displaced and a solid–liquid interface can be achieved[6].

Liquid–liquid emulsions

The foremost requirement for the existence of a liquid–liquid emulsion is the lowering of the interfacial tension between the two liquids. This is achieved in practice by the presence of surface-active agents, which lower the interfacial tension between water and many organic liquids from values in the range of 30–50 dynes/cm to values ranging from 0 to 10 dynes/cm.

The lowering of surface tension, however, does not necessarily impart stability to liquid–liquid emulsion. The emulsions are destabilized by aggregation of the small droplets, and by separation due to density differences between the two liquids. Oil-in-water emulsions are stabilized against aggregation by either or both of the following mechanisms:

(a) Formation of a strong film around individual droplets of the suspended liquid. Such films are formed, for instance, by denatured proteins, and many surface-active agents. These films are particularly effective when they are due to formation of a complex between several components adsorbed at the interface between the suspended oil phase and water. A good example of this type of interaction is the stabilization of fat globules in milk, which is due to the formation of a complex film of phospholipids, cholesterol, and other steroids and proteins.

(b) The existence of an electrostatically charged layer at the surface of the individual droplets. In food emulsions such charges usually originate in the adsorbed surface-active agents.

Stability against separation, such as creaming, is improved mainly by increasing the *viscosity* of the suspending medium. It is obvious that the higher the viscosity, the slower is the Brownian movement and the smaller are the chances for the particles to agglomerate and, therefore, the smaller are the chances for sedimentation or creaming to occur.

Otherwise stable emulsions, such as mayonnaise, consisting mainly of oil, egg yolk protein and water, may tend to show separation when stored at low temperatures. These phenomena are due to so-called "breaking temperatures" which usually depend on the type of oil or the proportions of the various components.

Milk on the other hand is a combination of practically all types of dispersed systems. The fat in it is distributed as an emulsion, the proteins (casein, albumin and globulin) are in a colloidal dispersion, while lactose, amino acids and a number of vitamins, salts, etc., are true solutions.

Surfactants are used in the stabilization of whipped cream products as well as in many similar products.

Foams

While suspensions are usually solids dispersed in liquids and emulsions generally consist of liquids dispersed in liquids, there is no such sharp distinction in many food products, where the systems are mostly much more complicated and very often contain several phases.

Foam, however, is a dispersed gaseous phase in a liquid medium, but even here the system is more complicated. In foams the air bubbles are surrounded by thin films of liquid. The air or gas may be dispersed in the liquid either by mechanical means, using suitable beaters, or by simple bubbling (using sprayers), or, again, by diffusion through porous dispensers. A recently patented process[7] makes use of a diffusion chamber made of some rigid ceramic porous material through which both air and liquid pass thereby causing a thin film of liquid to surround each tiny air bubble.

In foams the surface of the liquid is enormously increased. This results in extreme thermodynamic instability of the systems. Nevertheless it is possible in practice to produce foams which can be maintained for long periods of time. The theory of such *metastable* foams is complex and has not been completely elucidated. It appears, however, that the following factors aid in the achievement of "foam stability"[8]:

(1) high viscosity of the liquid;

(2) lowering of surface tension;

(3) formation of films with a high degree of *surface elasticity* and *surface viscosity*;

(4) existence of electrostatic charges on such films.

In practice, primarily in the baking and confectionary industries, proteins such as egg white, or other proteins from vegetable sources, are whipped in a solution of some carbohydrate until a maximum amount of air bubbles is produced to form a stiff mass. Such a foam achieves a certain degree of stability if the whipping is not overdone. It is generally known that over-whipping results in the so-called "protein fatigue" when the bubble structure breaks down and the specific gravity rises to leave very little foam stability. Minute changes in surface tension of the film can 'make or break' the foam.

In beer, the substance responsible for the foam adhesiveness is derived from the added hops, and is probably the compound *isohumulone*.

Other colloidal systems

As mentioned in Chapter 8, the viscosities of hydrocolloids, which in most cases are linear macromolecules, can vary considerably in accordance with the difference in the spatial configurations of the thread-like molecules. This principally depends on the degree of ionization of the hydrocolloid, or on the difference in viscosity in various dispersing media. When the hydrocolloid is ionized or when the dispersing medium, having a certain affinity towards the polymer, causes real solvation, the linear macromolecules become less coiled, and the more extended they are the higher the viscosity of the dispersed system (Fig. 16).

Another important factor is the attraction between linear macromolecules, this depending on the cohesive forces between the chains.

This interaction between the macromolecules greatly affects their flow properties. In the case of spherocolloids, and in the case of linear colloids in dilute solutions, and at elevated temperatures the flow behavior is typical *Newtonian* type. In this case the applied pressure is proportional to the rate of shear, and the proportionality constant is the viscosity.

In other colloidal systems the interaction between the colloidal particles causes deviations from this ideal, *Newtonian*, behavior. In these systems the ratio of applied pressure to the rate of shear is not constant, but varies with the conditions, such as pressure, rate of shear and time. In these systems it is not appropriate to speak of the viscosity as an inherent property of the liquid, but rather of *apparent viscosity*, or *consistency* which represents the ratio between the applied pressure and the rate of shear under the particular conditions at which it is measured.

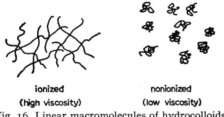

ionized   nonionized
(high viscosity) (low viscosity)

Fig. 16. Linear macromolecules of hydrocolloids.

In fact, many of these systems behave not as liquids which flow upon the application of the minutest pressure, but rather as soft solids, pastes and solids—they are called, therefore, *plastic systems*, which have a property called the *yield value*, which is the stress necessary to initiate flow.

Other colloidal systems show behavior intermediate between that of purely *viscous*, or *Newtonian* liquids, and that of *elastic* solids, and are called *visco-elastic* systems. The flow relations of these non-Newtonian systems are rather complex, and there are many combinations of elastic, plastic and viscous properties. Some of these non-Newtonian systems have moderate yield values and low apparent viscosities, *e.g.* mayonnaise and butter; others have high apparent viscosity while their yield value is zero, *e.g.* chocolate. The branch of science dealing with these complex manifestations of deformation and flow is called *rheology* (from the Greek: *"panta rhei"*— everything flows).

Thixotropy

The very important phenomenon of a reversible sol–gel transformation is often observed in many food products, such a concentrated juices, jellies, etc. On stirring, such gels liquefy. In these cases the apparent viscosity decreases with increasing rate of shear; however, if the disturbing force (*i.e.* stirring) ceases, the consistency may increase again so much that the system will set to a gel. This phenomenon, which is known as *thixotropy*, is explained by the fact that the long chains of linear macromolecules are normally linked by some secondary bonds, such as hydrogen bonds, which may be disrupted by simple mechanical treatment.

Non-dispersed systems

The so-called *non-dispersed colloidal systems* belong to an entirely different category. These systems occur, for instance, when a drop of fatty acid spreads on the surface of water. In a case such as this, a monomolecular film is formed, with the hydrophilic "heads" submerged into the water and the long hydrophobic "tails" projecting into the air (Chapter 16, page 238). Such monomolecular films, when dried over the surface of some products, may serve as an excellent protection against oxidation. In fact, a film of this kind is a colloidal system between the air and the water. Systems of this type, where the liquid or the solid is not dispersed, are called *diform systems*. Antifoams, for instance, may serve as an example of such systems.

REFERENCES

[1] A. M. GOLDSTEIN, Chemistry, properties and application of Gum Karaya, *Advances in Chem. Ser. No. 11*, (1954) 33.

[2] D. C. BEACH, History, production and uses of Tragacanth, *Advances in Chem. Ser. No. 11*, (1954), 38.

[3] R. L. WHISTLER, Guar gum, locust bean gum, and others, *Advances in Chem. Ser. No. 11*, (1954) 45.

[4] H. DEUEL AND H. NEUKOM, Some properties of locust bean gum, *Advances in Chem. Ser. No. 11*, (1954) 51.

[5] L. STOLOFF, Irish moss extractives, *Advances in Chem. Ser. No. 11*, (1954) 92.

[6] S. PRUSSIN, G. LIEBERMAN AND J. R. LINDQUIST, Practical aspects of dispersions, in physical properties of hydrocolloids, *Am. Chem. Soc. Science Ser. No. 25*, (1958) 82.

[7] J. J. ALIKONIS, *U.S. Patent 2,536,340*, (1951).

[8] J. A. KITCHENER AND C. F. COOPER, Current concepts in the theory of foaming, *Quart. Revs.*, 13 (1959) 71.

SELECTED BIBLIOGRAPHY TO CHAPTER 10

CLAYTON, W., *Colloidal Aspects of Food Chemistry and Technology*, J. and A. CHURCHILL, London, 1932.

FREY-WYSSLING, A., *Deformation of Flow in Biological Systems*, North-Holland Publishing Co., Amsterdam, 1952.

JIRGENSONS, B. AND K. E. STRAUMAMS, *A Short Textbook of Colloidal Chemistry*, J. Wiley and Sons, New York, 1956.

KRUYT, H. R., *Colloid Science*, Elsevier Publishing Co., New York, 1949.

LEWIS, W. K., L. SQUIRES AND G. BROUGHTON, *Industrial Chemistry of Colloidal and Amorphous Materials*, MacMillan Publishing Co., New York, 1942.

MOORE, W. J., *Physical Chemistry*, Prentice-Hall, Inc., New York, 1956.

SCOTT-BLAIR, G. W., *Foodstuffs, Their Plasticity, Fluidity and Consistency*, Elsevier Publishing Co., Amsterdam, 1953.

WARD, A. G., *Colloids*, Interscience, New York, 1946.

Society of Chemical Industry, *Texture of Food*, MacMillan, New York, 1960.

CHAPTER II

PROTEINS

Of the first rank

BERZELIUS

Occurrence

It has been mentioned earlier (Chapter 4) that proteins are formed during the first minutes after illumination, this being shown by chromatograms taken during photosynthesis. Proteins are very complex organic substances which, although also present in the plants, constitute the main structure of the animal and the human body. Their importance as one of the three major basic nutrients in foodstuffs, such as meat, eggs or milk curd, was appreciated long ago by intuition. Hence, their name *"protein"* suggested by BERZELIUS in 1838, coined from the Greek *proteios*—of the first rank.

All proteins contain, in addition to carbon, hydrogen and oxygen also nitrogen and often sulfur as well as phosphorus. Just to demonstrate their complexity, one may examine the elementary analysis of one of the "simple" proteins, *β-lactoglobulin*, found in milk, its molecular weight being only 42,000: $C_{1864}H_{3012}O_{576}N_{468}S_{21}$.

The presence of nitrogen is the most important characteristic of proteins and in order to estimate the total amount of proteins in a given food or similar product, it has become a widespread practice to multiply the percent nitrogen content by the factor 6.25, on the assumption that all proteins contain, on the average, approximately 16 % N.

The peptide bond

In spite of their complexity and immense diversity, all proteins have been found to consist of only about 20 structural units, the so-called *"amino acids"*.

All but two amino acids are of the general formula

$$R—CH·COOH$$
$$|$$
$$NH_2$$

i.e., α-amino acids, where both the carboxyl and the amino groups are attached to the α-carbon atom. In proteins the various amino acids are linked by peptide bonds, (—CO—NH—), *i.e.* the carboxyl group of one amino acid is linked with the amino group of the second amino acid with elimination of H_2O, thus forming an amide of the second acid:

$$
\begin{array}{cccc}
\text{HO}\vdots\text{OC} & \text{NH}\vdots_2 & \text{HO}\vdots\text{OC} & \text{NH}\vdots_2 \\
| & | & | & | \\
R^1\text{—CH} & R^2\text{—CH} & R^3\text{—CH} & R^4\text{—CH} \\
| & | & | & | \\
\text{NH}\vdots_2 & \text{HO}\vdots\text{OC} & \text{NH}\vdots_2 & \text{HO}\vdots\text{OC}
\end{array}
$$

$$
\begin{array}{cccccc}
& R^1 & O & & R^3 & O \\
& | & \| & & | & \| \\
\diagdown \text{CH}\diagdown & \diagup\text{C}\diagdown & \diagup\text{NH}\diagdown & \diagup\text{CH}\diagdown & \diagup\text{C}\diagdown & \diagup\text{NH}\diagdown \\
\text{C} & \text{NH} & \text{CH} & \text{C} & \text{NH} & \text{CH} \\
\| & & | & \| & & | \\
O & & R^2 & O & & R^4
\end{array}
$$

the peptide bond

R^1, R^2, etc., indicate different amino acid residues. However, all amino acids do not necessarily appear in a given protein and also some of them may recur many times in the same protein molecule.

Amino acids

When hydrolyzed by strong mineral acids or with the aid of certain enzymes, proteins can be completely decomposed into their component *amino acids*. Except for proline and hydroxyproline (see below) and for a few recently discovered and rarely encountered amino acids, like β-alanine, γ-aminobutyric acid a.o., all have the general formula

$$R \cdot CH \cdot (NH_2) \cdot COOH$$

In the simplest amino acid, glycine, R represents a hydrogen atom and in the next, alanine, R is CH_3. The following is a list of the known proteinogenic amino acids:

(I) *Aliphatic monoamino monocarboxylic amino acids*:

Glycine — $CH_2 \cdot (NH_2) \cdot COOH$

Alanine — $CH_3 \cdot CH \cdot (NH_2) \cdot COOH$

Valine —
$$
\begin{array}{l}
CH_3\diagdown \\
CH \cdot CH \cdot (NH_2) \cdot COOH \\
CH_3\diagup
\end{array}
$$

Leucine —
$$\begin{matrix} CH_3 \\ \\ CH_3 \end{matrix} \Big\rangle CH \cdot CH_2 \cdot CH \cdot (NH_2) \cdot COOH$$

Isoleucine — $CH_3 \cdot CH_2 \cdot CH(CH_3) \cdot CH \cdot (NH_2) \cdot COOH$

Serine — $HO \cdot CH_2 \cdot CH \cdot (NH_2) \cdot COOH$

Threonine — $CH_3 \cdot CH(OH) \cdot CH \cdot (NH_2) \cdot COOH$

(II) *Sulfur-containing amino acids*:

Cysteine — $HS \cdot CH_2 \cdot CH \cdot (NH_2) \cdot COOH$

Cystine —
$$\begin{matrix} S \cdot CH_2 \cdot CH \cdot (NH_2) \cdot COOH \\ | \\ S \cdot CH_2 \cdot CH \cdot (NH_2) \cdot COOH \end{matrix}$$

Methionine — $CH_3 \cdot S \cdot CH_2 \cdot CH_2 \cdot CH(NH_2) \cdot COOH$

(III) *Aliphatic monoamino dicarboxylic amino acids*:

Aspartic acid — $HOOC \cdot CH_2 \cdot CH \cdot (NH_2) \cdot COOH$

Glutamic acid — $HOOC \cdot CH_2 \cdot CH_2 \cdot CH \cdot (NH_2) \cdot COOH$

(IV) *Aliphatic, basic amino acids*:

Lysine — $NH_2 \cdot CH_2(CH_2)_3 \cdot CH \cdot (NH_2) \cdot COOH$

Arginine —
$$\begin{matrix} H_2N \\ \\ HN \end{matrix} \Big\rangle C \cdot NH \cdot CH_2 \cdot CH_2 \cdot CH_2 \cdot CH(NH_2) \cdot COOH$$

Histidine —
$$\begin{matrix} & CH & \\ N & & NH \\ | & & | \\ CH & = C \cdot CH_2 \cdot CH(NH_2) \cdot COOH \end{matrix}$$

(V) *Aromatic amino acids*:

Phenylalanine —
$$\langle \bigcirc \rangle CH_2 \cdot CH(NH_2) \cdot COOH$$

Tyrosine —
$$HO \langle \bigcirc \rangle CH_2 \cdot CH(NH_2) \cdot COOH$$

(VI) *Heterocyclic amino acids*:

Tryptophan —
$$\begin{matrix} & & C \cdot CH_2 \cdot CH(NH_2) \cdot COOH \\ & & \| \\ & NH & CH \end{matrix}$$

Proline —
$$\begin{matrix} & \\ NH & COOH \end{matrix}$$

References p. 149/150

Glutamine and asparagine, the amines of the resp. amino acids as well as the hydroxy derivates of lysine and proline appear also in proteins, the last two mainly in connective tissues.

Of this list of amino acids, eight are considered *essential* or *indispensable* for the diet of man. They are: lysine, tryptophan, phenylalanine, threonine, valine, methionine, leucine and isoleucine.

Except for the simplest amino acid, glycine, all are optically active and in each of them the carbon atom to which both the amino group and the carboxyl are attached, is the center of asymmetry. All amino acids forming natural proteins are L-configurations. The D-forms can be synthesized, but only in exceptional cases they are found in biological material.

Because an amino acid contains both a carboxyl and an amino group, it should be regarded as an *"inner-salt"* or a *"zwitterion"*.

$$R—CH—COO^-$$
$$|$$
$$NH_3{}^+$$

amino acid

A description of this sort shows that it is not a case of an electrolytic dissociation or of the presence of free ions. What we actually have here is an electric field between the two parts of the molecule. In other words, the amino acids are *"dipole compounds"*, which are in the state of ionization but not of dissociation. All amino acids have high melting points (above 230° C) and are difficultly soluble in organic solvents, however, their solubility in water is quite good.

The amino acids are, therefore, *amphoteric* substances, *viz.*, they act as acids in alkaline solution, and as alkalis in acid solutions:

$$\underset{NH_3{}^+}{R \cdot CH \cdot COOH} \quad \xleftarrow{\text{HCl}} \quad \underset{NH_3{}^+}{R \cdot CH \cdot COO^-} \quad \xrightarrow{\text{NaOH}} \quad \underset{NH_2}{R \cdot CH \cdot COO^-}$$

Accordingly, the molecules of amino acids will travel: in acid solutions to the cathode, as $R \cdot CH \cdot NH^+{}_3 \cdot COOH$; in alkaline solutions to the anode, as $R \cdot CH \cdot NH_2 \cdot COO^-$; and when their charge is zero, $R \cdot CH \cdot NH^+{}_3 \cdot COO^-$, the molecule will not travel at all. The latter state is attained at specific pH values for different amino acids and is called the *isoelectric point* of the particular amino acid. The difference in the isoelectric points is primarily due to the varied constitutions of the amino acids: in an amino acid in which there is only one carboxyl and one amino group, there is a sort of inner neutralization, however when there are more acidic residues, like in aspartic or glutamic acids, or when there are more amino groups, as in lysine or arginine, it is obvious that there will be different pH values for the appropriate isoelectric points. This property of the amino acids enabled TISELIUS to work out the very valuable method of *electrophoresis*, which enables one to differentiate not only between individual amino acids but also between different proteins (see further).

Introduction of nitrogen

The nitrogen required by the plant for the formation of amino acids during photosynthesis is derived from the soil in the form of nitrates. The reason for this is that all other nitrogenous compounds, such as ammonia, nitrites or organic substances, are quickly transformed in the soil into the more stable nitrates by the action of microorganisms (the nitrification bacteria).

In the plant, however, the nitrates are reduced first to nitrites and probably by way of hydroxylamine, into ammonia-containing compounds:

$$NO_3 \longrightarrow NO_2 \longrightarrow HONH_2 \longrightarrow R \cdot CO \cdot CH_2COOH \longrightarrow R \cdot CH \cdot (NH_2) \cdot COOH$$
nitrate   nitrite   hydroxylamine   keto acid   amino acid

The position at which this reduction takes place is not always the same in different plants: in most fruit plants, such as apples, apricots, all deciduous fruit trees, strawberries, etc., the reduction takes place in the roots and the nitrogen is transported from there to all parts of the plant in the form of amino acids; in other plants, such as cereals, tomato and tobacco, the roots are not the only organs in which nitrates are reduced—in these plants, nitrates are transported to the leaves where most of the reduction takes place.

When the rate of procurement of nitrogen from the soil is faster than its rate of reduction, an accumulation of nitrates is observed in the roots or in the leaves.

Nitrogen reduction is always accompanied by a considerable increase in respiration, sometimes up to 300 % of the normal rate. This is apparently due to the high energy requirements during the reduction process and such energy is acquired by the combustion of the carbohydrates during respiration. This phenomenon has been studied in a tomato plant which was starved for nitrates and then suddenly supplied with them after a time.

Amination and transamination

The introduction of NH_3 into the organic substance could be explained by some well-known deamination reactions, if they could be proved to be reversible. Unfortunately, this is found to be the case only in microorganisms and not in higher plants. In most of these reactions oxidative

References p. 149/150

deamination of the amino acid occurs which is then oxidized into the corresponding α-keto acid with the release of ammonia:

$$R\text{---}CH\cdot COOH + \tfrac{1}{2}O_2 \longrightarrow R\cdot C\cdot COOH + NH_3$$
$$\underset{NH_2}{\big|} \qquad\qquad \underset{O}{\big\|}$$

This type of reaction has been found to be reversible only in the case of glutamic acid when it is converted into α-ketoglutaric acid in the presence of the enzyme *glutamic acid dehydrogenase*, which contains the previously mentioned coenzyme, DPN (diphosphopyridine nucleotide) (see Chapter 6). The reaction proceeds in two steps:

$$
\begin{array}{ccccc}
\text{COOH} & & \text{COOH} & & \text{COOH}\\
| & & | & & |\\
\text{HCNH}_2 & \underset{\text{DPNH}_2}{\overset{\text{DPN}}{\rightleftharpoons}} & \text{C}=\text{NH} & \underset{}{\overset{\text{H}_2\text{O}}{\rightleftharpoons}} & \text{C}=\text{O} \quad + NH_3\\
| & & | & & |\\
\text{CH}_2 & & \text{CH}_2 & & \text{CH}_2\\
| & & | & & |\\
\text{CH}_2 & & \text{CH}_2 & & \text{CH}_2\\
| & & | & & |\\
\text{COOH} & & \text{COOH} & & \text{COOH}\\
\text{glutamic acid} & & \text{iminoglutamic acid} & & \alpha\text{-ketoglutaric acid}
\end{array}
$$

In the first stage of this reaction, DPN is reduced to $DPNH_2$ which can be further oxidized by other oxidative biological systems and finally the hydrogen is oxidized by molecular oxygen. VON EULER succeeded in making this reaction proceed from right to left, starting with α-ketoglutaric acid and ammonia in the presence of the reduced diphosphopyridine nucleotide ($DPNH_2$). *In vitro*, VON EULER was compelled to add constantly the enzyme-containing $DPNH_2$ in order to continue with the synthesis of glutamic acid. However, *in situ*, this enzyme can be supplied by the reactions of the respiration cycle.

Using isotopes, this path of amination has now been proved to exist also in higher plants and it is assumed that it is the principal amination reaction since both glutamic acid and DPN are widely distributed in the plant kingdom.

A second important reaction which contributes to the complete understanding of the formation of amino acids is the reaction of *transamination* discovered in 1937 by BRAUNSTEIN AND KRITZMAN[1]. These investigators found that glutamic acid and pyruvic acid may interchange the amino group for the carbonyl group in the presence of an enzyme, *transaminase*:

$$\underset{\text{glutamic acid}}{\begin{array}{c}\text{COOH}\\|\\\text{HCNH}_2\\|\\\text{CH}_2\\|\\\text{CH}_2\\|\\\text{COOH}\end{array}} + \underset{\text{pyruvic acid}}{\begin{array}{c}\text{COOH}\\|\\\text{C}=\text{O}\\|\\\text{CH}_3\end{array}} \underset{\xleftarrow{\hspace{1cm}}}{\xrightarrow{\text{transaminase}}} \underset{\text{α-ketoglutaric acid}}{\begin{array}{c}\text{COOH}\\|\\\text{C}=\text{O}\\|\\\text{CH}_2\\|\\\text{CH}_2\\|\\\text{COOH}\end{array}} + \underset{\text{alanine}}{\begin{array}{c}\text{COOH}\\|\\\text{CH}\cdot\text{NH}_2\\|\\\text{CH}_3\end{array}}$$

In fact, glutamic acid is capable to transfer its amino group to any α-keto acid. It appears, therefore, that glutamic acid is the chief transporter of the amino group to various other amino acids. The derivatives of pyridoxine, pyridoxamine and pyridoxal, the group of substances known as Vitamin B$_6$, are now found to act as coenzymes in the transamination reaction. Both forms taking part in this reaction are esterified by phosphoric acid:

pyridoxine   pyridoxamine   pyridoxal   pyridoxal phosphate

It is assumed that the enzyme participates in the transamination reaction in the following manner:

amino acid 1   pyridoxal phosphate

α-keto acid 1   pyridoxamine phosphate

pyridoxamine + phosphate + α-keto acid 2 → pyridoxal phosphate + amino acid 2

References p. 149/150

Classification of proteins

Solubility properties of the proteins present a good means for separating various proteins. Water, salt solutions, alkaline and acid solutions and ethanol are used for such separations. Fractional precipitation from ammonium sulfate solution is a very useful method for the purification of proteins. Solubility is, therefore, commonly used as a means of classifying them, although this method of classification is quite inadequate. The following groups can be distinguished:

(I) *Scleroproteins —totally insoluble proteins*. These form the greater part in animal tissues, such as wool, silk (fibroin), hair (keratin), etc.

(II) *Spheroproteins*. These are classified in five sub-groups according to solubility:

(a) *Albumins*—soluble in water and in salt solutions, *viz.*, the white of an egg;

(b) *Globulins*—insoluble in water, but soluble in salt solutions, *viz.*, serum globulin of blood;

(c) *Glutelins*—insoluble in the above, but soluble in alkali and acids, *viz.*, wheat glutelin, oryzenin in rice;

(d) *Prolamines*—soluble in 50–80 % ethanol, *viz.*, wheat gliadin, zein in maize;

(e) *Histones*—proteins of comparatively low molecular weights containing a large number of basic amino acids; they are soluble in water and in acids;

TABLE IV

SOLUBILITY OF SPHEROPROTEINS

Protein	Water	Salt solutions	Alkali	Acids	50–80 % ethanol
albumins	+	+			
globulins	—	+			
glutelins*	—	—	+	+	
prolamines*	—	—	—	—	+
histones	+	+			

* Not generally accepted.

Properties of proteins

Although proteins are built only of amino acids linked together by peptide bonds, as shown before, they have specific properties of their own with the general properties of polymers of very large molecular weights. In the first place, all of them like polysaccharides, are of a colloidal nature, and in addition they behave like dipolar ions, *i.e.*, they exhibit amphoteric properties in similarity to amino acids. Since in proteins the α-amino and the α-carboxyl groups of the amino acids are engaged in the peptide linkage, their amphoteric properties depend on the ionizable groups in the amino acid side chains, such as the additional ε-amino group of lysine, the guanidino group of arginine, the γ-carboxyl of glutamic acid and the sulf-hydryl group of cysteine, etc.

Strong acids, such as concentrated nitric acid, picric and trichloracetic acids cause irreversible coagulation of protein sols from solution. However, when heated for several hours with 30 % solutions of H_2SO_4 or HCl, the proteins undergo complete hydrolysis into their component amino acids. Catalyzed by special enzymes, such as *pepsin, trypsin* and *chymotrypsin*, the proteins undergo a similar hydrolysis in the animal and in the human body at a temperature of about 37°C. The human body, as well as that of the animal, is then capable of synthesizing its own specific proteins from the structural units obtained after such hydrolysis.

Due to the action of such *proteolytic enzymes*, the large protein molecule is first disrupted into smaller units called *peptones* or *proteoses*. EMIL FISCHER was the first to succeed in synthesizing such units consisting of several amino acids and called them *peptides*. The larger peptide synthesized by FISCHER consisted of 18 amino acid molecules (15 molecules of glycine and 3 of leucine) with a molecular weight of 1213. The polypeptide behaved like a natural peptone and was even attacked by proteolytic enzymes. *Glutathione* is such a peptide found in nature, in fact it is a tripeptide consisting of glutamic acid, glycine and cysteine:

$$
\begin{array}{cc}
\text{COOH} & \text{CH}_2\text{SH} \\
| & | \\
\text{NH}_2 \cdot \text{CH} \cdot \text{CH}_2 \cdot \text{CH}_2 \cdot \text{CO} \diagdown \quad \diagup \text{CH} \diagdown \quad \diagup \text{NH} \diagdown \quad \diagup \text{COOH} \\
\text{NH} \qquad \text{CO} \qquad \text{CH}_2
\end{array}
$$

glutathione

A large number of such peptides have been found in nature and particularly in microorganisms which produce peptides that have antibacterial activity toward other microorganisms, in peptide hormones and in muscles (carnosine, anserine).

The ability of strong acids to hydrolyze proteins into smaller units of peptides and polypeptides is used commercially in the food industry for preparing the so-called *protein hydrolysates* from plant materials. In this process, proteins from various plant sources are hydrolyzed by strong hydrochloric acid, usually in glass-built apparatus, and the product is then neutralized with alkali. The resulting mixture of peptides is then concentrated and sold in this form as protein hydrolyzates. These are widely used for soup mixtures and similar food preparations.

Molecular weights

One can not determine molecular weights of proteins by the classical methods used in organic chemistry, such as the boiling point or cryoscopic methods, since with such large macromolecules the differences in such indices are indeed very small. Here are a few examples of the most probable molecular weights of proteins:

ribonuclease,	12,700;
lactalbumin (cow),	17,500;
trypsin,	24.000;
gliadin,	27,000;
zein,	35,000;
β-lactoglobulin,	35,400;
insulin,	38,000;
egg albumin,	42,000;
hemoglobin,	68,000;
serum globulin,	167,000;
urease,	480,000.

Methods used for the determination of the molecular weights of proteins include the following:
(a) osmotic pressure;
(b) light and X-ray scattering;
(c) viscosity;
(d) diffusion;
(e) sedimentation in an ultracentrifuge.
Each of the above methods has its inherent advantages and disadvantages. The sedimentation, diffusion and viscosity methods, for example, all depend on the determination of the resistance of the molecules to their motion through the surrounding liquid medium. This resistance, however, depends not only on the molecular weight, but also on the shape of the molecules and the amount of water which moves with the molecule, *i.e., hydration.* Unless the shape and hydration are independently determined, the determination of the true molecular weight is impossible by any *one* of these methods. The light scattering methods are similarly affected by shape factors.

The osmotic pressure is theoretically independent of shape and hydration of the molecules, but the determination of molecular weight by this method s complicated by electrochemical factors (*Gibbs–Donnan effect*) and by deviation from ideal solution behavior.

One difficulty common to all methods is the tendency of protein molecules to aggregate. Depending on conditions of temperature, solvent, pH, etc., the proteins may reversibly change their molecular weight. Insulin, for instance, appears to have a minimum molecular weight of 6,000; under most normal conditions, however, it appears in solution as a unit having a molecular weight of 36,000–48,000, apparently due to some form of association, or aggregation.

SVEDBERG, who devised the ultracentrifuge method, suggested an empirical formula for the approximate evaluation of molecular weights of proteins. According to this formula, the number of amino acids in a protein can be $2^4 \cdot 3^2$ or multiples of this number, *e.g.*, 144, 288, 576, 1152, etc. Since the average molecular weight of all amino acids is 120 (taking the smallest amino acid, glycine, as 57, and the largest, tryptophan, as 187), the molecular weights of all proteins should lie in the region of: $144 \cdot 120 = 17,300$; or $288 \cdot 120 = 34,500$; or $576 \cdot 120 = 52,500$, etc. If one compares these figures with the actual molecular weights shown above, one can find a quite close approximation. Further studies showed, however, that many proteins do not obey this oversimplified formula, since it assumes that all amino acids appear with equal frequency, which is not true.

Electrophoresis

The amphoteric properties of amino acids as well as the fact that proteins tend to migrate in an electric field in solution, are made use of in the determination of the isoelectric point of an isolated protein or in ascertaining how many single proteins constitute an unknown protein material. Such methods are known as *electrophoresis*.

In its simplest form, electrophoresis is used in determining the isoelectric point by admixing into a solution of a given protein very fine particles of an inert material, such as SiO_2 or TiO_2. These particles are soon coated with a thin film of the protein, thereby forming a suspension. A direct electric current is now passed through the suspension and the migration of the particles towards the anode or the cathode can be easily followed with a microscope. By carefully changing the pH of the solution it is then possible to arrive at a certain pH—a point at which the migration of the particles will be arrested. This pH is the isoelectric point of the protein in question.

In 1933, ARNE TISELIUS developed more complicated procedures in electrophoresis by means of which it is possible, by analyzing a given mixture of protein material, to ascertain how many proteins are involved. The instruments and procedures used for this purpose are very complicated and only a very brief description of the basic principle can be given here. The proteins dissolved in a buffer of a known ionic strength are placed in a U-tube (Fig. 17), and the buffer is added on top of the protein solution so as to create a sharp demarcation line between the two. When the direct

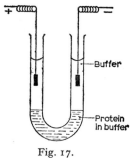

Fig. 17.

current is turned on, the protein solution will move according to its electrophoretic mobility and the separating line will ascend in one arm and correspondingly descend in the other. This movement of the separating line can be followed up by means of an optical system which registers the *rate of the change in the index of refraction*: as the recording instrument scans through the boundary between buffer and protein it registers a considerable change, although the registering line is not very sharp due to the influence of convection currents. After passing the demarcation line the refractive index remains steady again. Fig. 18 shows such an electrophoretic diagram of a homogeneous protein:

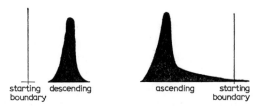

Fig. 18. Electrophoretic pattern of a single protein.

In the case of a mixture of several proteins, each of them will migrate in the electric field at different velocities because of differences in their molecular weights, their spatial configuration and their distinct isoelectric points. In other words, each protein will possess its specific mobility and the scanning diagram will, therefore, show several peaks, their number corresponding to the number of single proteins in the mixture:

starting   descending   ascending   starting
boundary   boundary

Fig. 19. Electrophoretic pattern of a mixture of proteins.

Fig. 19 shows that the analyzed mixture contains at least five single proteins. The optical technique involved in this technique is known as the *"schlieren scanning method"*, and the diagram shows that the boundary line has moved upward in the arm containing the cathode (ascending boundary) and has moved downward in the other tube (descending boundary).

Protein structure

The fact that proteins are built of a number of different amino acids joined together by a peptide bond is not sufficient to enable the exact structure of a given heteropolymer of this type to be elucidated. It is true that on complete hydrolysis by acids or by suitable proteolytic enzymes, it is now possible to determine which amino acids are present in the composition of a given protein as well as the relative amounts of the amino acids, provided that during the hydrolysis no destruction of any of the amino acids takes place. However, the main difficulty lies in the determination of the exact sequence of the amino acids in the protein.

The analysis of protein hydrolyzates is now achieved mainly by several chromatographic procedures, two-dimensional paper chromatography, which is not very well suited to the quantitative estimation of amino acids, partition chromatography on starch or on silica gel, and ion-exchange chromatography. In addition, microbiological methods are applied, using *Lactobacilli* as biological indicators of concentrations of various amino acids in a protein hydrolyzate. Recently, new procedures have been developed by SANGER[2] for the identification of the amino acid residue bearing the free α-amino group of a peptide chain (N-terminal residue), the one bearing the free α-carboxyl group (C-terminal residue) and also for the determination of the amino acid sequences of segments of the peptide chain.

In his brilliant work on the structure of insulin, SANGER found this protein to be composed of two peptide chains joined by disulfide bonds. He then

References p. 149/150

proceeded to isolate and identify many fragments and finally established the unequivocal sequence of the amino acids (Fig. 20).

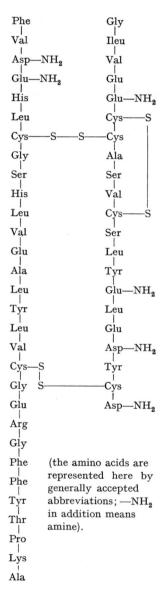

Fig. 20. Structure of beef insulin.

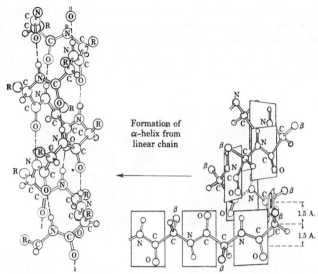

Formation of
α-helix from
linear chain

Fig. 21. Schematic representation of the process of coiling an extended polypeptide chain into the α-helical configuration (*Proc. Intern. Wool Textile Research Conf.*, B (1955) 249).

The primary structure of the enzyme ribonuclease (124 amino acids), of the tabac-mosaic virus (158 amino acids) and of hemoglobin (574 amino acids) has been elucidated.

The basic secondary structure of many of the proteins is considered now to be a helix, which is held together primarily by a number of hydrogen bonds (see Fig. 21). Disulfide bonds and other types of intramolecular linkages may also be involved.

In addition, the mere shape of the protein molecule, as well as its spatial arrangement (the tertiary structure), apparently play an important part in the nature of the proteins. The vast majority of known proteins do not behave as long fibers, but tend to be circular in shape. These are named *"globular"* or *"corpuscular"* proteins. They consist of polypeptide chains folded or coiled in a regular pattern (see Fig. 23). The other proteins have a *"fibrous"* structure (see Fig. 24) and are characteristic of those which make up the animal body. The globular proteins play an important part in metabolic activities, possess a large degree of specificity (see Chapter 12) and are easily denatured by unfolding and uncoiling (see further).

Denaturation

The most important property of proteins is that termed *"denaturation"*. Denaturation is a distinct change in the natural properties of the protein.

Such changes may be caused by a number of factors, such as heat, strong acids and bases, certain solvents and solutes, ultraviolet rays or heavy metals. All these can bring about large changes in the molecule of protein; however, if they are handled with extreme care, using low temperatures and less strong reagents, it is possible to regain the original properties of the

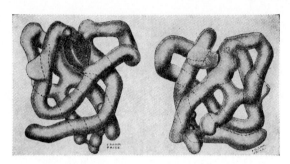

Fig. 22. Photograph of a model of the myoglobin molecule. The haem group is shown as a forshortened dark grey disk (Courtesy Dr. H. M. DINTZIS, G. BODO, H. M. DINTZIS, J. C. KENDREW and H. W. WYCKOFF, The cristal structure of myoglobin, *Proc. Roy. Soc., London*, A, 253 (1959) 70).

protein; this is a state of *reversible denaturation*. With stronger agents the sulfhydryl groups, which are responsible for the cross-linking in the protein molecule, are displaced and the molecule undergoes unfolding and uncoiling of the chains which are often irreversible. Such is the case when whey proteins, for instance, formed due to high temperatures during the processing of cottage cheese, interfere with the manufacturing process. These proteins from whey become less soluble and hinder the formation of the

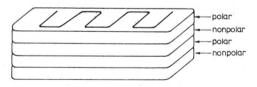

Fig. 23. Schematic representation of globular proteins.

casein curd. Some of these proteins contain the sulfhydryl groups (—SH) hidden in the inner coils of the protein helix and when these break, the exposed protein chains unfold and become much more reactive and sensitive to side reactions. Exposure of —SH groups contributes to a large extent to the specific flavor of cooked milk. Moreover, these groups give place to

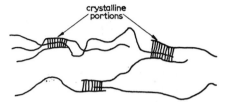

Fig. 24. Schematic representation of fibrous proteins.

new combinations and to the formation of aggregates according to the following scheme:

$$\begin{array}{ccc}
\mathrm{-SH} & \mathrm{-S} & \mathrm{-S\!-\!\!-\!\!-\!S-} \\
 & & \\
+ & \rightleftharpoons & \mathrm{-SH} \\
 & \mathrm{-S} & \\
\mathbf{R_1} & \mathbf{R_2} & \mathbf{R_1} \qquad \mathbf{R_2}
\end{array}$$

Denaturation, therefore, is a property which may contribute largely to both the texture and flavor of many foods containing proteins. From the nutritional point of view, light denaturation of proteins, may sometimes make them more susceptible to the attack of proteolytic enzymes and, therefore, facilitates digestion.

Proteolytic enzymes

It has been mentioned earlier that enzymes are biological catalysts, themselves proteins with or without a supplemented non-proteinic moiety called "coenzyme" or "prosthetic group".

A large number of enzymes, derived from various sources, specifically engaged in the breakdown of proteins are known today. In the first place, all organisms which can use proteins as a source of nitrogen are equipped with such proteolytic enzymes, which are capable of performing the cleavage of the peptide bond first and of synthesizing their own special proteins later. This part of biochemistry is in the domain of general biochemistry and nutrition and will be dealt with here only very cursorily. On the other hand, attention will be called to the role of proteolytic enzymes which may be used in foods during the process of manufacture or preparation.

Proteolytic enzymes are classified into two major groups:

(a) *proteinases*, which are capable of attacking whole protein molecules;

(b) *peptidases*, which catalyze the cleavage of relatively small fragments — peptides.

All of these enzymes are of a relatively high specificity (see Chapter 12). However, whereas the *proteinases* can cleave the protein both into peptides as well as into amino acids, the resulting compounds of *peptidase* activity are single amino acids. Another important difference between the two groups of enzymes is that *proteinases* are capable of attacking linkages hidden inside the protein helices and are therefore called *endopeptidases*, while the *peptidases*, also called *exopeptidases*, are restricted in their action to the hydrolysis of peptide bonds adjacent to terminal α-amino or α-carboxyl groups on the outside of protein helices.

A number of well-known *proteinases* are found in the gastro-intestinal tract of mammals:

Pepsin initiates the digestive breakdown in the stomach at the very low pH of about 1.0. This enzyme, which has been crystallized from beef, salmon and tuna, causes the degradation of nearly all proteins; however, its specificity lies in its favoring the hydrolysis of the peptide bond near an aromatic amino acid, such as tyrosine.

Trypsin and *Chymotrypsin* are two important *proteinases* present in the mixture of proteolytic enzymes found in the pancreas. *Trypsin* has also been crystallized, its isoelectric point being near pH 10.5 and its optimum activity near pH 8. *Trypsin* is an *endopeptidase* and its specificity is demonstrated by its action on CO—NH linkages in the vicinity of amino acids of strongly basic character, such as arginine or lysine. Provided these specificity requirements of *trypsin* are met, it can also act upon ester linkages as well as upon amide bonds.

Chymotrypsin actually represents a group of several closely related *endopeptidases* (usually marked by the Greek letters α, β, γ, δ and π). The specificity of this group of proteolytic enzymes lies in their ability to attack the peptide bond in the vicinity of a benzene ring or some other bulky group, such as phenylalanine.

All three *proteinases* mentioned above, *pepsin*, *trypsin* and *chymotrypsin*, are respectively derived from their inactive precursors: *pepsinogen*, *trypsinogen* and *chymotrypsinogen*. The most interesting thing about this is that the conversion of these precursors into the active enzymes is catalyzed by the respective enzymes themselves; these reactions, therefore, are autocatalytic. This process provides an example of an enzyme, which is in itself a protein, acting on another protein (in this case the precursor) to produce a structural change, which leads to the formation of more enzyme.

Another extraordinary phenomenon regarding these enzymes is that *pepsin*, for instance, *can digest itself*. In other words, it can cleave its own molecule into smaller peptides, which are dialyzable and which still retain the *pepsin's* enzymatic activity.

To complete the digestion of foods in the gastrointestinal tracts of mammals, several *peptidases* (*exopeptidases*) are known which cleave the smaller peptide chains into amino acids. Those attacking the peptides from the carboxyl end of the chain are termed *carboxypeptidases*; the others, found in the intestinal mucosa, catalyze the hydrolysis of peptide linkages adjacent to a free α-amino group and are termed *aminopeptidases*.

In addition, animal tissues can undergo a process of *"autolysis"*, which involves extensive degradation of their proteins into peptides and amino acids. The autolysis of such tissues is caused by intracellular enzymes named *cathepsins*. The possible use of such enzymes from beef muscle is of considerable interest to the food industry in the matter of enzymatic tenderization of meat during aging. Today, the tenderizing of meat is enhanced by proteolytic enzymes from plant sources, *papain, bromelin* and *proteases* from microbial sources[3].

To conclude the list of the numerous proteolytic enzymes derived from animal sources, mention must be made of the enzyme *rennin*, probably known since ancient times, and found in the fourth stomach of the calf. *Rennin* causes the coagulation of milk casein by converting it into paracasein which is precipitated in the presence of suitable concentrations of calcium ions. This important step in the manufacture of cheeses is performed at an optimal pH of 5; however, the nature of the linkages cleaved by this enzyme have not yet been elucidated.

The next important source of proteolytic enzymes is the plant kingdom, where they are widely distributed in various plant tissues.

Finally, microorganisms constitute an important source of proteolytic enzyme, since bacteria, yeasts and fungi contain a large variety of *proteinases* and *peptidases*. Although the greater part of these have not been extensively purified, many of them are used in the food industry, especially in the ripening of special cheeses (Limburger, Camembert and Cheddar). In such processes the microbial culture functions as a source of extracellular *proteinases* which slowly hydrolyze the proteins during the aging of the cheeses to give them a smooth, buttery texture[4].

Examples of some food proteins

The amount of research work which has contributed to the elucidation of various proteins is very large indeed and the literature on the subject is vast; however, comparatively little has been done on the proteins found in plants and especially in foods. It will be appropriate to mention briefly a few important examples.

Milk proteins. Although milk is the first and foremost food used by man, progress towards the isolation and identification of the proteins contained in cow's milk has only been achieved recently[5-7].

It is considered, at the present time, that there are two major types of proteins in milk. A relatively small amount is adsorbed in the film surrounding the milk fat globules. The nature of these proteins is not clear, but it appears that some of the milk enzymes are present in this group. Removal of this film which surrounds the fat globules often results in appearance of "free fat", which may alter the solubility characteristics of whole milk powders.

The bulk of milk proteins is retained in *skim milk* after the separation of most of the fat globules.

The skim milk proteins may be separated into four fractions:

casein,	76–86% of the total proteins;
lactalbumin,	9–18%;
lactoglobulin,	1.4–3.1%;
proteose-peptone,	2–6%.

Their separation can be performed according to the following scheme:

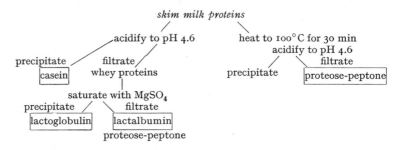

The above fractions have been found to be heterogeneous, and the names given to some of them, for example "lactoglobulin" and "lactalbumin" have now only historical value. The protein components which have been isolated from the individual fractions are:

Casein	Lactoglobulin	Lactalbumin	Proteose-Peptone
α-casein	euglobulin	β-lactoglobulin A	several components isolated, but their nature is largely unknown
(consists of several components)	pseudoglobulin	β-lactoglobulin B	
β-casein		blood serum albumin	
γ-casein		α-lactalbumin	

Many of the changes in flavor and in texture which different milk products undergo during processing are no doubt due to the degree of denaturation of these proteins. Relatively mild treatments such as *pasteurization* of milk cause little change in the state of proteins. Prolonged exposure to higher temperatures, however, causes protein denaturation. The whey proteins are most susceptible to denaturation, but drastic treatments may also alter the casein fraction. The most pronounced change in the properties of the milk proteins are loss of solubility and a tendency to coagulate. Flavor changes, which are often associated with unmasking of the sulfhydryl groups of β-lactoglobulin may also be of importance.

In order to stabilize milk against subsequent heat coagulation it is often necessary to add *sequestering agents*, such as phosphates or citrates, which alter the ionic balance of the milk. Sequestering agents are reagents which tie up a particular ion. The addition of phosphates or citrates results in the binding of more Ca^{++} in the form of soluble complexes thereby decreasing the activity of Ca^{++} ions. This practice is common in the evaporated milk industry.

Wheat proteins. Because of the universal nutritive importance of bread, wheat proteins have been investigated more extensively. The principal protein in wheat is *gluten*, which is the ingredient responsible for the unique ability of wheat flour to form the well-known leavened bread structure. Gluten makes possible the formation of a dough, which can retain the carbon dioxide produced during the fermentation of the dough by yeast or by chemical leavening ingredients. The continuous phase created by the gluten has peculiar rheological properties: it is spongy, elastic and, at the same time, rigid enough to form the well-known "comb texture". This extraordinary texture also depends on the relative amount of gluten compared to the starch grains. Because gluten has the ability to hydrate, *i.e.*, to imbibe large quantities of water, it follows that the more gluten contained in bread the better are its keeping qualities, and the longer it will stay fresh.

Unfortunately, the proteins of other cereals, such as rice, maize or corn, barley, etc., predominantly used in many countries instead of wheat, do not possess the qualities of gluten and are, therefore, unsuitable for the manufacture of leavened bread.

Gluten is, in fact, composed of two different proteins: *gliadin*, which is a

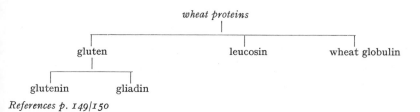

prolamine (dissolves in 50 % alcohol), and *glutenin*, which dissolves in alkali and acids. The wheat proteins contain, in addition, globulin and leucosin (an albumin).

There are only slight differences in the wheat proteins found in spring wheat and in winter wheat, as shown in Table V; however, there are apparently great differences in the specific structure of different wheats, soft and hard wheats: the gluten of very hard wheat, *Durum*, does not possess the ability to create an appropriate continuous phase for the desired bread texture—it is, therefore, used for the production of macaroni.

TABLE V

Protein	Spring wheat (%)	Winter wheat (%)
glutenin	4.68	4.17
gliadin	3.96	3.90
globulin	0.62	0.63
leucosin	0.39	0.63

The molecular weight of gliadin, determined by osmotic pressure and by ultracentrifuging, is 34,000. That of glutenin has not yet been determined —this protein does not lend itself to electrophoresis. On the other hand, glutenin has been found to consist of several fractions by fractional solubility methods.

The complete hydrolysis of wheat proteins shows that they contain all the amino acids known and that *glutamic acid* alone constitutes nearly one-half of the total. Other cereals contain more or less similar proteins. Zein is the main protein of maize, has a molecular weight of 35,000 and does not seem to be homogeneous. Some of the amino acids contained in the proteins are shown in Table VI.

TABLE VI

Protein	Amino acid found (%)				
	Arginine	Leucine and isoleucine	Valine	Glutamic acid	Proline
Gliadin	3.2	6.0	3.0	46.0	13.2
Glutenin	4.7	6.0	1.0	27.2	4.4
Zein	1.6	3.0	3.0	35.6	9.0

The proteins of seeds (not cereals), such as oil-rich seeds, soy-bean, etc., are of quite a different composition. Their molecular weights are of an order of magnitude of 300,000.

Conjugated proteins

In addition to the various proteins mentioned so far in this chapter, there are a great number of the so-called *conjugated proteins* which besides their protein molecule, contain a non-protein moiety, usually termed the *prosthetic group*. This general class of conjugated proteins comprises several sub-groups:

(1) Many of the enzymes with their prosthetic groups, also called "*coenzymes*", are treated in the next chapter.

(2) *Chromoproteins*—in which the prosthetic group is a metalloporphyrin, such as chlorophyll, which is linked in the plant tissue with a protein, or the hemin which is bound to the protein to form hemoglobin. Some of the metalloporphyrins, linked with proteins, constitute the already mentioned enzymes: *peroxidase, catalase* and *cytochromes* (see Chapter 2).

(3) *Glycoproteins*—proteins bound to carbohydrates.

(4) *Lipoproteins*—proteins conjugated to lipids.

(5) And, finally, the most important sub-group of conjugated proteins, the *nucleoproteins*. These are the proteins containing as their prosthetic group the *nucleic acids*, which are engaged in the processes of reproduction and of heredity in plant and animal.

Nucleoproteins

The living cell comprises the *cytoplasm*, in which the *nucleus* and the *chromoplasts* are in suspension. All three constitute the *protoplasm*, each of them being built of different proteins. In spite of their specific name, *nucleoproteins* are also found in cell components other than the nucleus. The nucleoproteins consist of two groups:

(a) *Ribonucleoproteins*—found mainly in the cytoplasm, their prosthetic group being *ribonucleic acid* (RNA for short).

(b) *Desoxyribonucleoproteins*—found mainly in the nucleus, having as their prosthetic group *desoxyribonucleic acid* (DNA for short).

In the early stages of protein research, it was customary to distinguish between the nucleoproteins of seeds, which were regarded as reserve proteins necessary for the early development of the plant, and the protoplasmic proteins, which were characterized as taking part in the metabolic activity of the cell. Accordingly, those obtained from yeasts were called plant nucleoproteins in distinction from animal nucleoproteins, which were obtained from the thymus gland. Both modes of classification have become out-of-date now since both RNA and DNA are found in cytoplasm as well as in the nucleus, although in different proportions. It is true, however, that the structure of RNA was first elucidated from studies of yeast.

References p. 149/150

Both ribonucleic acid (RNA) and desoxyribonucleic acid (DNA), when hydrolyzed in weak alkali, result in four so-called *nucleotides*, each of which consists of one molecule of phosphoric acid, one molecule of ribose (a pentose) or desoxyribose, and one molecule of a nitrogenous base which is either a purine or a pyrimidine:

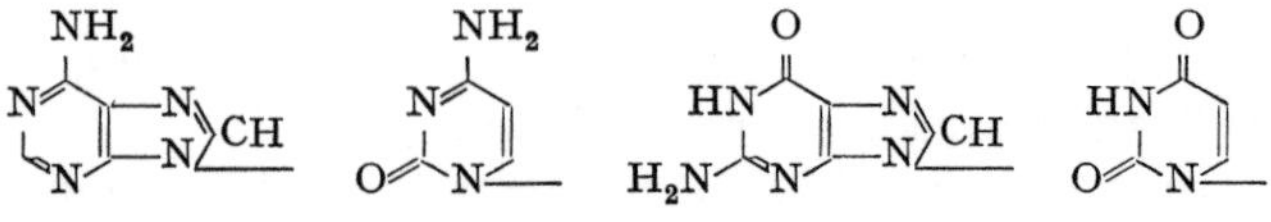

adenine   cytosine   guanine   uracil

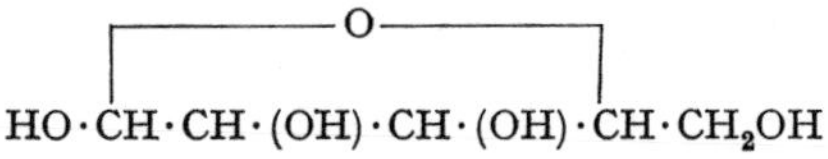

$$HO \cdot CH \cdot CH \cdot (OH) \cdot CH \cdot (OH) \cdot CH \cdot CH_2OH$$

ribose

In desoxyribonucleic acid (DNA), the ribose is replaced by desoxyribose:

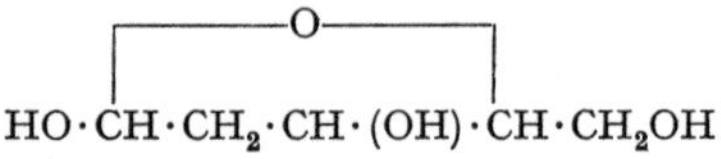

$$HO \cdot CH \cdot CH_2 \cdot CH \cdot (OH) \cdot CH \cdot CH_2OH$$

and the uracil is replaced by thymine:

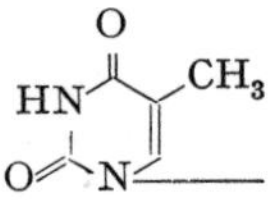

The following may serve as a general scheme for the breakdown of nucleoproteins:

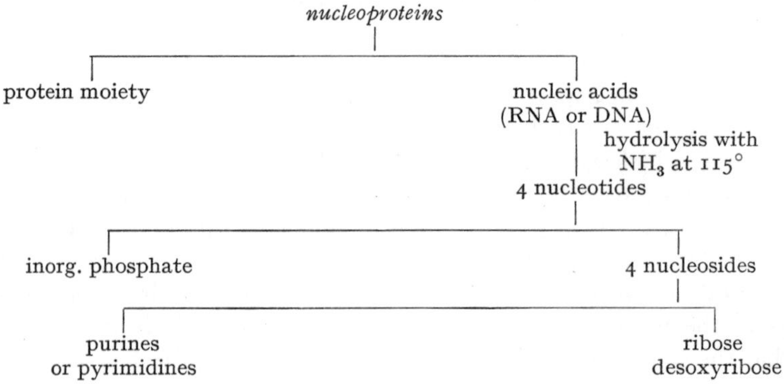

nucleoproteins

protein moiety   nucleic acids
                                  (RNA or DNA)
                                        hydrolysis with
                                          NH₃ at 115°
                                  4 nucleotides

inorg. phosphate   4 nucleosides

        purines   ribose
        or pyrimidines   desoxyribose

The schematic structure of RNA is assumed to be as follows: in it a purine molecule alternates with a pyrimidine, each one being linked to a ribose molecule to form a nucleoside. Each nucleoside is bound to the other by a phosphate bond. It is probable that the phosphoric acid di-ester connects the ribose molecules between C_3 and C_5 and not, as shown in Fig. 25, between C_2 and C_3.

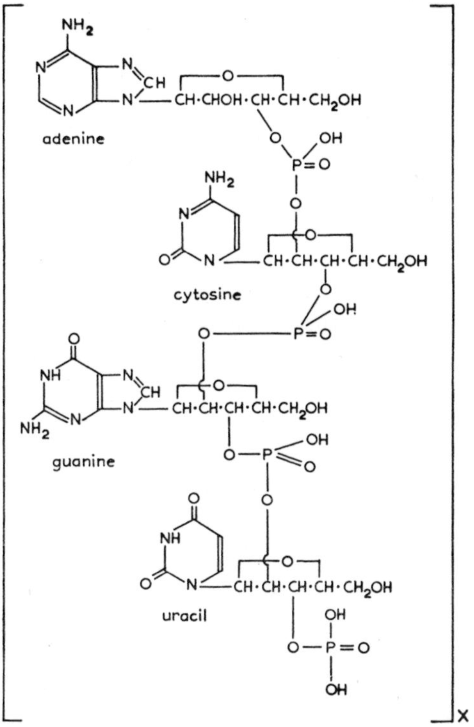

Fig. 25. The structural formula of RNA.

The quantitative relation between the different pyrimidine–purine pairs is probably not $1:1$.

In studying the products of degradation of an RNA molecule, it was originally presumed that its molecular weight was about 1500, *i.e.*, one such grouping. Later it was found that its molecular weight is about 20,000, which means that one molecule of RNA consists of about 15 units, as presented above.

The schematic of desoxyribonucleic acid (DNA) is assumed to be as follows, see formulas on p. 144, Fig. 26. One characterises a AT-type and a GC-type of DNA. In the first adenine–thymine prevails, in the latter guanine–cytosine.

Desoxyribonucleic acid extracted from the thymus gland is of a much higher molecular weight and varies between 500,000 and 2,000,000 according to different investigators.

More recent investigations shed some doubt on the hypothesis of these aggregates of tetranucleotides because of the discovery of some new nitrogenous bases, namely, 5-hydroxymethylcytosine, and 6-methylaminoadenine both, however, in rather small quantities:

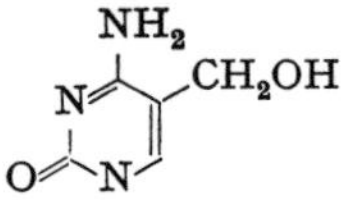

5-hydroxymethylcytosine 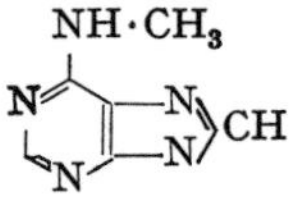   6-methylaminoadenine

The opinion is held that the nucleosides are arranged rather as doughnuts on a tray, one behind the other, connected by phosphoric acid residues. This kind of "packaging" seems to be very dense, for the specific gravity of

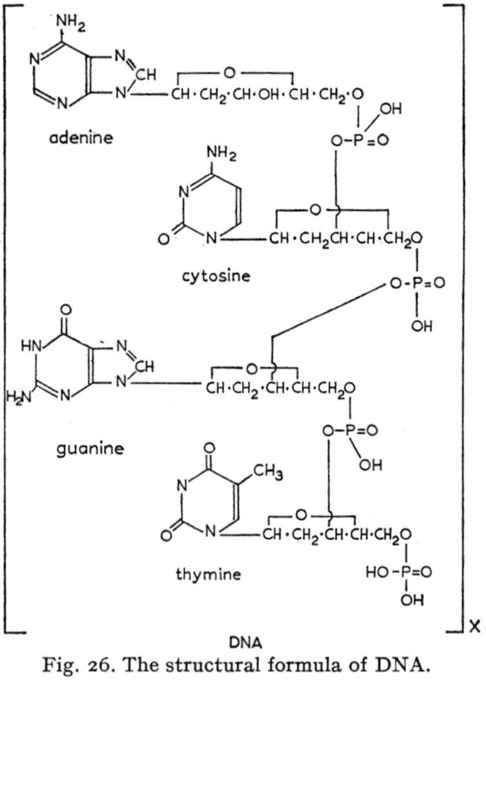

Fig. 26. The structural formula of DNA.

nucleic acids is relatively high, 1.65 g/ml, and the distance between one nucleoside and the other is 3.3–3.4 Å.

The majority of the proteins of the nucleoproteins are of the histone type. Very recently the protein structure of the enzyme *RNAase*, which catalyzes the breakdown of ribonucleoprotein, has been elucidated and the sequence of the amino acids in this protein determined.

The structure of chromosomes[8]

The chromosomes, those bodies responsible for the hereditary characteristic of all living matter, contain mainly DNA and protein and very little RNA. The point of view held until recently was that the specificity of the chromosomes was caused by the protein moiety, as was the case with all enzymes (see Chapter 12). However, it is accepted now that in this case the specificity lies in the prosthetic group, namely in the desoxyribonucleic acid itself: the amount of DNA is not the same in all chromosomes, however in different species the quantities of DNA are of the same order of magnitude. It was originally thought that the amounts of the four nitrogenous bases was the same in every molecule of DNA. More exact determinations have now shown that, while in various species these quantities differ, as far as one living species is concerned or in very closely related species, the amounts of the nitrogenous bases are quite constant irrespective of the part of the animal or plant from which they are derived.

X-ray diffraction is the only method which gives us the possibility of learning something of the order in which the atoms are arranged in the molecule. The distance between two bonded atoms in a molecule is about 1.5 Å, and that between atoms which are not linked together is 3–4 Å. X-rays are of a sufficiently short wave (1.5 Å) to enable us to penetrate the secret of atomic and molecular combinations, however, they do not lead themselves to focusing and the X-ray diffraction image is not a photographic picture in the proper sense. Such pictures of DNA taken from various species showed very similar images, notwithstanding the fact that the amounts of the nitrogenous bases were quite different. It has been finally found that, owing to the helical structure of the protein, only one in every ten twists of the helix can be detected by the X-rays.

Fig. 27 gives a schematic presentation of a model of a DNA molecule showing the scheme for possible duplication. In this figure, the white pentagons represent desoxyribose, while the black pentagons and hexagons represent the purines and the pyrimidines; the ribbons connecting them are phosphoric acid molecules. It will be noted that the nitrogenous bases of one chain are linked by hydrogen bonds to those of the other chain; it is, however, always in a strict order so that the adenine of one chain is always

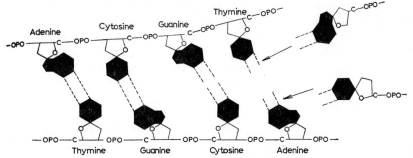

Fig. 27. Model of the structure of DNA showing the scheme of possible duplication. (White pentagons represent ribose, the black polygons show the nitrogenous bases).

hydrogen-bonded to the thymine of the other, and the guanine of one chain is linked to the cytosine of the other[9]:

adenine   thymine

The "pairing" of the nitrogenous bases in DNA preparations, together with X-ray diffraction data, provided the basis for the proposed helical structure for nucleoproteins.

These chains have the ability to duplicate themselves. The possible way of such duplication is apparently the loosening of the hydrogen bonds first. To each of these separated chains appropriate free nitrogenous bases from the general metabolic pool cling by their own hydrogen bonds so that two new molecules are formed from the originally split halves. These is obviously an oversimplified description of this multiplication process of the nucleoproteins, however, it is clearly observed in the behavior of chromosomes and in viruses, as will be presently explained (Fig. 28).

We are still very much in the dark as to the exact functional paths of the nucleoproteins in the living cell, however, one thing is clear, that while all the other metabolic processes catalyzed by numerous enzymes, i.e., the metabolism of the carbohydrates of lipids and proteins, the processes of respiration, fermentation and all others, deal with the subsistence of the individuum, the nucleoproteins are involved in its future. The nucleoproteins are evidently the primary component parts of the genes, the chromosomes and, as such, influence the growth of all living matter, its development, reproduction, the art of adaptation and its modes of evolution.

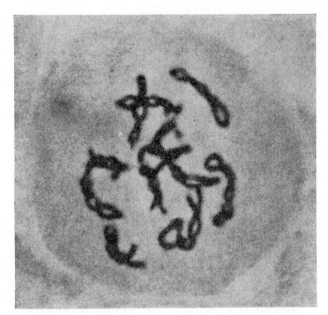

Fig. 28. Conjugated chromosomes in the cell, as seen by the electron microscope.

Viruses

In the former discussion of nucleoproteins we have touched upon the question of multiplication, and it is appropriate to allot here a little space to the description of viruses, those very strange bodies which occupy the borderline between inanimate molecule and living matter.

It was in 1892 that BEIJERINCK ascertained the existence of viruses. Tobacco plants were often struck by the so-called tobacco mosaic disease. BEIJERINCK found that the juice of the tobacco leaves was capable of transmitting this disease to healthy plants even after the juice had been thoroughly filtered to remove all microorganisms. Such diseases, known as virus diseases, are very dangerous in agriculture and have been found in cucumbers (*Cucumber mosaic virus*), in tomatoes (*Tomato bushy stunt*), in potatoes (*Potato X virus*), in tobacco (*Tobacco ringspot*) and in citrus (*Quick decline*). All these are dangerous virus diseases, which are easily transferred from one cell to another. In recent years, many virus diseases have been detected in both animals and human beings. Only in 1935 did STANLEY succeed in isolating the tobacco mosaic virus in a crystalline form. From that moment viruses became a point of interest not only to biologists and medical people but also to chemists.

References p. 149/150

It was found that an isolated virus can be preserved in cold storage for many years without showing any change at all. The moment, however, when the virus finds "appropriate surroundings" it begins to "live and to multiply". Such "appropriate surroundings" for the virus is a living cell body; without such a living cell, the virus is only a complex inanimate molecule. The living cell necessary to start the biochemical activities of the virus may be a plant cell for some viruses or an animal cell or a micro-organism for others.

Viruses differ in size: some are so small that they can only be detected by the electron microscope, others may approach the size of a red blood corpuscle. The smallest virus is 25 mμ in diameter, something like the molecule of hemocyanin. The largest virus known approaches the size of small bacteria, about 150–175 mμ in diameter.

Their shapes are also very different: some viruses are spherical in shape, others are like small rods, still others are sperm-shaped, these being called *bacteriophages*. Their molecular weight is of the order of 17,000,000, but some are even larger and approach 40,000,000. All viruses consist of proteins. The plant viruses contain about 6 % RNA, the remainder, 94 %, is a protein of the globulin type. The animal viruses are more complex, their molecular weights are higher, and they contain DNA.

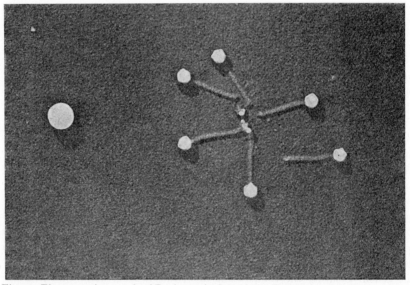

Fig. 29. Electron micrograph of P-1 bacteriophage from *Escherichia Coli* (Enlargement ×69,000). Spherical particle is polystyrene (average diam. 880 Å). (Courtesy ROBERT F. BILS of M.I.T. Cambridge, Mass.).

The year 1953 showed great progress in the study of viruses. In that year, it was possible, by using the isotopes of sulfur (^{35}S) and phosphorus (^{32}P) to establish the structure of the virus body.

It has been found that bacteriophages, for instance (Fig. 30), consist of a tube enveloped on the outside by an helix of protein while inside the tube are found desoxyribonucleic acids (DNA).

These bacteriophages, when they come into contact with a microorganism, such as *Bacterium coli*, will adhere by the tail of their rod, carrying a positive charge, to the surface of the microorganism, which carries a negative charge.

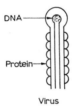

Fig. 30. Schematic structure of a bacteriophage.

Apparently, at that stage, the DNA molecules from the head of the bacteriophage are released into the bacterium. After a short time the bacterium cell dies and explodes, releasing a host of viruses at the rate of 150 new viruses to every bacteriophage adhered to the bacterium (Fig. 31).

Fig. 31. Schematic representation of the reproduction of viruses.

The researches have shown that it is not the virus itself that multiplies (as is the case with microorganisms) but rather the nucleoproteins caused the formation of new viruses of the same type inside the foreign cell and of structural units and enzymes found in this cell. The virus is, therefore, a parasitic body capable of living and reproducing itself only by means of a foreign body. Whether or not the virus is an early form of life is still an open question.

REFERENCES

[1] A. E. BRAUNSTEIN AND M. G. KRITZMAN, *Enzymologia*, 2 (1937) 129.
[2] F. SANGER et al., *Biochem. J.*, 60 (1955) 541.
[3] V. S. BAVISOTTO, Meat tenderizing by enzymes, *Proc. 10th Research Conf. Am. Meat Inst. Foundation* (1958).

[4] B. S. Schweigert, Food aspects of enzymes affecting proteins, in H. W. Schultz, *Food Enzymes*, Avi Publishing Co., Westport, Conn., 1960, p. 97.

[5] T. L. McMeekin and B. D. Polis, Milk protein, *Advances in Protein Chem.*, 5 (1949) 201.

[6] R. Jenness and S. Patton, *Principles of Dairy Chemistry*, John Wiley and Sons, Inc., New York, 1959.

[7] J. R. Brunner, C. G. Ernstom, R. A. Hollis, B. L. Larson, R. McL. Whitney and C. A. Zettle, Nomenclature of the proteins of bovine milk-first revision, *J. Dairy Sci.*, 43 (1950) 901.

[8] F. H. C. Crick, The structure of hereditary material, in The physics and chemistry of life, *Sci. American Book*, Simon and Schuster, New York, 1955.

[9] D. O. Jordan, A. R. Mathieson and Sheila Matty, *J. Chem. Soc.*, (1956) 154, 158.

SELECTED BIBLIOGRAPHY TO CHAPTER 11

Altschul, A. M. *Processed Plant Protein Foodstuffs*, Academic Press, New York, 1958.

Bell, R. P., *Acids and Bases*, Methuen and Co., London, 1952.

Chargaff, E. and J. N. Davidson, *The Nucleic Acids*, Academic Press, New York, 1955.

Davidson, J. N., *The Biochemistry of Nucleic Acids*, 2nd edn., Methuen and Co., London, 1953.

Fox, S. W., and J. F. Foster, *Introduction to Protein Chemistry*, J. Wiley and Sons, New York, 1957.

Haurowitz, F. *Chemistry and Biology of Proteins*, Academic Press, New York, 1950.

Lederer, E., and M. Lederer, *Chromatography*, 2nd edn., Elsevier Publishing Co., Amsterdam, 1957.

Meister, A., *Biochemistry of the Amino Acids*, Academic Press, New York, 1957.

Neurath, H., and K. Bailey, *The Proteins*, Academic Press, New York, 1954.

Pauling, L., *Harvey Lectures*, 49 (1955) 216.

Schroedinger, E., *What is Life*, Cambridge Univ. Press, 1945.

The physics and chemistry of life, *Sci. American*, 1955.

CHAPTER 12

ENZYMES

In the yeast

KÜHNE

Definition

Another most important class of conjugated proteins are the *enzymes* or *ferments*, which have been mentioned at various occasions throughout this book. It is now the appropriate place to go into further detail regarding the constitution of these biological catalysts and the mode of their action.

It was BERZELIUS who suggested in 1836 the term "catalysts" for "substances that are able to set into activity affinities which are dormant at a particular temperature by their presence alone". He ascribed these phenomena to some mysterious "catalytic power". This belief in such a mysterious power persisted for a long time, even after many of these enzyme preparations had been well established. As late as 1926, WILLSTAETTER delivered a lecture before the German Chemical Society in which he summarized his researches on the isolation of pure enzymes, and in that lecture he related his work on *peroxidase*, which consisted of a protein and a non-protein moiety containing iron. The activity of this enzyme continued even when its concentration was diluted to such an extent that no more protein or iron could be detected in the substrate—this led WILLSTAETTER to believe in a *new natural force* created in some way by the enzymes.

In the same year, 1926, SUMNER[1] succeeded in isolating and crystallizing from Jack beans the enzyme *urease*, which cleaves urea into CO_2 and NH_3, while NORTHROP and his collaborators crystallized the proteolytic enzymes *pepsin, trypsin* and *chymotrypsin*. Many scientists did not believe that these crystals were enzymes or that they even contained enzymes, and it was another 20 years before NORTHROP, STANLEY and SUMNER received the Nobel prize for their brilliant achievements.

Many biological reactions can, of course, proceed *in vitro* as ordinary chemical reactions when relatively high temperatures or concentrations of acids or alkalies are applied. As already mentioned, proteins can be hydrolyzed into amino acids, for instance, by boiling for several hours in acids or alkalines, or again starch can be converted into glucose, etc. However, all such reactions proceed *in vivo* at body temperatures albeit with the active participation of enzymes. The name "enzyme" was coined in 1878 by KÜHNE from the Greek εν ζύμη—"in yeast". It was accepted at that time that enzymes could do their work only in the living cell.

In 1897, the BUCHNERS[2] found for the first time that enzymatic activity was not necessarily limited to the living cell: they triturated yeast cells with sand in a mortar and pressed out the "yeast juice", which, after thorough filtration in order to eliminate any cell particles, still preserved the ability to ferment sugar into alcohol and carbon dioxide. This was a great discovery at that time, for it separated for the first time biological phenomena from the concept of some mysterious "vital power".

We now define enzymes as *organic, colloidal catalysts, mostly soluble in water, formed* (as far as now known) *inside the living cell of plants or animals, but capable of acting also outside the cell and without any connection with it.*

Today, the activities of many hundreds of enzymes are acknowledged but, however, only some 75 have been crystallized. All enzymes, without exception, contain proteins, as shown by their elementary analysis. *Urease*, for instance, has the following composition: C, 51.6%; H, 7.1%; N, 16%; S, 1.2%.

Classification

There is no unanimity today in classifying the many enzymes and most of the textbooks use different systems: some arrange the enzymes according to the reactions they catalyze, others do it by the substrates on which the enzymes act. It is more common now to divide the enzymes into two main groups: (a) the hydrolyzing enzymes—the *hydrolases*, and (b) all the others— *desmolases*.

I. Hydrolases

A. *Esterases*—all enzymes responsible for the cleavage as well as the synthesis of all esters in accordance with the general formula:

$$R \cdot COOR' + H_2O \rightleftarrows RCOOH + R'OH$$

These enzymes are also capable of hydrolyzing esters of polyhydric alcohols, such as the glycerides of fatty acids. Here are examples:
1. *Lipases*—found in the pancreas; will hydrolyze all fats and oils in the plant and animal kingdoms (see Chapter 16).
2. *Chlorophyllase*—cleaves phytol from chlorophyll (see Chapter 2).
3. *Phosphatases*— ⎫ cleave phosphoric acid and sulfuric acid, respectively,
4. *Sulfatases*— ⎭ from the corresponding esters.
5. *Pectinesterases* (see Chapter 9).

B. *Carbohydrases*—all enzymes responsible for the breakdown and the synthesis of carbohydrates:

1. *Polyases*—catalyze the reactions of polysaccharides, such as α- and β-amylases, *α-amyloglucosidase, enzyme Q,* etc. (see Chapter 8). The pectolytic enzymes, PG (*polygalacturonase*), and *polymethylgalacturonase* belong to this category.

2. *Glycosidases* or *hexosidases*—enzymes engaged in the cleavage of disaccharides or of glycosides, *i.e.,* they remove the aglucone from sugar; examples are α- and *β-glucosidases, maltase, invertase, lactase, α-galacturonase,* etc. (see Chapter 7).

C. *Proteolytic enzymes* or *proteases*—all enzymes engaged in the hydrolysis and synthesis of proteins:

1. *Proteinases*—capable of cleaving the peptide (—CO—NH—) bond into peptides or single amino acids, such as *pepsin, trypsin, chymotrypsin, papain, bromelin, ficin,* etc. (see Chapter 11).

2. *Peptidases* (*carboxypeptidases* and *aminopeptidases*)—capable of breaking down peptides into amino acids.

3. *Amidases* — enzymes which cleave the C—N link other than the peptide bond, such as *urease* and *arginase* (see later).

II. Desmolases

A. *Oxidoreductases* — enzymes engaged in the oxidation and reduction of biological systems; these are conveniently classified in two sub-groups—the *oxidase* and *dehydrogenases*:

1. *Oxidases* are again subdivided into those containing:

   a. Fe in their prosthetic group, such as *Cytochrome c,* or *peroxidase,* which transfers hydrogen to another acceptor,

   $$2H_2O + A \rightleftharpoons H_2O_2 + AH_2$$

   and *catalase,* which breaks down H_2O_2

   $$2H_2O_2 \longrightarrow O_2 + 2H_2O$$

   b. Cu is the main component of the other *oxidases,* such as *phenolase, tyrosinase, ascorbinase* (see Chapter 19).

2. *Dehydrogenases*

   a. Those containing diphosphopyridine nucleotide (DPN, TPN).

   b. Those containing the riboflavonucleotides (FMN, FAD).

B. *Phosphorylases*—various enzymes engaged in phosphorylation or dephosphorylation and also sometimes in cleaving larger molecules and attaching the phosphate group (see Chapters 6 and 8). To this class belongs also *hexokinase* which works in conjunction with the important adenylic system, ATP (see Chapter 5).

References p. 174/175

C. *Isomerases*—the complex *zymase* contains a number of enzymes which take part in various reactions of isomerization, mutation, etc. (see Chapter 6).

D. *Carboxylases*—these are engaged in detaching CO_2 from various products, such as *pyruvic acid carboxylase*, containing phosphorylated thiamine as its coenzyme (see Chapter 6), or *Coenzyme A* (see Chapter 18).

E. *Coagulating enzymes*—such as *rennin* (see Chapter 11).

The prosthetic group

Generally speaking, all enzymes can be divided into three distinct groups in accordance with their composition:

(1) Enzymes, which are built of protein only. Here the protein alone is responsible for the catalytic action upon a given biochemical reaction as well as for the specificity of the enzyme towards the substrate. Such enzymes are, for instance, the *amylase*, the *proteinases* and many others.

(2) Enzymes, which in addition to their protein possess a non-proteinic moiety, called *coenzyme* or *prosthetic group*. In such enzymes, the prosthetic group is the center of the chemical activity, while the protein part is responsible for the specificity of this enzyme. So there are many instances when the same prosthetic group may be combined with different proteins, thus forming different enzymes. For instance, several *dehydrogenases*, containing different proteins, may have the same prosthetic group, FMN (flavin-mononucleotide), and will exert the same dehydrogenation activity but on quite different substrates. In this group of enzymes, it is usually possible to separate, by dialysis, the prosthetic group from the protein, without destroying the enzyme, the enzyme regaining its activity when the protein and the prosthetic group are recombined.

(3) The third class of enzymes also consists of two moieties, the protein and the coenzyme, only they are practically inseparable without the complete destruction of the enzymatic potency. For instance, such are the *metalloproteins*, enzymes containing Fe, Cu, Co, etc.

In these last two groups, the following denominations are accepted:

holoenzyme	=	apoenzyme	+	coenzyme
(the whole enzyme)		(the protein moiety)		(the prosthetic group)

While the coenzyme is usually thermostable, the protein moiety (apoenzyme) is naturally very thermolabile.

At this stage, it is suitable to mention a few examples of prosthetic groups and the mode of their action:

Dehydrogenases

In the previous chapter (Chapter 11), when discussing the mode of introduction of nitrogen into amino acids, mention was made of the enzyme *glutamic acid dehydrogenase*, which contains the compound DPN—diphosphopyridine nucleotide—as its prosthetic group. We have also met the same enzyme in the EMBDEN–MEYERHOF fermentation scheme (Chapter 6). This compound also goes under the name *Coenzyme I* or *Cozymase*. In honor of the investigators who isolated this prosthetic group, the enzyme is also called "Warburg and Christian new yellow enzyme".

The formula of DPN, or NAD, as given on page 64, contains nicotinamide, adenine, two molecules of ribose and two molecules of phosphoric acid. With three molecules of phosphoric acid the same combination constitutes another prosthetic group, TPN, *triphosphopyridine nucleotide*, or *Coenzyme II*:

structural formula of TPN

The third molecule of phosphoric acid in TPN is connected to the ribose of the adenine.

Nicotinamide is now found to be the PP—pellagra prevention factor. It should be pointed out that many of the vitamins, especially those of the B group, play the role of a prosthetic group in various enzymes (see Chapter 14).

Before they discovered the "new yellow enzyme", DPN, WARBURG AND CHRISTIAN found in yeast another enzyme, the "old yellow enzyme". This is an enzyme, also a *dehydrogenase*, containing the compound FMN, flavin-mononucleotide, as its prosthetic group. FMN is a phosphorylated 6,7-dimethylisoalloxazine ribityl; without the phosphoric acid it is vitamin B_2 (riboflavin),

formula of flavin-mononucleotide (FMN)

This prosthetic group can combine with different apoenzymes and so create several *dehydrogenases*, which act as hydrogen carriers. They can transfer the hydrogen obtained to *Cytochrome c*, which in its turn transfers it directly to molecular oxygen. The prosthetic group can be easily dialyzed and separated from the apoenzyme. The enzyme then loses its potency. However, on simply mixing them together, the enzyme regains its full activity.

It is possible to understand the chemical part played by FMN during dehydrogenation from the following formulae:

FMNH$_2$ — (reduced enzyme)   FMN — (oxidized enzyme)

Altogether there are eight such yellow enzymes, however, only two of these contain riboflavin by itself. The others contain, besides riboflavin, other groups, for example adenine, as in the case of FAD (flavin–adenine dinucleotide):

adenine moiety

riboflavin moiety   formula of flavin–adenine dinucleotide (FAD)

The protein–coenzyme bond

Very little is known yet of the manner in which the prosthetic group is bound to the protein. THEORELL[3], a Swedish Nobel prize laureate (1955) was the first to succeed in separating by dialysis (using an acid solution) the colorless apoenzyme from the yellow coenzyme FMN in the "old yellow enzyme of Warburg".

Further studies on this enzyme suggest that the prosthetic group is probably linked at certain points to the apoenzyme by hydrogen bonding, as may be represented schematically as follows:

FMN   apoenzyme

In this connection, it is necessary to examine the ATP compound in somewhat more detail. When dealing with the phosphorylation of sugars in Chapter 5, mention was made of the important compound adenosine tri-phosphate (ATP), which plays a vitally important role as an energy carrier in all biological systems. At that particular point, ATP was mentioned as a prosthetic group of the enzyme *hexokinase*. However, there is a great number of biochemical reactions in which ATP is involved and in which is no absolute certainty that ATP is a coenzyme in the proper sense of the word. Besides the phosphorylation of sugars and their fermentation (see Chapter 6), ATP contributes towards photosynthesis (Chapter 4); it is also involved in the respiration cycle (Chapter 18), together with another enzyme (CoA); in the synthesis of lipids (Chapter 16), and of amino acids. Some of these reactions are coupled enzymatic reactions in which the conversion of ATP to ADP and phosphate is linked to other reactions, such as the synthesis of thiol esters of coenzyme A:

$$\text{acetate} + \text{CoA} + \text{ATP} \rightleftharpoons \text{acetyl–CoA} + \text{ADP} + H_3PO_4$$

Another example of such coupled reactions is in the respiration cycle, when the electron carriers (DPN or TPN) are reoxidized through the flavoproteins by the molecular oxygen while the resulting energy is further transferred to ATP by phosphorylation of ADP.

As can be seen, ATP plays an important part in biochemical reactions and can probably do so either in "cooperation" with different enzymes or by forming each time a prosthetic group with another apoenzyme.

There are, however, a great number of enzymes where the bond between the apoenzyme and the prosthetic group is apparently much stronger and, in order to separate them, it is necessary to bring the protein to the verge of denaturation. Such is the case always when the prosthetic group contains heavy metals as, for instance, in metal porphyrins, which constitute the prosthetic group of *cytochromes, peroxidases, catalase,* etc. Here, not only the prosthetic group is linked to the protein but also the metal itself is bound to it, see formula below for the reduced form of cytochrome *c*:

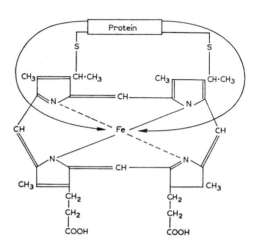

Schematic attachment of the porphyrin moiety to the protein in *Cytochrome c.*

A great number of enzymes apparently belong to this group and, in some cases, the metals are connected in some way with the protein even without a porphyrin moiety. Such is the case of the Cu in the numerous *polyphenolases* and in *ascorbinase,* and the Mg in several *peptidases* and *phosphatases.*

Finally, the above brings us to a possible understanding of the important role played in agriculture by the so-called "minor elements", such as Mn, Fe, Cu, Co, Zn, Mg and B. All these are apparently necessary for the plants to build their enzymes, which are required for normal growth and metabolism.

The term "coenzyme" for the non-proteinic moiety of the enzyme given by early investigators was later substituted by the name "prosthetic group". Some biochemical literature distinguishes between the different terms reserving "coenzyme" for the organic fragments that are normally not isolated with the apoenzyme, while "prosthetic group" represents a group firmly attached to the protein, such as a metalloporphyrin, the term "activator" being reserved for metals or other catalyzing agents. The common denominator for all these substances is that they have a comparatively low molecular weight and are comparatively thermostable.

Decarboxylases

It will be recalled that, when discussing the EMBDEN–MEYERHOF scheme for fermentation in Chapter 6, an account was given of an enzyme *pyruvate carboxylase*, which is capable of detaching a molecule of CO_2 from pyruvic acid to leave acetaldehyde. This particular decarboxylation reaction is performed by an enzyme, which has as its prosthetic group phosphorylated thiamine (see formula on page 192) and needs Mg^{++}. The mechanism of the chemical action of this cofactor is not yet known. Moreover, a number of *carboxylases* have been found, each of which has an entirely different prosthetic group. When discussing the respiration cycle in Chapter 18, mention is made of three different *carboxylases* which successively cleave pyruvic acid: *pyruvic acid carboxylase, oxalosuccinate carboxylase* and *α-ketoglutarate carboxylase*—each of them having a different constitution, the first and third of these containing *Coenzyme A.*

Decarboxylation reactions are known in many other instances: a large series of *amino acid carboxylases* are known, some of them highly specific and requiring pyridoxal phosphate as their coenzyme. A chemical decarboxylation of a similar kind, called "Strecker degradation", is also known to occur during the browning of foods (see Chapter 20).

Some of these reactions are accompanied by oxidation; there are the so-called "oxidative decarboxylations", which proceed in the presence of a hydrogen acceptor, an example of these being the above-mentioned decarboxylation of α-ketoglutaric acid, coupled with dehydrogenation, to form succinic acid as will be shown in Chapter 18.

Finally, in the Calvin scheme for the formation of carbohydrates during photosynthesis, one may recall that ribulose diphosphate *combines* with CO_2 to give two molecules of PGA (phosphoglyceric acid), this being, of course, again activated by a carboxylating enzyme, a carboxy dismutase (Chapter 4).

Transferring enzymes

Although not specifically referred to in the classification of enzymes mentioned earlier in this chapter, mention should be made of the ability of certain *hydrolases* to participate in a number of transferring reactions, which apparently play a most important part in biosynthesis.

With regard to the introduction of nitrogen into an organic substance, a description has already been given in Chapter 11, of the enzyme *trans-*

aminase, which is capable of transferring an amino group from glutamic acid to different α-keto acids, thereby forming new amino acids.

Similar transfers take place in carbohydrates. In these, enzymes of this type, *"transglycosidases"*, can catalyze the transfer of fructofuranosyl groups not only to water (as is the case with *invertase,* which hydrolyzes sucrose), but also to various alcohols and sugar, thereby forming new glycosides. Another enzyme, the *Q enzyme,* is capable of transferring the glycosidic 1:4 bond to a new 1:6 bond, thereby achieving the branching of the amylopectin molecule (see Chapter 8).

The importance of such hydrolytic enzymes in catalyzing bimolecular reactions, in which a substrate reacts not with water but with an amine or an alcohol, has been appreciated only quite recently. These phenomena have been of particular interest in experiments conducted with the view of elongating a peptide chain. Enzymes of this type, called *transamidases,* are capable of transferring the terminal amino group of one peptide to the end of a newly created peptide:

$$
\underset{\text{alanyl-phenylalaninamide}}{\overset{\overset{\displaystyle CH_3 \qquad\quad CH_2C_6H_5}{|\qquad\qquad\quad |}}{NH_2 \cdot CH \cdot CO—NH \cdot CH \cdot CO—NH_2}} + \underset{\text{alanyl-phenylalaninamide}}{\overset{\overset{\displaystyle CH_3 \qquad\quad CH_2C_6H_5}{|\qquad\qquad\quad |}}{NH_2 \cdot CH \cdot CO—NH \cdot CH \cdot CO—NH_2}} \;\overset{-NH_3}{\underset{}{\rightleftarrows}}
$$

$$
\rightleftarrows \;\; \overset{\overset{\displaystyle CH_3 \quad CH_2C_6H_5 \quad CH_3 \quad CH_2C_6H_5}{|\qquad\quad |\qquad\quad |\qquad\quad |}}{NH_2 \cdot CH \cdot CO—NH \cdot CH \cdot CO—NH \cdot CH \cdot CO—NH \cdot CH \cdot CO \cdot NH_2}
$$

This type of polymerization reaction, in which there is little or no change in the free energy (because they are purely hydrolytic reactions, and are consequently, in most instances, reversible) have been demonstrated with other dipeptide amides which can serve as substrates for the enzyme *catepsin C.* In the case of glycyl-tyrosine amide, it was possible to build up an octapeptide by this reaction of transamidation[4]. It should be noted that although very little energy is required for such reactions they are still endergonic. However, when proteins are synthesized *in vivo,* the above peptides entering the reaction must get from somewhere the energy required to build up their (CO—NH) peptide bonds.

Finally, the reader is referred to the description of a possible biosynthesis of the chlorophyll molecule and the importance of Fe in its formation. There, the iron changes places with Mg most probably through the action of such transferring enzymes (see Chapter 2).

Intracellular, or *constitutive,* enzymes act inside the living cell, whereas *induced* or *extracellular* enzymes are either adsorbed on the surface of cells and tissues, or have the ability to pass through the plasma membrane of the cell in order to perform their catalysis outside the cell. Normally enzymes, consisting of a large protein molecule, are unable to permeate the cell wall. Such is the case when microorganisms act upon a given substrate; the latter penetrates the plasma membrane of the organism, while the final products of reaction find their way out of the cell, as for instance during alcoholic fermentation.

However, cases of extracellular activity are quite widespread, but the mechanism by which such activity takes place in microorganisms is not yet known. The only plausible explanation for this phenomenon is probably the fact that the plasma membrane is not fully continuous and the enzymes find their way from the living cell through such apertures.

The oxidative enzymes, both those containing Cu—the *phenolases*, as well as those containing iron porphyrins—*peroxidase, catalase* etc., are discussed in more detail in Chapter 19.

Specificity of enzymes

With the exception of only a few enzymes the majority of enzymes act in aqueous solutions. In water, the molecules are in constant thermal movement and, generally speaking, they can react only when they collide in an appropriate fashion. In the absence of enzymes, such collisions may bring about a chemical reaction in only one of a trillion collisions; however, if enzymes are present, the chances of a reaction taking place are considerably better. This is ascribed to the ability of the enzyme to form a complex or an addition compound with the appropriate substrate for at least a very short time. Since the mere presence of an enzyme cannot accelerate the movement of the molecules in solution and does not, therefore, increase the frequency of their collisions, one is to assume that by combining with the substrate molecules the enzyme brings about some change in the molecular architecture of the substrate, thus increasing its reactivity. There is ample evidence, for instance, that in some cases this reactivity is brought about by the enzyme detaching some electrons from the molecules of the substrate, thus converting them into ions or free radicals of a given charge.

The formation of an enzyme–substrate complex has recently been confirmed spectrophotometrically in the breakdown of hydrogen peroxide by *catalase*. When H_2O_2 was added to a solution of *catalase* the original pattern in the ultraviolet region changed to show the pattern of the newly formed complex; however, the spectrogram returned to its original pattern after all the H_2O_2 had been exhausted.

In this case of *catalase* and H_2O_2, the substrate–enzyme complex is formed each time for only a 85,000th of a second. This combination between the enzyme and the substrate is, however, limited to specific cases: each enzyme will combine with one substrate, or at best with one group of substrates, hence the "*specificity*" of enzymes—their most important property.

In order to understand this property of specificity, the analogy of "the key and the lock" was proposed a long time ago. To open a door the "key" (the substrate) must fit the "lock" (the enzyme), otherwise the reaction will not take place. Moreover, as sometimes happens, the key inserted into the lock not only does not open the door, but becomes stuck and one is unable to pull it out. The very same thing may happen with the enzyme. For example, the enzyme *succinic acid dehydrogenase* catalyzes the transformation of succinic acid into fumaric acid (see Chapter 18):

$$
\begin{array}{ccc}
\text{COOH} & & \text{COOH} \\
| & & | \\
\text{CH}_2 & \xrightarrow[\text{dehydrogenase}]{-2\text{H}} & \text{CH} \\
| & & \| \\
\text{CH}_2 & & \text{CH} \\
| & & | \\
\text{COOH} & & \text{COOH}
\end{array}
$$

This enzyme is very specific and will not dehydrogenate any other substance. However, if malonic acid is added to the substrate, it will compete with succinic acid, due to their close similarity in structure ($\text{COOH—CH}_2\text{—COOH}$), by combining with the enzyme and making it unavailable for its duty, while malonic acid itself will not be dehydrogenated. Here, malonic acid is the "key" which does not fit, for some reason, the "lock" (*succinic acid dehydrogenase*) and, at the same time, interferes with the opening of the door (the true reaction).

Substances which react similarly to malonic acid in this case are called *antimetabolites*, namely, compounds which, while not being themselves attacked by enzymes, are capable of forming with them a complex and so compete with the substrate. Antimetabolites were discovered for the first time by Woods[5] in 1940 while working with microorganisms. An example of these is the substance *p-aminobenzoic acid* which is required by certain bacteria during their growth: most probably this substance plays the part of a prosthetic group in some enzyme vital to their metabolism. It has been

$$
\begin{array}{cc}
\text{NH}_2 & \text{NH}_2 \\
\bigcirc & \bigcirc \\
\text{COOH} & \text{SO}_2\cdot\text{NH} \\
\textit{p-aminobenzoic acid} & \textit{p-aminophenylsulphonamide}
\end{array}
$$

found, however, that the compound *p-aminophenylsulphonamide* can prevent the growth and development of these bacteria by playing the role of an antimetabolite, *i.e.*, by combining with the enzyme just as *p*-aminobenzoic acid did and preventing it from exerting its powers.

This important discovery led the pharmaceutical industry to develop a large number of so-called *sulpha-drugs*, which are used in medicine. In fact, they are all antimetabolites which interfere with the further development and multiplication of pathogenic microorganisms.

In a similar way, it is possible to explain the action of some of the chemical or antibiotic preserving agents used in the conservation of foods (see Chapter 4).

Perhaps the most convincing experiment to explain the "key and lock" concept is that performed by BARRON *et al.*[6] who were engaged in the study of the enzymatic oxidation of acetic acid as part of the lipids metabolism. When they tried the same enzymatic reactions on substances very similar to acetic acid, namely, monofluoracetate and monochloracetate, they found that while the latter did not enter the reaction at all, the former acted as an antimetabolite. The only difference between these three substances is that in one the hydrogen of the α-carbon atom is substituted by F and in the other by Cl, and it is most interesting to note the differences in the length of these three bonds:

$$\varDelta = 0.32 \text{ Å} \begin{cases} \text{H—C} & \text{in acetic acid} = 1.09 \text{ Å} \\ \text{F—C} & \text{in monofluoracetate} = 1.41 \text{ Å} \\ \text{Cl—C} & \text{in monochloracetate} = 1.76 \text{ Å} \end{cases} \varDelta = 0.35 \text{ Å}$$

In both cases the difference is about the same but quite sufficient to make the two other substances unsuitable for the specific enzyme oxidizing acetic acid. An oversimplified drawing in Fig. 32 tries to convey the idea of the

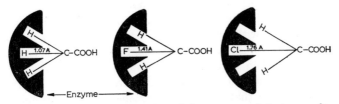

Fig. 32. Schematic representation of the enzyme–substrate complex.

"key and lock" concept. Here, the enzyme is represented as a black spot, while acetic acid (on the left) normally fits this specific enzyme; the monochloracetate (on the right) does not fit at all and is not activated by it.

References p. 174/175

In the case of monofluoracetate (in the center) the fit is too tight and this substance acts as an antimetabolite.

Finally, mention should be made of the proposed[7] "polyaffinity theory" of enzyme action, which is illustrated by the following diagram:

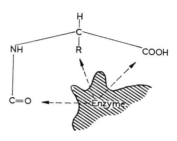

Fig. 33. Scheme showing the "polyaffinity" hypothesis.

This theory suggests that in order for an enzymatic reaction to proceed, there must be a specific mutual orientation of the side-chain group of the terminal amino acid residue in the substrate (in case of a protein) and one of the groups in the apoenzyme, and that there must be at least three points of specific interaction between the enzyme and the substrate. According to this hypothesis, the active center of an enzyme must have an asymmetric character. This theory also leads to a clearer understanding of the competitive action of antimetabolites: such inhibitors may have groups in common with the substrate and, in that case, these groups can combine with one or more of the three essential points in the active center of the enzyme so as to prevent the approach of the corresponding groups of the substrate. The polyaffinity theory has been successful in explaining the steric specificity of the proteolytic enzymes.

There are several types of enzyme specificity:

(a) *Steric specificity.* Many of the organic compounds taking part in the metabolic processes, with which biochemistry is concerned are optically active substances and of the two stereo-isomeric configurations possible, only one is usually found in nature. Carbohydrates, for instance, are usually D-isomers while the amino acids are naturally present as L-forms. It is interesting to observe that the known enzymes act only on one of these optical configurations and not on its enantiomorph. This observation is quite in agreement with the "key and lock" philosophy.

Example: the hydrolytic enzyme, *arginase*, catalyzes the cleavage of the amino acid, L-arginine, into urea and L-ornithine, but will not do so with D-arginine:

$$
\begin{array}{c}
\text{NH } \text{NH}_2 \\
\diagdown\diagup \\
\text{C} \\
| \\
\text{NH} + \text{H}_2\text{O} \\
| \\
(\text{CH}_2)_3 \\
| \\
\text{CH}\cdot(\text{NH}_2)\cdot\text{COOH} \\
\text{L-arginine}
\end{array}
\quad\underset{\longleftarrow}{\overset{\textit{arginase}}{\longrightarrow}}\quad
\begin{array}{c}
\text{NH}_2 \text{ NH}_2 \\
\diagdown\diagup \\
\text{CO} \\
+ \\
\text{NH}_2 \\
| \\
(\text{CH}_2)_3 \\
| \\
\text{CH}(\text{NH}_2)\cdot\text{COOH} \\
\text{L-ornithine}
\end{array}
$$

Further example: the enzyme *lactic acid dehydrogenase*, isolated from muscle, and containing DPN as its prosthetic group, will catalyze the conversion of L(+)lactic acid into pyruvic acid, but it will not attack the D-form:

$$
\begin{array}{c}
\text{CH}_3 \\
| \\
\text{HOCH} \\
| \\
\text{COOH} \\
\text{L(+) lactic acid}
\end{array}
\quad\underset{\text{FMN}}{\overset{-2\text{H}}{\rightleftarrows}}\quad
\begin{array}{c}
\text{CH}_3 \\
| \\
\text{C}=\text{O} \\
| \\
\text{COOH} \\
\text{pyruvic acid}
\end{array}
$$

Note that when the same enzyme acts on pyruvic acid, which is optically inactive, it will convert it into the L-form only; its enantiomorph will never appear with this enzyme. There is, however, another specific *dehydrogenase*, found in many microorganisms, such as *Bacillus delbrückii*, capable of forming only the D-lactic acid. This particular enzyme is used industrially in the production of lactic acid.

A third example of steric specificity is concerned with the *cis–trans* isomerism. The *succinic acid dehydrogenase* mentioned above oxidizes succinic acid into fumaric acid, which is a *trans*-configuration and never into maleic acid, which is the *cis*-form of the same molecule:

$$
\begin{array}{c}
\text{CH}_2\text{COOH} \\
| \\
\text{CH}_2\text{COOH} \\
\text{succinic acid}
\end{array}
\quad\underset{\text{s.a. dehydrogenase}}{\rightleftarrows}\quad
\begin{array}{c}
\text{CH}\cdot\text{COOH} \\
\| \\
\text{HOOC}\cdot\text{CH} \\
\text{fumaric acid} \\
(\textit{trans})
\end{array}
\qquad
\begin{array}{c}
\text{CH}\cdot\text{COOH} \\
\| \\
\text{CH}\cdot\text{COOH} \\
\text{maleic acid} \\
(\textit{cis})
\end{array}
$$

Of the various enzymes, the *esterases* usually possess the steric specificity.

(b) *Other types of specificity*. The other types known depend primarily on the *degree of their specificity*. This could be best explained with examples of *hydrolases*. Their general action can be represented by the following schematic formula:

$$
\text{A—B} + \text{H}_2\text{O} \quad\underset{\longleftarrow}{\overset{\textit{hydrolase}}{\longrightarrow}}\quad \text{A}\cdot\text{OH} + \text{B}\cdot\text{H}
$$

References p. 174/175

where A—B represents a molecule of the substrate built of two parts A and B and the bond between them. Accordingly, there are three types of specificity:

(1) when only the type of the linkage is important to the enzyme, no matter what A and B are—*low specificity*;

(2) when the linkage and only one of the components of the molecule are important to the enzyme—*group specificity*, and

(3) when both moieties as well as the bond linking them are required by the enzyme to be able to act—*absolute specificity*.

As an example of the low specificity type enzymes, one can take the *lipases*: practically all *lipases* can cleave the linkage between the acid and the alcohol in the lipid, as long as it is an ester linkage; they will equally easily cleave an ethylbutyrate as well as a triglyceride.

Some *glycosidases* are limited in their action to only a glycosidic bond, and some *peptidases* to only the peptide bond. However, in Chapter 11 when speaking of proteolytic enzymes, mention was made of the specific requirements of *carboxypeptidase*, the structural requisite of which is the presence of a free α-carboxyl group adjacent to the peptide linkage to be hydrolyzed:

$$\overset{\displaystyle R_1}{\underset{\displaystyle \uparrow}{RCO - NH \cdot CH \cdot COOH}}$$

This enzyme will not hydrolyze the peptide bond of a peptide of this type:

$$\overset{\displaystyle R_2}{\underset{\displaystyle \uparrow}{R \cdot NH - OC \cdot CH - NH_2}}$$

for which a different *peptidase*, an *aminopeptidase*, is required. The requirements of *aminopeptidase*, are, therefore, the presence of a free α-amino group adjacent to the sensitive peptide bond.

The enzymes, *carboxypeptidase* and *aminopeptidase*, are both examples of the second type of specificity—*group specificity*. This is the most common type among the enzymes.

Another example of group specificity is the digestive enzyme, commonly called *maltase* since it splits maltose into two glucose molecules. In fact, however, *maltase* obtained from the gastrointestinal tract of mammals will hydrolyze other glucosides besides maltose. The main requirement of the enzyme *maltase* is the presence of D-glucose and a glucosidic bond in the α-position; it is not concerned, however, with the nature of the aglucone R:

$$\text{CH}_2\text{OH structure} + \text{H---OH} \longrightarrow \text{CH}_2\text{OH structure} + \text{R}\cdot\text{OH}$$

This enzyme would not act if the aglucone R was β-glucosidic, nor if the glucose were even slightly changed, such as 6-methylglucose glucoside or 2-desoxyglucose glucoside:

6-methylglucose glucoside   2-desoxyglucose glucoside

Such an enzyme should not, therefore, be called *"maltase"* at all, for it is not specific to maltose. It should be called *α-glucosidase* for it belongs to the type of enzymes with group specificity; such enzymes as *β-glucosidase* or *α-galactosidase*, etc., are also group-specific in accordance with the sugar moiety and the type of the glycosidic bond.

Absolute specificity. This is the case of an enzyme which necessitates that all three parts of the substrate upon which it acts should fit the requirements, namely, each of the moieties A and B as well as the bond between them. A suitable example for this type of absolute specificity is the true enzyme *maltase*, found in germinating barley, *malt-maltase*. This enzyme will attack maltose only and will not act upon any other glucoside, as described in the previous paragraph; the name *maltase* is, therefore, the appropriate designation for it.

Similarly, the enzymes *arginase* or *succinic acid hydrogenase*, mentioned above in connection with steric specificity, are enzymes of absolute specificity. *Arginase* is specific for arginine and will not cleave the urea from such compounds as δ-N-methyl arginine or α-N-methyl arginine in which one of the amino groups is substituted by a methyl. Similarly, *succinic acid hydrogenase* is specific for succinic acid and not for malic acid.

Before closing the discussion on the specificity of enzymes, it is interesting to mention one more example of an exceptional case. In 1902, SCHARDINGER discovered in milk an enzyme capable of catalyzing the oxidation of a large number of various aldehydes into corresponding acids. This enzyme, having only group specificity has, since then, been named the *Schardinger enzyme.* Twenty years later, in 1922, MORGAN found in milk another enzyme of a very specific nature, which could convert xanthine and hypoxanthine into uric acid:

xanthine

xanthine oxidase

uric acid

hypoxanthine

This enzyme, *xanthine oxidase*, will not use as a substrate any purines other than the two mentioned. It seems, therefore, that this enzyme possesses nearly absolute specificity.

The curious thing about it, however, is that the *Schardinger* enzyme and *xanthine oxidase* have been found to be identical, which means that we are confronted, in this case, with an enzyme which has an absolute specificity towards one type of reaction and a group specificity towards another type*.

In summary, one is bound to assume that all enzymes cannot be strictly classified into the above-mentioned three groups of specificity and that some intermediate stages may exist. Moreover, as methods for the isolation and purification of enzymes improve with time, one may expect that more and more enzymes, which are now probably only mixtures, will be ultimately upgraded from the "low specificity class" to the upper ranks of group and absolute specificity.

Non-proteinic enzymes

Recently BINKLEY[8] drew attention to the curious behavior of some *aminopeptidases* when they are cleaved into smaller protein units. This investigator started with an *aminopeptidase* which had been originally shown by electrophoresis to be an homogeneous protein. The enzyme was then subjected to ion exchange chromatography, whereby it was possible to obtain fifteen smaller fragments of molecular weight around 6,000. Each of

---

* A highly purified preparation of *xanthine oxidase* has been found to contain an ironporphyrin together with FAD and in addition also molybdenum as cofactor [7a].

these fragments preserved the enzymatic activity of the original *amino-peptidase* notwithstanding the fact that they were far from being true proteins, for each contained a mononucleotide, a glucosamine and a small peptide consisting of two or three amino acids (glutamic acid, aspartic acid and leucine). Only one of these fragments contained a relatively more complicated peptide, consisting of alanine, histidine, leucine, glutamic acid, aspartic acid, lysine and arginine. The amino acids in these peptides were bound to the glucosamine, while the latter was linked to uridine and guanosine diphosphate; the nucleotide–peptide units are cross-linked by phosphoric acid molecules as in ribonucleic acid.

This finding is of considerable importance in biochemistry, for it leads to a way of synthesizing such enzymes with small protein moieties.

Another attempt was made recently to synthesize organic molecules which resemble the structural and spatial configuration of a prosthetic group or a cofactor of an enzyme. The first model of such a catalyst was prepared by WANG[9]—a triethylene tetramine linked to a molecule of Fe and used to catalyze the decomposition of H_2O_2. Although this compound is not as effective as the enzyme catalase, it shows that there may exist a possibility of artificially creating enzymes or at least closely related substitutes to the biological catalysts:

$$CH_2{-}CH_2$$
$$CH_2{-}NH \quad NH{-}CH_2$$
$$Fe^{3+}$$
$$CH_2{-}NH_2 \quad NH_2{-}CH_2$$

triethylene tetramine

Inactivation of enzymes by heat

As is the case with all proteins, enzymes can be easily denatured in several ways mentioned earlier, among them, heat. The enzymes are, therefore, very thermolabile and it is sufficient to apply a temperature of 70 to 80°C for two to five minutes in order to destroy most of the enzymes.

This fact of complete inactivation of enzymes by heat is very widely used in the food industry. In most cases of food preservation, it is desired that there should be no continuation of any enzymatic activity: not only should all the microorganisms be completely destroyed but the activity of the enzymes outside the living cell should also be arrested. A continuance of enzymatic action may cause, for instance, a change in the green color of the chlorophyll (Chapter 2) or of the carotenoids (Chapter 3) or cause browning of various foods (Chapter 19); it may change the taste of carbo-hydrates (Chapters 6 and 7) or cause rancidity in oils (Chapter 16); it may cause changes in the aroma (Chapter 17) or in the nutritive value of proteins (Chapter 11) or of vitamins (Chapter 14) and, finally, the presence of pecto-lytic enzymes may cause complete changes in the texture of foods (Chapter 9).

Among the various methods of food preservation, the use of heat, either as *pasteurization* or *sterilization*, is the most convenient way of inactivating enzymes. Unfortunately, enzyme inactivation by heat often takes more time than the attainment of complete sterility from microorganisms. In some cases, however, such as in milk, for instance, a test for the absence of *phosphatase* enzyme is a good indication of whether the milk is adequately pasteurized, since this enzyme is completely inactivated at a temperature high enough to destroy such resistant pathogens as *B. tuberculosis*. (The test for *phosphatase* is to allow the enzyme to act on phenolphthalein-phosphate or upon *p*-nitrophenylphosphate, both of which are colorless; if the enzyme is still active it will hydrolyze these compounds to yield colored products.)

From the industrial point of view, it is also important to know the proper distribution of the enzyme in the given food product: whether the enzyme is equally well distributed throughout the product (such as *phosphatase* in milk) or dissolved in it (such as the *lipases* in oils and fats) or, again, the enzymes may be adsorbed on solid particles (as is the case with *pectolytic enzymes* or *phenolases*, which are adsorbed on the pulp of various fruit juices).

Situations are known in food technology when, although they have been inactivated, some enzymes may become regenerated and their activity renewed after some time. Such enzyme regeneration sometimes concerns the above-mentioned enzyme *phosphatase* in milk[10] and also *pectolytic* enzymes in citrus juices. Recently, with the introduction of a new method of "end-over-end" sterilization, where the food is heated at 125° for a short time (as against 115°C in the accepted rotary sterilizers for a longer period), the regeneration of *peroxidase* activity was observed after 24 hours, although their presence could not be demonstrated immediately after processing[11,12].

The general contention in the food industry is that the shorter is the time of heat treatment the greater are the chances for the regeneration of enzyme activity[12].

This phenomenon of enzyme regeneration in heat processed foods cannot, for the time being, be explained very well. One can only surmise that the proteins of these enzymes, which have been unfolded or uncoiled during denaturation, find themselves, after a while, partially recombined by the hydrogen or sulfhydryl bonds and thus their activity is restored.

Use of enzymes in the food industry

Earlier it was shown how enzymes are inactivated in food products, by heat or otherwise, when it is important to prevent undesirable changes due to the continuation of the enzymatic activity. However, it is often necessary to bring about some quite desirable alterations in foods and it is important to show now how enzymes can be advantageously applied as a part of the processing operation in the food industry. Some of these desirable enzymatic procedures have been mentioned throughout this book, however, it seems appropriate to summarize all such processes under the present sub-title. Mention will not be made, however, of all the fermentation processes in which the enzymic activity is brought about by microorganisms *in situ*: for such processes one is referred to special treatises on biotechnology[13,14].

Enzymes are widely used today in food industries such as brewing, manufacture of cheese, of corn syrups, in the tenderization of meat, in wine making and fruit juices.

Industrial enzymes are obtained from three major sources, plants, animals and microorganisms:

(1) *Malt diastase, papain, bromelin* and *ficin* are obtained from plants. *Malt diastase* is obtained by germinating barley or wheat. *Papain* is produced from the melon-like fruit of the tree *Carica papaya*; it is usually extracted from the milky latex of the green fruit. *Bromelin* is found in the pineapple plant and is usually a by-product of the pineapple industry. *Ficin* is obtained from the latex of tropical trees of the genus *Ficus* and contains a powerful proteolytic enzyme system.

(2) Enzymes prepared industrially from animal sources comprise *pancreatic enzymes, pepsin, catalase* and *rennin*. The pancreas is particularly rich in a number of important enzymes used for preparing protein *hydrolysates* and in dairy products to prevent an oxidized flavor. Various animal glands are the best sources for enzymes, however, their collection in small quantities from slaughter houses, as well as the necessity to preserve the animal tissues quickly by drying or freezing, makes the utilization of these sources both cumbersome and expensive.

(3) The microbial source for the production of industrial enzymes is the most promising. Many such enzymes are now prepared on a large scale: *invertase* from the yeast *Saccharomyces cerevisiae*; *amylases* and *proteinases* are obtained from bacterial sources, such as *Bacillus subtilis*, or from the fungus *Aspergillus oryzae*, while *amylo-glucosidase, pectinases, glucose oxidase* and *catalase* are produced industrially from *Aspergillus niger*.

After selection of the microorganism which gives the optimal quantities of the desired enzyme, the usual microbiological technique is applied to the production of enzymes industrially. Suitable conditions for the propagation of the selected microorganism, such as the medium, optimal temperature and pH, as well as the oxygen supply, must be carefully chosen, since it is not uncommon for the optimal conditions for the best enzyme yield to be different from those for their growth. In order to extract the enzymes it is necessary to autolyze or mechanically disrupt the cells and to separate the clear enzyme solutions by filtration or centrifugation, to concentrate them in a vacuum and to dry at low temperature. A comprehensive review on the production of industrial enzymes has been recently published by the Wallerstein Laboratories (see General References at the end of this chapter).

Baking. It was an old practice in the baking industry to supplement the dough with malts produced by germinating barley or wheat, in the form of malt syrups or dried malt preparations. These additives, all of which contain *amylase* enzymes, as well as *proteinases*, help to convert the starches into dextrins and sugars and cause slight hydrolysis of the gluten, the major flour protein. These changes in the dough are very desirable since they make possible more vigorous fermentation and this can be readily observed in the improved elastic properties of the dough, and of the loaf characteristics in the baked products. While *β-amylase* (which is capable of cleaving single maltose units from a straight amylose chain) is present in abundance in normal flour, *α-amylase* (which is required for breaking up the large amylo-pectin molecules) is present in flour only in micro-quantities. That is why the addition of *α-amylase* is very desirable.

α-Amylase and *proteinase* are now produced from bacterial sources and especially from the fungi *Aspergillus oryzae*. Improved techniques in industrial enzymes now permit the preparation of these fungal-enzyme supplements with any ratio of *proteinase* to *α-amylase*, thus enabling the baking industry to control the condition of the dough more easily. The malt additions are now usually made to the flour at the mill. In the United States, the addition of fungal enzymes is permitted, however, only to the dough at the bakery and not to the flour at the mill.

The enzyme activity of industrial enzyme concentrates is many times more potent than that of barley or wheat malts, and there is some preference for the use of enzymes from fungal sources rather than from bacterial sources due to the fact that the latter require a higher temperature for their inactivation when the enzymatic activity should be finally arrested[15, 16].

The major credit for having the foresight to apply our basic knowledge about enzymes to their use in industry probably goes to JOKICHI TAKAMINE, who obtained a U.S. Patent in 1894 for a process for making a diastatic enzyme from fungi.

Manufacture of beer. In Chapter 8 mention was made of the use of diastatic enzymes in the manufacture of beer. In this, corn and other cereals from which beer is brewed are first subjected to the action of amylases, which are usually obtained from malt. So far, little use has been made of industrial enzymes obtained from fungi. Malt is prepared by germinating barley or wheat during which an abundant quantity of these enzymes is formed. It is then added to the brewers mash either as a malt syrup or in the dry form.

Chillproofing of beer. The manufacture of beer in the United States was confronted with the peculiar problem of how to prevent formation of haze in chilled beer. Such cloudiness (which, incidentally, is quite unimportant in other countries) is due to the coagulation of proteins, their source being the cereals or the autolysis of yeast. It may also be caused by tannins or leuco-anthocyanins from hop flowers and leaves, which are used in beer manufacture. It was WALLERSTEIN[17] who patented, in 1911, a process for the chillproofing of beer by introducing a proteolytic enzyme, *collupolin,* to be used during processing. In this case, the preliminary hydrolysis of the proteins prevents the formation of undesirable colloidal suspension on chilling. *Papain,* alone or in combination with other *proteinases,* is also used as a commercial chillproofer.

Tenderization of meat. For many years it has been the practice to subject meat to aging by storing it at temperatures above freezing for several weeks, thereby improving its texture. Today, such tenderization of meat can be achieved by using proteolytic enzymes. This increase in tenderness is thought to be attributed in a large degree to the action of the *cathepsin* enzymes present in the muscle. It has already been mentioned, that when proteins in a certain food are denatured by means of heat or otherwise, they become good substrates for the action of enzymes, which can then get at the unfolded large molecules more easily. However, it must be remembered that enzymes are also proteins and become denatured themselves, thus becoming largely inactivated. In such cases, when the action of enzymes is desired, one cannot rely upon the natural enzymes present in this food, and it is necessary to get them from another source. Tenderization of such meats can be done by using proteolytic enzymes from plant sources, such as *papain, bromelin* and *ficin*[18]. The usual procedure is to dip the meats in diluted enzyme preparations containing approximately 1 % *papain* in a salt base to which spices and monosodium glutamate are often added.

Clarification of wines and fruit juices[19, 20]. When discussing the action of pectolytic enzymes in Chapter 9, mention was made of the use of fungal enzyme preparations which are now widely used in clarification of fruit juices and wines. There are now several such preparations on the market (*Pectinol, Mylase,* etc.) which are very helpful during the extraction and filtration of juices containing pectin. The admixing of such industrial enzymes to the crushed fruit pomace, allowing them to act for 30 to 60

References p. 174/175

minutes greatly increases the free run juice and facilitates pressing. If a certain fruit is particularly rich in pectin, the addition of pectic enzymes to the crushed fruit may elevate the methanol content since *pectin esterase* hydrolyzes the methoxyl groups from the pectin molecule. In most cases when the pectin content is not too high, the methanol content remains below the legal limit of 0.35 %. However, if such fermented juices are used for brandy distillation, the use of pectic enzymes is questionable.

The use of pectolytic enzymes can be further extended in cases when it is desired to achieve high concentrations of juice concentrates without causing gelation. Such concentrates of apple juice, for instance, of 72 Brix are widely used as bases in the production of jellies, and it is desirable to ship or to use them in a liquid form. This makes it necessary to remove the pectin by means of commercial pectolytic enzymes. The enzyme is allowed to act upon the apple juice for some time before concentration. In practice, the enzyme is added to the partially concentrated juice, about 35 Brix, because at higher concentrations the rate of enzymatic activity is drastically reduced. Similar treatment is applied to bitter orange marmalade bases to prevent pregelation on storage[21].

Confectionary. In order to prevent crystallization of sucrose in the manufacture of hard candies, and in general whenever inversion of sucrose is desired at low temperatures and at not too low pH, the enzyme *invertase* can be successfully used. Industrially, *invertase* is usually prepared from *Saccharomyces cerevisiae.* Crude *invertase* preparations are also used in the production of high-test molasses.

Lactose hydrolysis. A commercial enzyme preparation, *lactase*, has recently been advocated for the enzymatic hydrolysis of lactose in skim milk and in whey, making it possible to use low lactose products in the manufacture of ice cream and other foods where lactose crystallization presents a problem[22].

Other examples of the use of industrial enzymes are mentioned elsewhere in this book, such as the decolorization of anthocyanins by fungal enzymes (Chapter 15), the elimination of glucose by *glucose oxidase* and *catalase* to prevent browning (Chapter 20), and the reconstitution of flavor by the action of enzymes on specific flavor precursors (Chapter 17).

REFERENCES

[1] J. B. SUMNER, *J. Biol. Chem.*, 69 (1926) 435.
[2] E. AND H. BUCHNER, *Ber.*, 30 (1897) 117.
[3] H. THEORELL, *Biochem. Z.*, 278 (1935) 263.
[4] J. S. FRUTON, W. R. HEARN, V. M. INGRAM, D. M. WIGGANS AND M. WINITZ, Synthesis of polymeric peptides in proteinase-catalyzed transamidation reactions, *J. Biol. Chem.*, 204 (1953) 891.
[5] D. D. WOODS, *Brit. J. Exptl. Pathol.*, 21 (1940) 74.

[6] E. S. G. Barron and F. Ghiretti, Pathways of acetate oxidation, *Biochim. et Biophys. Acta*, 12 (1953) 239.

[7] M. Bergmann and J. S. Fruton, *Advances in Enzymol.*, 1 (1941) 63.

[7a] D. E. Green et al., *Biochem. J.*, 33 (1939) 1694.

[8] F. Binkley, Isolation and characterization of resistant peptidate, *J. Am. Chem. Soc.*, 81 (1959) 1257.

[9] J. H. Wang, *J. Am. Chem. Soc.*, 77 (1955) 822, 4715.

[10] H. Fram, The reactivation of phosphatase in high-temperature short-time (H.T.S.T.) pasteurized dairy products, *J. Dairy Sci.*, 40 (1957) 19.

[11] S. Schwimmer, Regeneration of heat-inactivated peroxidase, *J. Biol. Chem.*, 154 (1944) 487.

[12] R. B. Guyer and J. W. Holmquist, Enzyme regeneration in H.T.S.T. sterilized canned foods, *Food Technol.*, *Australia*, 7 (1955) 199.

[13] S. C. Prescott and C. G. Dunn, *Industrial Microbiology*, 3rd edn., McGraw-Hill Co., New York, 1959.

[14] H. Tauber, *The Chemistry and Technology of Enzymes*, J. Wiley and Sons, New York, 1949.

[15] B. S. Miller and J. A. Johnson, Fungal enzymes in baking, *Baker's Dig.*, 29 (1955) 95.

[16] L. P. Carroll, B. S. Miller and J. A. Johnson, The application of enzymes in pre-ferment processes for bread production, *Cereal Chem.*, 33 (1956) 303.

[17] L. Wallerstein, *U.S. Patent No. 995,820*, (1911).

[18] A. K. Balls, Enzymes affecting proteins, p. 85, in H. W. Schultz, *Food Enzymes*, Avi Publishing Co., Westport, Conn., 1960, p. 85.

[19] C. E. Neubeck, Pectic enzymes in fruit juice technology, *J. Assoc. Offic. Agr. Chemists*, May (1959) 374.

[20] W. V. Cruess, R. Quacchia and K. Ericson, Pectic enzymes in wine making, *Food Technol.*, 9 (1955) 601.

[21] A. H. Rouse and C. D. Atkins, Pregelation in bitter orange marmalade bases, *Proc. Florida State Hort. Soc.*, 70 (1957) 223.

[22] J. J. Sampey and C. E. Neubeck, Low lactose concentrate makes better ice cream, *Food Eng.*, January (1955) 68.

SELECTED BIBLIOGRAPHY TO CHAPTER 12

Ausgewählte Kapitel aus der Allgemeinen Biochemie, Sandos A.G., Basel, 1954.

Beckhorn, E. J., Production of industrial enzymes, *Wallerstein Labs. Communs.*, 23 (1960) 201.

Byer, P. D., H. A. Lurdy and K. Myrbäck, *The Enzymes*, Vol. 2, Academic Press, New York, 1960.

Dixon, M., and E. C. Webb, *Enzymes*, Academic Press, New York, 1958.

Green, E. D., *Currents in Biochemical Research*, Interscience, New York, 1956.

Haldane, J. B. S., *Enzymes*, Longmans, Green and Co., London, 1930.

Laidler, K. J., *Introduction to the Chemistry of Enzymes*, McGraw-Hill, New York, 1954.

McElroy, W. D., and B. Glass, *The Mechanism of Enzyme Action*, Johns Hopkins Press, Baltimore, 1954.

Neilands, J. B., and P. K. Stumpf, *Enzyme Chemistry*, 2nd edn., J. Wiley and Sons, New York, 1958.

Nord, F. F. *Advances in Enzymology*, 22 Vols., Interscience, New York, 1941–1960.

Northrop, J. H., M. Kunitz and R. M. Herriott, *Crystalline Enzymes*, 2nd edn., Columbia Univ. Press, New York, 1948.

Schulz, H. W., *Food Enzymes*, Avi Publishing Co., Westport, Conn., 1960.

Sumner, J. B. and K. Myrbäck, *The Enzyme*, Academic Press, New York, 1950–1952.

Sumner, J. B., and G. F. Somers, *Chemistry and Methods of Enzymes*, 3rd edn., Academic Press, New York, 1953.

Tauber, H. *The Chemistry and Technology of Enzymes*, J. Wiley and Sons, New York, 1949.

CHAPTER 13

ENZYME KINETICS

Is a science only when you can measure it?

LORD KELVIN*

Thermodynamics

Contrary to antiquated belief all biological reactions are subject to the basic laws of thermodynamics, and it is appropriate to see now how these laws apply to enzymatic reactions.

The first law of thermodynamics states that the sum of all energies involved in a closed system remains constant:

$$\Delta E = Q - W$$

i.e. ΔE the increase in the internal energy of a system is equal to Q the amount of heat energy supplied to the system, less W the amount of energy expended by the system in doing work on the surroundings.

Of particular interest in chemical thermodynamics are the changes in energy at constant pressure. Under these conditions the work done by the system is $P\Delta V$, *i.e.* the constant pressure P multiplied by the change in volume. Thus when the system absorbs heat from the surroundings: $Q = \Delta E + P\Delta V$. This change in heat energy at constant pressure is called the change in *enthalpy* and denoted by the symbol ΔH. If heat is evolved in a reaction ΔH is negative and the reaction is termed exothermic, if the heat is absorbed by the system ΔH is positive and the reaction called endothermic.

This total change of heat which accompanies chemical reactions may be measured in a calorimeter. It has been established, however, that not all of the energy involved in ΔH is available for actual work, such as operating machines, or breaking chemical bonds. That portion of the energy change, which can be utilized for actual work is called *free energy*, and designated by the symbol ΔF.

---

* Lord Kelvin: "I often say that when you can measure what you are speaking about, and express it in numbers, you know something about it; but when you cannot express it in numbers, your knowledge is of a meagre and unsatisfactory kind; it may be the beginning of knowledge, but you have scarcely, in your thoughts, advanced to the stage of Science, whatever the matter may be."

In a reversible heat machine, for example, where ΔH is the total energy supplied to it at a temperature (T_1) which decreases to a lower value (T_2) in the course of the process, the actual work done (ΔF) is invariably smaller than the energy supplied (ΔH):

$$\Delta F = \Delta H \frac{T_1 - T_2}{T_1} = \frac{\Delta H T_1}{T_1} - \frac{\Delta H T_2}{T_1} = \Delta H - \left(\frac{\Delta H}{T_1}\right) T_2$$

In other words, the free energy change (or the work exercised by the heat machine) can only then be exactly equal to the amount of energy supplied to the machine when $T_2 = 0$; that is, when the temperature of the exhaust or the condenser is at absolute zero. In so far as this is impossible, or rather unrealistic, the change in free energy will always be smaller than the change in enthalpy $(F < H)$. The fraction $(\Delta H/T_1)$, to which the symbol ΔS is often assigned, is the change in entropy and designates the measure of the energy not exploited in the actual work of the reversible heat machine. In general, therefore, the following relation prevails:

$$\Delta F = \Delta H - T(\Delta S)$$

Our main object is always to learn the value of ΔF; however, while it is possible to measure ΔH directly by means of a calorimeter, it is impossible to do the same for the entropy. One thing is clear, namely that:

when $\Delta F = 0$, the system is in equilibrium;

when $\Delta F > 0$, free energy is flowing into the system and the reaction will not proceed without the supply of energy from the outside—an *endothermic reaction*, ΔH then has a positive value;

when $\Delta F < 0$, free energy is flowing out of the system and the reaction can proceed on its own—an *exothermic reaction*, the ΔH then has a negative value.

A few biochemical reactions are now given as examples. When glucose is oxidized into H_2O and CO_2 heat flows out of the system, the reaction is exothermic and the values of ΔF and ΔH are negative:

$$C_6H_{12}O_6 + 3\ O_2 \longrightarrow 6\ CO_2 + 6\ H_2O, - 686\ \text{kcal}$$

The difference between the enthalpies, ΔH is $- 673$ kcal

The value of $T\Delta S$ is then $+ 13$ kcal

As an example of an endothermic reaction, let us remember the photosynthetic process in which CO_2 and water, reacted to form carbohydrates of

References p. 186

high potential energy (Chapter 4). The chemical energy, ΔF, required for the synthesis of a mole of glucose from CO_2 and water is about 690 kcal and it is supplied by the radiant energy of visible light.

Activation energy

The mere presence of an enzyme will not start a reaction. It is clear, therefore, that all enzymatic reactions can take place only if they are thermodynamically feasible, *i.e.*, if they are accompanied by a loss of free energy as is the case in all metabolic processes, unless energy is supplied from the outside, as can only happen in an anabolic process. Whether the reaction will indeed take place is quite another question and depends on certain conditions. The first and most important condition is that the molecules entering the reaction must be in an *activated state*. This was explained at some length in Chapter 4 (see page 28). There we saw that the relationship between the rate of reaction, the activation energy and the temperature were expressed by ARRHENIUS' equation

$$K = A\mathrm{e}^{-E_a/RT}$$

meaning that the slightest change in the activation energy or in the temperature will influence enormously the rate of the reaction.

It is in the nature of enzymes, as biological catalysts, to reduce the activation energy to a great extent. For the time being, there is no plausible explanation of this phenomenon, however, Table VII shows the differences between the activation energy in various reactions without enzymes in comparison with those taking place in their presence.

TABLE VII

Reaction	Enzyme	Activation energy-E_a (cal/mol)	
		No catalyst or with H^+ only	*In the presence of the enzyme*
Breakdown of H_2O_2	*Catalase*	18,000	5,000
Sucrose hydrolysis	*β-Fructosidase*	26,000	11,500
Casein hydrolysis	*Trypsin*	20,600	12,000
Lipid hydrolysis (ethyl butyrate)	*Lipase*	13,200	4,200

In all these instances the activation energies required in the presence of enzymes are considerably smaller than in their absence or when the reaction is activated by the hydrogen ion alone, and because of the exponential character of the relationship between the rate of reaction and the activation energy, it is not difficult to calculate that a decrease from 20,000 to 10,000 cal/mole may correspond to an increase in the rate of reaction of about 500,000 times.

Influence of temperature

The second factor which may considerably influence the rate of a reaction, as shown by the ARRHENIUS' equation, is temperature. Although the general range of temperatures suitable for enzymatic reactions is very narrow, slight changes have considerable influence. The optimal temperature for most enzymatic reactions, with a few exceptions, lays between 30°C and 40°C. With the rise of temperature the reaction rate increases, and for most enzymes, a rise of 10°C will often double or even triple the rate of the reaction. So, for instance, for *invertase (β-fructosidase)* K, the velocity constant, between 0° and 20°C, will be:

$$\frac{K_{t+10}}{K_t} = 2.0$$

The point of denaturation of the enzymes also lays very near to the optimum temperature of the enzymatic reaction, so that for most enzymes the rate of reaction *versus* temperature curves are of the form shown in Fig. 34.

At temperatures between 50°C and 90°C most enzymes are completely inactivated. On the other hand at low temperatures enzymatic activity

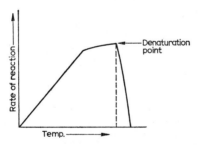

Fig. 34. Relation between the rate of an enzymatic reaction and the temperature.

proceeds very slowly but is not entirely arrested. This should be taken into consideration in the frozen food industry: many a frozen food undergo considerable deterioration after prolonged storage, for even at such temperatures as —18°C (0°F) some enzymatic reactions continue to take place.

References p. 186

The enzyme–substrate complex

The reason why enzymes require a much lower activation energy to start a reaction is generally ascribed to the fact that the enzyme first forms a complex with the substrate and, in doing so, the whole molecule is, in some way, "shattered" or "deformed" and thus the reaction can take place more quickly and more easily. MICHAELIS AND MENTEN[1] were the first who tried to explain this phenomenon. According to them, the enzyme–complex compound is very labile due to its complicated and specific structure. In the case of hydrolytic enzymes, for instance, they assume that the substrate after combining with the enzyme, even for a very short time, becomes so weakened by the large molecule of the enzyme that it is prepared for the hydrolysis at a lower hydrogen ion concentration than in the absence of the enzyme.

The concept of the enzyme–substrate complex, described in the previous chapter, was very beneficial to the study of enzymology, although it remained no more than a working hypothesis for a long time. Schematically, one can represent it as in Fig. 35.

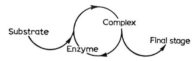

Fig. 35. Schematic representation of an enzymatic reaction.

Recently, however, some investigations indicated the actual presence of such complexes. CHANCE[2] working on the decomposition of hydrogen peroxide found, in 1943, that the enzyme *horseradish peroxidase* forms, upon addition of H_2O_2, a complex of green color with strong absorption maxima at the wavelengths of 410 and 624 mμ. The absorption maxima shifted to 418, 527 and 555 mμ during the reaction, only to return to their original spectra when the reaction was completed.

The turnover number

However, if the old concept, that a catalyst does not actually participate in the reaction, does not apply, how can one explain the fact that only very minute quantities of the enzyme are sufficient to make the reaction proceed. The cause of this is attributed to the high rate at which the enzymes activity can be restored.

The enzyme *invertase*, for instance, is capable of hydrolyzing every second an amount of sucrose ten times greater than that of its own weight, while *amylase* can produce 40 times its weight of maltose from starch. Moreover, if one takes into consideration the tremendous differences in molecular weights between the enzymes and their substrates it is possible to understand why some enzymes can have a turnover of between 100 and 3,000,000 times per minute.

The *turnover number* of a given enzyme is defined as the *number of substrate molecules capable of being catalyzed by one molecule of the enzyme during one minute*.

Table VIII gives some idea of the turnover numbers of a few enzymes.

TABLE VIII

Enzyme	Substrate	Turnover number
Catalase	H_2O_2	$5 \cdot 10^6$
Urease	Urea	$4.6 \cdot 10^5$
Invertase	Sucrose	$4 \cdot 10^4$
Aldolase	Hexose diphosphate	$7 \cdot 10^3$
Carboxylase	Pyruvic acid	$8 \cdot 10^2$
DPN	Hydrogen transfer	$5 \cdot 10^1$

Rate of enzymatic reactions

Of the various factors influencing the rate of an enzymatic reaction, mention has been made so far of the state of activation, temperature and the turnover number. Additional important factors controlling the rate of these reactions are the pH of the substrate and the concentration of both the enzyme and the substrate.

Influence of pH. The catalytic action of the enzymes is attained in comparatively narrow limits of pH. Generally, every enzymatic reaction has its optimal pH; however, if the same enzyme acts with different substrates, it can have different optima in each case. Thus, for example, *carbohydrase* requires different optimal pH for the various sugars on which it acts, while *pepsin* has only a narrow optima of pH limits in the range 1.5–2.5, depending on the various proteins on which it acts. Nearly all curves depicting the relation of the rate of enzymatic activity (*V*) *versus* the pH have similar characteristics, as shown in Fig. 36.

This general curve is very similar to the one which depicts the *degree of ionization* of a simple ampholyte, such as glycin, at various values of pH. It should be remembered (see Chapter 11) that all amphoteric substances, such as amino acids and proteins, undergo certain minimum or maximum changes of their properties (solubility, osmotic pressure, conductivity, viscosity, etc.) at their corresponding isoelectric points. It is accepted that these changes are caused by the different ionic states of these ampholytes:

References p. 186

being a zwitterion, the protein can form different ionic configurations. One has to assume that an enzyme, which of course is also a protein, can also appear in different ionic configurations and that only one of these forms is capable of exerting catalytic properties. It may be that at a given optimal pH this particular configuration is in greater abundance and thus this allows it to act as an enzyme.

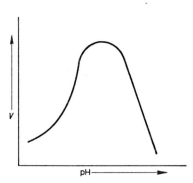

Fig. 36. Relation of pH to the rate of an enzymatic reaction.

Enzyme concentration. When all other factors comply with the optimal requirements, the rate of the enzymatic reaction depends on the concentration of the enzyme. In fact, the reaction velocity is directly proportional to the enzyme concentration, as shown by the curve presented in Fig. 37,

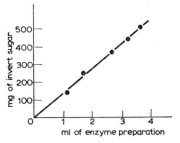

Fig. 37. Rate of reaction *versus* enzyme concentration.

showing the inversion of sucrose by *invertase*, and, since the given reaction will not proceed without the enzyme, it is clear that the curve should pass through the zero point, *i.e.*, the point of interaction of the two coordinates.

Concentration of substrate. The rate of an enzymatic reaction will, of course, normally rise with the concentration of the substrate, however, only up to a certain degree. From that point, the reaction velocity will change very little with the concentration of the substrate and ultimately the curve will flatten out, *i.e.* the rate will become constant. With more enzyme in the substrate, a higher curve will be obtained but this will still follow the same pattern. Fig. 38 shows the results of an experiment carried out with *invertase* acting

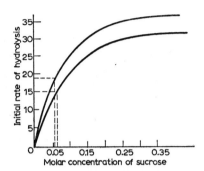

Fig. 38. Rate of sucrose hydrolysis by *invertase* at different concentrations of the substrate.

upon sucrose (with higher concentration of enzyme the hyperbolic curve was higher).

This is one of the experiments used by MICHAELIS in explaining his theory and substantiating the hypothesis of the existence of an enzyme–substrate complex, as will be seen presently. However, before proceeding with the discussion of the rates of enzymatic reactions, one should strictly remember that we have to deal here with *molar* concentrations and not simple concentrations in percent of weight. This should be borne in mind especially because enzymes are proteins of very high molecular weights in comparison with most of the substrates.

In accordance with the Mass Law, the rate of a chemical change is proportional to the product of the concentrations of the reactants. In the presence of only one reactant, the rate of change (v) is proportional to the concentration of this substrate $[S]$.

This is a monomolecular reaction or a *reaction of the first order*. Many hydrolytic reactions are such monomolecular reactions and, therefore, their velocities are proportional to the substrate which undergoes hydrolysis. During the hydrolysis of sucrose, for instance, by H^+ ions, one molecule of water reacts with each molecule of sucrose to be hydrolyzed; however, the concentration of water in comparison with that of the sucrose is so great that any considerable change in the concentration of the latter will have practically no effect upon the concentration of the water. The rate of this

References p. 186

reaction, therefore, can be measured by the concentration of the sucrose alone:

$$v \propto [S]$$

i.e. the velocity of this reaction (*v*) is directly proportional to the concentration of the substrate, sucrose [S]. Substituting the velocity constant (*K*) for the concept "proportional":

$$v_o = K\,[S]$$

After the reaction has run for some time (*t*), the concentration of the substrate will diminish somewhat and will become [S—*x*], the reaction velocity will then be

$$v = \frac{dx}{dt} = K\,[S-x]$$

which means that the reaction velocity at a given time is equal to the velocity constant multiplied by the concentration of the substrate at that particular time. By integrating the above equation, a more useful form can be obtained:

$$K = \frac{2.303}{(t_2-t_1)}\log_{10}\frac{[S]}{[S-x]}$$

or:

$$K = \frac{1}{t}\ln\frac{[S]}{[S-x]}$$

meaning that the constant of velocity equals the reciprocal of time (in seconds, minutes or hours) multiplied by the natural logarithm of the initial substrate concentration, divided by its final concentration at the time (*t*). Thus, it is not difficult to calculate the velocity constant from the concentrations at the beginning and end of the reaction, the values [S] and [S—*x*] being the concentrations of the substrate at times t_1 and t_2. If the values of *K* at two different time intervals are more or less equal, the reaction is considered to be of the first order.

In Fig. 38, the curves, representing the rate of sucrose hydrolysis, at first indicate a monomolecular reaction, *i.e.*, the initial reaction velocities are directly proportional to the concentrations of the substrate. However, in due course, the above curves approach asymptotically a limit at which the reaction rates are constant no matter what the concentration of the substrate is.

This phenomenon is apparently due to the presence of enzymes. When sucrose is hydrolyzed by *invertase*, one could assume, on the basis of the enzyme–substrate complex theory, that with low concentrations of the substrate (in this case upto about 4 % of sucrose) not all of the enzyme molecules participate in forming the complex. Ultimately, however, when sucrose concentrations are high (10–20 %) all the enzyme molecules are engaged in the reaction and are constantly forming complexes with the substrate; from that moment, additional sucrose will not change the velocity rate because all the enzyme molecules are engaged at their full turnover capacity. When the rate of reaction is no longer dependent on the substrate concentration, the reaction is considered to be of *zero-order*. Using the same symbols as before, the differential equation for a zero-order reaction is

$$\frac{dx}{dt} = K, \text{ which upon integration gives } K = \frac{\Delta x}{\Delta t}.$$

The MICHAELIS *equation*

Let us consider now the principle already discussed of the enzyme–substrate complex in the light of the Mass Law. The enzyme at a concentration $[E]$ forms with the substrate $[S]$ a temporary complex of concentration $[ES]$:

$$[E] + [S] \rightleftharpoons [ES]$$

Accordingly, the equilibrium constant is:

$$K = \frac{[E] \cdot [S]}{[ES]}$$

However, due to the formation of the complex, one should deduct this bound quantity from both the enzyme concentration as well as from that of the substrate. The above equation should, therefore, read:

$$K = \frac{([E] - [ES]) \; ([S] - [ES])}{[ES]}$$

The concentration of the complex is so small in comparison with the amount of substrate that it can indeed be ignored as far as the substrate is concerned. The same equation could therefore be simplified to:

$$K_m = \frac{([E] - [ES]) \; [S]}{[ES]}$$

This last form of the equation for the equilibrium constant of enzymatic reactions is called the MICHAELIS *equation* and the constant, K_m, is accepted in biochemistry as the MICHAELIS *constant*.

Fig. 39 shows theoretical curves based on the MICHAELIS equation and it is of interest to note that these correspond very closely with the curves

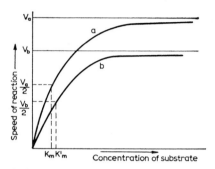

Fig. 39. Theoretical reaction-velocity curves based on MICHAELIS equation.

obtained from actual experiments (see Fig. 38). This equation gives a rectangular hyperbolic curve with the following characteristics:

(a) the limit of the reaction velocity is an asymptotic value to which the velocity approaches with rise of the substrate concentration;

(b) the MICHAELIS constant, K_m, corresponds to that substrate concentration at which the velocity of the reaction reaches one-half of its maximum rate;

(c) in the case of a large excess of substrate, the limit velocities are directly proportional to the concentration of the enzyme (as discussed earlier), as can be seen from the differences in the heights of curves a and b.

In addition, MICHAELIS curves do not only predict the velocities of enzymatic reactions on the basis of substrate concentrations, but also give a fairly good idea of the specificity of the enzymes involved. If the curves a and b in Fig. 39 represent two different enzymes of low specificity acting on the same substrate, it is obvious that enzyme a has a greater affinity to the substrate than b and that it would be necessary to use much more of the enzyme b in order to obtain the same K_m as in a, which is apparently more specific.

REFERENCES

[1] L. MICHAELIS AND M. L. MENTEN, *Biochem. Z.*, 49 (1913) 333.
[2] B. CHANCE *et al.*, *Mechanism of Enzyme Action*, Johns Hopkins Press, Baltimore, 1954.

SELECTED BIBLIOGRAPHY TO CHAPTER 13

BALDWIN E., *Dynamic Aspects of Biochemistry*, 3rd edn. Cambridge Univ. Press, 1957.
BULL, H. B., *Physical Biochemistry*, 2nd edn., J. Wiley & Sons, New York, 1951.
KLOTZ, I. M., *Chemical Thermodynamics*, Prentice-Hall Ltd., New Jersey, 1950.
NEILANDS, J. B. AND P. K. STUMPF, *Enzyme Chemistry*, J. Wiley & Sons, New York, 1958.
ROSSINI, F. D., *Chemical Thermodynamics*, J. Wiley & Sons, New York, 1950.
WEISSBERGER A., *Physical Methods of Organic Chemistry*, 2nd edn., Interscience Publishers, New York 1949.

CHAPTER 14

VITAMINS

Accessory food factors

SIR FREDERIC HOPKINS, 1906

History

For a long time it was appreciated that some substances, then of an unknown nature, are required in the diet of man to prevent certain diseases. As far back as in 1747, a doctor in the British Navy, Captain LIND[1], showed that the very dangerous disease, scurvy (*scorbutus*), which frequently prevailed in older times with seamen who were at sea for many months, was caused only because of the lack of fresh fruit and vegetables in their diet. LIND also found, through long empirical tests, that the only way to prevent scurvy in such cases was to add to the daily diet of men at sea a teaspoonful of citrus juice*. Since 1804, the British Navy has had strict instructions never to sail without lime juice—they have since been nicknamed the "limies".

One hundred and fifty years later, a Dutch doctor, EIJKMAN, demonstrated in 1897 that a very common disease, beri-beri, which prevailed at that time in the Dutch East Indies, was caused through feeding on only polished rice. To the vital substance, contained in the rice bran (hulls and germ) and which apparently prevented beri-beri, as well as to other compounds the lack of which caused scorbut and pellagra, FUNK, in 1912, gave the name *Vitamine*, in the belief that it was an amine. Since then, the denotation *vitamins* has been reserved for this class of compounds.

It was only in 1912 that HOPKINS[2], the renowned British biochemist, proved that every animal body requires for its well being and normal growth, in addition to the main nutrients (carbohydrates, proteins, fats, a few minerals and water), some important "accessory food factors". In his first very simple but ingenious experiments, HOPKINS fed his rats with synthetic feeds containing purified major nutrients and found that the rats could not sustain normal conditions unless they received, in addition, 3 ml

---

* Even before LIND, the use of lemons or oranges seems to date from 1601 when Sir JAMES LANCASTER introduced it to the ships of the East India Company.

of milk daily. That year of 1906 was an important turning point in the science of nutrition. EIJKMAN AND HOPKINS were jointly awarded the Nobel laureateship in 1929.

Vitamins are organic substances of very diversified composition required by the animal body usually in very minute quantities. Some of them, especially the so-called B group, take an active part in various enzymatic reactions as coenzymes. Most of the vitamins are directly or indirectly supplied to the animal body by the plants, which are capable of producing them. Animals cannot generally synthesize vitamins. Vitamins supply neither energy to the body nor any structural units for body building substances. They play, however, a most important role in the energy transfer as well as in the control of many metabolic processes.

In contrast to enzymes, most of the vitamins are thermostable and, in the absence of oxygen, are stable even at temperatures of over $100°C$. So far, some 20 vitamins with well defined functions have been isolated and, in addi-, tion, many so-called "factors" have been demonstrated, although their exact performance has not yet been established.

Because there is no structural relationship among the different vitamins, their classification is practically impossible. One important distinction does exist, namely their solubility properties; the vitamins are, therefore, divided into two groups: the water-soluble vitamins comprising vitamin C, all the vitamins of group B, vitamin PP, inositol and biotin, and those soluble in fats—vitamins A, D, E and K. In this book, the alphabetical order will be followed in general although this order has been rather inconsistent throughout the years.

Vitamin A (synonyms: axerophthol)

Deficiency in this vitamin causes the eye disease called *xerophthalmia*, which is now uncommon except in very undeveloped countries of Africa and Asia, especially in children. In adults, long before the eyes actually become infected, lack of vitamin A is indicated by *night blindness*, inability to see in dim light. Vitamin A is also considered to be essential as an important growth promoting factor. This, however, is regarded today as true of *all* vitamins, since vitamins are obviously necessary for proper health and full growth.

Vitamin A, as such, is not found in plants, yeast, fungi or bacteria, and the herbivorous animal obtains it only in the form of its precursors, carotenes, which are, therefore, called *provitamins A* (see Chapter 3). The animal is capable of converting the carotene by the intestinal mucosa into vitamin A and from there it is carried by the blood stream into the liver, where it is deposited and stored. Animals and humans can, of course, receive their supplies of vitamin A by directly eating the liver of other animals or fish.

Small but not insignificant quantities of vitamin A and of the provitamin are found in the yolk of eggs and in milk and, because both of them are soluble in fats, they are found in cream and butter*.

In the human body, vitamin A is found in the form of esters of oleic, palmitic and stearic fatty acids; however, a small quantity of free vitamin "wanders" about in the blood stream.

As mentioned in Chapter 3, vitamin A is an alcohol and consists of one-half of the molecule of its precursor, β-carotene (see page 20).

This all-*trans* form of vitamin A is found in the livers of sea fish, however, in some fresh-water fish another form of this vitamin has been isolated, with two less hydrogens, which has been named vitamin A_2 (note the additional double bond in the ring structure):

vitamin A_2-alcohol

So far, it has been impossible to convert β-carotene enzymatically *in vitro* into vitamin A, a transformation which takes place, as said, in the intestines. On the other hand, scientists in both the United States and in Holland have succeeded in synthesizing this vitamin in recent years.

Vitamin A crystallizes in yellow prisms with a melting point of 63–64°C; it does not dissolve in water but is soluble in most organic solvents. It can be distilled (by molecular distillation) at 137 to 139°C under a reduced pressure of 10^{-3} mm Hg. It is obviously not destroyed at high temperatures, however, it is easily oxidized in the presence of oxygen. Sulfur dioxide can prevent such oxidation. In commerce, vitamin A is now sold in more stable forms: as an ester of acetic acid ($R—COCH_3$) or of palmitic acid, $R—CO(CH_2)_{14}CH_3$, for the enrichment of such foods as margarine, etc.

Recently, an easy method was found to oxidize the vitamin A-alcohol into its aldehydic form, called *retinene*. When a solution of vitamin A-alcohol in petroleum ether is kept over solid MnO_2, it is soon converted into retinene, the form of vitamin A found in the eye:

retinene A_1—vitamin A_1-aldehyde

---

* HIPPOCRATES (*ca.* 500 B.C.) knew of night blindness and of its cure by eating liver.

References p. 219/220

This finding has greatly facilitated the elucidation of the mechanism of vitamin A's action in the eye to prevent night blindness. There are two kinds of vision:

(a) *photopic vision* in full daylight, which is stimulated by cone-like receptors in the retina of the eye;

(b) *scotopic vision* in dim light at twilight or at night, which is achieved by rod-like receptors.

It usually takes between 5 and 30 minutes for a human eye to adapt itself for scotopic vision. The pigment in the retina responsible for vision in the dark, the visual purple, is now called *rhodopsin*. Rhodopsin is found to be a combination of retinene with a protein, *opsin*. The first stage, however, is the dehydrogenation of vitamin A-alcohol into vitamin A-aldehyde (retinene) with the aid of DPN, which is thereby reduced to $DPNH_2$:

$$C_{19}H_{27} \cdot CH_2OH + DPN \quad \underset{+2H}{\overset{-2H}{\rightleftarrows}} \quad C_{19}H_{27} \cdot CHO + DPNH_2$$

$$\text{vitamin A} \hspace{5cm} \text{retinene}$$

In the dark, retinene combines spontaneously with the protein opsin to form rhodopsin, only to separate again in the light. The bleaching of rhodopsin requires energy which is supplied by the light. This is a very interesting case of a very labile connection between a protein and a prosthetic group in the performance of a biological function, as already mentioned in Chapter 12.

What is even more interesting is that when retinene combines with opsin, its natural all-*trans* configuration is curved into one of its *cis* geometrical isomers:

neo-retinene b

When retinene is released from its combination with opsin, it returns to its *trans* isomer, a configuration most favored by nature which always appears in synthetic preparations.

At least five *cis–trans* stereoisomers are possible with vitamin A or with retinene, however, they differ widely from each other in their ability to regenerate from the rhodopsin combination. Various synthetic preparations have been examined by means of bio-assays and their potency, or biological activity as vitamins, has been compared with the natural vitamin, as:

All-*trans* vitamin A,	100 %;
Neo-vitamin A-aldehyde (6 mono-*cis* and 2:6 di-*cis*),	91 %;
Neo-vitamin A-acetate (2-mono-*cis*),	75 %;
2:4 *cis* vitamin A-aldehyde,	47 %;
2:4 di-*cis* vitamin A-acetate,	23 %;
6 mono-*cis* and 2:6 *cis* vitamin A-aldehyde,	18 %;

Theoretically, one molecule of β-carotene should produce in the animal body two molecules of vitamin A. However, bio-assays have shown that the biological activity is less than that. Moreover, carotenoids with one open ionone ring will produce only one-half the amount of vitamin A, and such carotenoids as lycopene, with no ionone rings, cannot serve as precursors to vitamin A at all.

Very little is known at the present time regarding the *systemic action* of vitamin A in the human body, namely, its action as a growth promoting factor. The particular chemical reactions in the body (except vision) in which vitamin A participates have still to be elucidated.

The *international unit* (I.U.) accepted for this vitamin is 0.6 γ (microgram) of pure β-carotene or 0.3 γ of pure vitamin A-alcohol. Green and yellow vegetables contain between 1,500–20,000 I.U. vitamin A per 100 g; butter 1,000–4,500 I.U. and calf liver between 10,000–160,000 I.U. vitamin A per 100 g.

The recommended requirements for the average adult are about 5,000 I.U. from combined sources (of carotene or vitamin A).

Prior to the availability of synthetic vitamin A, the most important natural source of it was the fish liver oils, from which it was recovered by molecular distillation, after appropriate saponification.

The recommended human allowance can be easily provided by one egg a day, plus one liter of milk, 25 g of butter and 100 g of fresh tomatoes. Animals are provided with vitamin A by eating grass containing ample quantities of carotene.

Alfalfa, for instance, is used in livestock feeding as a rich source of carotene. However, due to the enzymatic oxidation by *lipoxidase*, drying hay or alfalfa in the field leads to the destruction of 45–90 % of the carotene. Artificial drying, which causes the inactivation of the *oxidase*, keeps the carotene level in the freshly dried meal high. On the other hand, ZIMMERMAN[3] has found that heat may exert a deleterious effect on the nutritive protein value of alfalfa meal, as shown by a significant reduction in digestibility and biological value for rats.

Since both vitamin A and its precursor, β-carotene, are soluble in fats and oils, there is always a danger that when the oils become rancid (due to oxidation) the vitamin will suffer considerable losses. This is true to a large extent of such food products as butter or vitamin-enriched margarines subjected to prolonged storage.

Vitamin A can also be destroyed to some extent by the action of light and, in particular, by the ultraviolet portion of the spectrum. The effect of packaging is therefore an important factor in the retention of vitamin A in products packed in glass, such as milk, or in other transparent forms of packaging[4].

To prevent deterioration of carotene in fruits and vegetables during canning or dehydration, the processes of steam blanching or deaeration are used.

The vitamin B group

The whole group of vitamins designated by the symbol B have been isolated principally from yeast and from the bran of various cereals. Today, some twelve vitamins are known in this group, and all of them have been found to be responsible for certain metabolic activities, their deficiency being the cause of abnormal conditions in man, or at least in experimental animals. However, not all have been properly separated, so that the prevailing idea nowadays is not to attach any particular disease to the lack of a given vitamin, but rather to regard them as responsible for various metabolic processes, since most of them have been found to act as prosthetic groups in certain enzymes. In the absence of one of the vitamins of this group, the corresponding enzyme is deficient in its action and, therefore, the whole metabolic process suffers, bringing about general derangement in the body, a condition which may express itself in a certain disease.

Vitamin B_1 (synonyms: in the U.S.A.—thiamine; in Europe—aneurin)

Chronologically, vitamin B_1 was the first to be demonstrated in 1897 by EIJKMAN in rice bran, isolated from yeast and crystallized by WINDAUS and synthesized by WILLIAMS.

Vitamin B_1 consists of two nuclei, a pyrimidine and a thiazole nucleus (see page 65) in other words, it is a quarternary thiazolinium salt. The synthetic compound is sold as a hydrochloride:

(pyrimidine moiety)   (thiazole nucleus)
vitamin B_1
(in the chloride–hydrochloride form)

It crystallizes in needles, melting point 248–250°C and is very soluble in water: 1 g in 1 ml.

Most important for the food technologist is the behavior of vitamin B_1 towards sulfur dioxide or any sulfite salt. In their presence, this vitamin splits into two parts: the sulfited pyrimidine moiety and the thiazole residue:

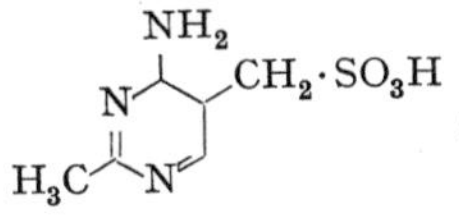

$$NH_2$$

2,5-dimethyl-4-aminopyrimidine
sulphonic acid

Both these residues are water-soluble but they no longer show vitamin B$_1$ potency. It is important to remember, therefore, that a food of which the nutritive value depends largely on its vitamin B$_1$ content, should never be preserved by SO$_2$ or sulfites.

As mentioned before (see Chapter 6), vitamin B$_1$ when esterified by two molecules of phosphoric acid (thiamine pyrophosphate) forms the prosthetic group of *pyruvic acid carboxylase*, the enzyme which detaches a molecule of CO$_2$ from pyruvic acid during alcoholic fermentation to convert it into acetaldehyde. The same process of decarboxylation of pyruvic acid takes place in the human body during the breakdown of glucose.

Lack of thiamine in the human diet causes "beri-beri", which used to strike many inhabitants of the Far East countries where it was customary to eat polished rice. Today, it has been established, without doubt, that the bran and the germ of all cereals contain vitamin B$_1$ as well as other vitamins of the B group. Although, nowadays, cases of death from beri-beri have become rare, thiamine deficiency is still a frequent occurrence, mainly because large sections of population, who lack a balanced diet prefer white bread to bread made of whole-meal flour. A *high-extraction rate* means that a high proportion of the grain, including the germ and particularly the protective covering of the germ, the *scutellum*, pass into the flour during the milling operations. Naturally, the higher the extraction, the darker the flour and the breads made from it although it is richer in important nutrients and particularly in vitamin B$_1$. (White flour has an "extraction rate" of about 72–75 %; however, during World War II most countries introduced a unified flour of 85 % extraction rate. Since then, white low-extraction flours are often reinforced by addition of synthetic thiamine, nicotinic acid and iron.)

Vitamin B$_1$ is quite thermostable at a pH of 3.5 up to 120°C. On the other hand, it is much more labile in neutral and even more so in alkaline solutions. It is obvious, therefore, that non-acid food products are apt to lose their thiamine content easily at higher temperatures.

The daily requirement for the "normal man" is considered to be 1.6 mg. The principal sources of vitamin B$_1$ are wheat germ, whole-meal cereals, pulses and nuts, yeast, egg yolk, liver, heart, kidney and pork. The approximate content, in micrograms, of thiamine per 100 g of food are as follows: dried brewer's yeast, 9,500 γ; whole wheat 560 γ, whole egg, 120 γ.

References p. 219/220

Vitamin B$_2$ (synonyms: riboflavin, lactoflavin)

The second important vitamin in the B group is vitamin B$_2$, or *riboflavin*. For a long time it has been considered to be the anti-pellagra vitamin, however, when it was isolated in a pure state from the other members of the B complex, it turned out that the vitamin responsible for the prevention of the pellagra disease was another member of the group—nicotinic acid.

Riboflavin was first discovered by WARBURG AND CHRISTIAN[5] and was shown to be a constituent of the so-called "yellow oxidation enzyme". It was obtained in a crystalline state from whey by KUHN[6], who established its nature as a vitamin.

Deficiency of vitamin B$_2$ in man is characterized by severe inflammation at the corners of the mouth (*cheilosis*) or of the tongue (*glossitis*). Serious deficiency may result in impaired growth and cause inflammation of the digestive tract with marked diarrhea; also, there are changes in the cornea of the eye.

The structural formula of riboflavin was elucidated by KARRER[7], who also succeeded in preparing it synthetically. It is the dimethyl derivative of isoalloxazine with a five-carbon alcohol, ribitol, attached as a side chain to the nitrogen in position 9 (see page 155):

vitamin B$_2$ (riboflavin)
6,7-dimethyl-9(D-ribityl)isoalloxazine

Pure riboflavin crystallizes in fine, orange-yellow needles melting at 282°C with decomposition. It is soluble in water (12 mg in 100 ml) and only slightly soluble in a few organic solvents. In alkaline solutions, it is exceedingly soluble and, in this form, it shows considerable optical rotation ($[\alpha]_D^{20} = -114°$), while in neutral or acid media its optical activity is very small.

One of the most striking properties of riboflavin is its sensitivity to light: when illuminated in a neutral solution, the ribitol residue is completely split off.

As already mentioned in Chapter 12, riboflavin, with an additional molecule of phosphoric acid, forms the prosthetic group of a number of *dehydrogenases, flavin-mononucleotides* (FMN) and *flavin–adenine-dinucleotides*

(FAD), when they are in combination with adenine. In the form of *de-hydrogenases*, riboflavin plays an important role in a number of enzymatic reactions in the human body, all of them engaged in hydrogen transfer. FMN possesses a strong fluorescence when the enzyme is illuminated by ultraviolet rays. This fluorescence disappears when the enzyme is reduced to $FMNH_2$. The suggested scheme by which vitamin B_2 is linked to the protein moiety in the enzyme has been given on page 157. THEORELL succeeded in separating this coenzyme from its apoenzyme by dialysis. By combining the protein from one flavoprotein with the prosthetic group from another, new flavoprotein enzymes can be formed.

The daily requirement for an "normal" adult is 1.8 mg, and the best food sources are green, leafy vegetables (such as cabbage, spinach and tomatoes), the bran of cereals, milk, egg white, liver and kidney.

In order to prevent losses of this vitamin, it is recommended to avoid excessive blanching of vegetables before processing. Processing by heat does not impair the vitamin B_2 potency. Packaging material may play an important role in food products as far as riboflavin is concerned: milk which is allowed to stand in glass containers on the consumer's doorstep may lose as much as 85 % of its riboflavin after two hours' exposure to bright sunlight[8].

Pantothenic acid (synonyms: chick antidermatitis factor; filtrate factor)

Before this vitamin had been isolated and its name firmly established as *pantothenic acid* by WILLIAMS[9], much confusion existed in the field of the vitamin B group due to the fact that B_2 was originally considered to be a single compound. Later, several vitamins were isolated from this mixture by adsorbing them on Fuller's earth while others went into the filtrate. Today, all such denotations as vitamin B_3, B_4 and "filtrate factor" are obsolete. The following scheme clearly shows the relationship:

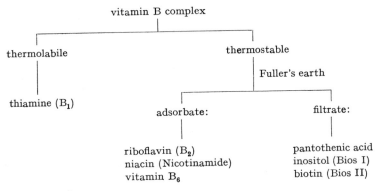

Pantothenic acid (from the Greek word, *pantothen*, indicating its ubiquitous distribution) is, therefore, now the accepted name for this vitamin, which has been discovered, isolated and characterized solely by means of microorganisms, by the work of WILLIAMS[10] and his coworkers.

The structure of pantothenic acid is:

$$\text{HO—CH}_2\text{—}\underset{\overset{|}{\text{CH}_3}}{\overset{\overset{\text{CH}_3}{|}}{\text{C}}}\text{—}\overset{\overset{\text{OH}}{|}}{\text{CH}}\text{—CO—NH—CH}_2\text{—CH}_2\text{—COOH}$$

(α,γ-dihydroxy-β,β'-dimethyl-butyryl-β-alanide)

Pantothenic acid, has since been found to constitute the major part of the so-called Coenzyme-A (CoA), *i.e.*, the one concerned in acetylation reactions, hence the connotation "A".

Coenzyme A is composed of 2-mercaptoethylamine condensed with *pantothenic acid*[11] which, in turn, is combined through two molecules of phosphoric acid and the phosphorylated pentose, D-ribose, with adenine as follows:

Coenzyme-A

The function of this coenzyme is described further in Chapter 18 as a participant in the condensation of pyruvic acid with oxaloacetic acid to form citric acid during the respiration cycle. The mechanism of action of

CoA centers around its terminal sulfhydryl group, which is alternately acetylated and deacetylated. This ability to transfer the acetyl group has been demonstrated[12] in the biosynthesis of fatty acids (see Chapter 16), according to the general scheme:

$$CH_3-\underset{\substack{\| \\ O}}{C}-OH + HS-CoA \rightleftharpoons CH_3-\underset{\substack{\| \\ O}}{C}\sim S-CoA + H_2O$$

acetyl   CoA   acetyl
compound   coenzyme-A

Because of the great importance of Coenzyme-A, one can readily understand the acceptance of panthothenic acid as a vitamin. However, as its name indicates, it is very widely distributed in all living cells and, therefore, no apparent deficiency has been found in man. Specific deficiencies can be produced in experimental animals. The pantothenic acid content in a few foodstuffs is shown in the following few examples:

brewer's dry yeast,	200 γ/g;
beef liver,	76 γ/g;
egg yolk,	63 γ/g;
kidney,	35 γ/g;
buckwheat,	26 γ/g;
spinach (fresh),	26 γ/g;
wheat bran,	30 γ/g;
roasted peanuts,	25 γ/g;
whole milk powder,	24 γ/g;
bread,	5 γ/g.

The daily amount in a normal diet is more than adequate.

Nicotinic acid (synonyms: niacin in U.S.A.; nicotinamide in U.K.; vitamin PP—pellagra preventive)

The history of this vitamin is a good example of the development of scientific knowledge. The disease, pellagra, has been known for over 200 years; it manifests itself in dermatitis, diarrhea and dementia. As far back as 1735, CASAL ascribed pellagra to a toxin which, in his opinion, was discharged by certain microorganisms. In 1918, GOLDBERGER[13], of the Public Health Office of the United States, was able to show that pellagra was a disease caused by a dietary deficiency. At that time, a large number of deaths caused by pellagra were common, not only in countries like Italy, Rumania, Egypt, etc., where peasant populations were forced to rely almost exclusively on maize as their staple food, but also in many southern parts of the United States, where 11,000 deaths from pellagra were recorded in 1915.

In 1930, it became clear that nicotinic acid was very good at preventing pellagra. However, a great difficulty presented itself in accepting this compound as a vitamin, due to the fact that small quantities of milk added to the diet of a diseased person, quantities which contained only insignificant amounts of nicotinic acid, brought about a complete recovery. To explain this inconsistency, scientists thought that the milk nourished certain bacteria in the intestines, and these bacteria were able to synthesize the necessary nicotinic acid.

In 1940 an important observation was made, namely, that large sections of the population in India, whose sole nourishment was rice, containing only 5 mg of nicotinic acid per day, did not show any signs of pellagra, while the inhabitants of Moldavia, in Europa, who ate mainly maize, with 15 mg per day of nicotinic acid, were subject to severe attacks by this disease.

It was only in 1945 that ELVEHJEM found that the rice in India contained, in addition to a small quantity of nicotinic acid, a large proportion of *tryptophan* and that this amino acid, as a precursor, was capable of being transformated in the human body into nicotinic acid:

tryptophan   nicotinic acid   nicotinamide

Moreover, it has been demonstrated that maize does contain, in addition, some unknown toxic factor capable of provoking some signs of pellagra, at least in rats. In the meantime, it has been learned that tryptophan is an excellent precursor of nicotinic acid.

The daily requirement of nicotinamide or nicotinic acid, which is easily converted in our body into nicotinamide, is about 12–16 mg per day, and the best sources for it are foods: yeast, meat, fish and milk. Niacin is quite thermostable in both acid and alkaline media and is not easily oxidized.

Nicotinamide is a component part of the two important coenzymes, DPN and TPN, which are *dehydrogenases* containing also adenine, ribose and phosphoric acid and which have been described at length earlier in Chapters

5 and 12. In addition to the chemical mechanism described there, a more recent suggestion has been made by PULLMAN[14]. According to this view, the nicotinamide moiety of these enzymes, which behaves as a weak quaternary base, is readily reduced and oxidized in the following manner:

| ethyl alcohol | DPN | DPNH + H$^+$ | acetaldehyde |

This is an example of DPN oxidizing an alcohol into an aldehyde, whereby DPN is reduced, one of the hydrogens entering the pyridine ring in position 4 (*para* to the nitrogen). The other hydrogen can be regarded as splitting into a proton and an electron. This electron pairs off with the charged nitrogen in the ring, while the proton becomes attached to the oxygen of one of the phosphoric acid residues in equilibrium with the water in the medium. Reduced DPN, according to the older ideas, was marked DPNH$_2$. At present, both mechanisms are accepted in various textbooks.

Recently, it was demonstrated[15] in Mexico that during the roasting of coffee beans their nicotinic acid content rises from 1.29 to 32.01 mg per 100 g. It turned out that, of all foods, coffee is probably the richest source of this vitamin, except for dry yeast and wheat bran. Apparently, *trigonelline* is the precursor of nicotinic acid in this case, the conversion being achieved by heat:

| trigonelline | nicotinic acid |

This alkaloid is also found in peas and in many cereals.

Vitamin B$_6$ (synonyms: *pyridoxine, adermin*)

Although vitamin B$_6$ is essential in the diet of man for reasons which will soon be apparent, deficiency in this vitamin does not show specific syndromes. Large deficiencies in a child's diet may cause convulsions. Experimental animals which lack vitamin B_6 are less capable of storing fats and develop dermatitis of the extremities, commonly called "rat pellagra".

As already mentioned in Chapter 11, vitamin B_6 is the prosthetic group of the enzyme *transaminase*, engaged in transferring the amino group from glutamic acid to α-keto acids to form other amino acids. In other enzymatic reactions, the decarboxylation of tyrosine and of some other amino acids, vitamin B_6 participates as a coenzyme of a *carboxylase*. Also other enzymatic reactions apparently require the presence of pyridoxal. The active coenzyme form is no doubt the pyridoxal phosphate, however, all these derivatives of pyridoxine are interconvertible.

Commercial pyridoxine hydrochloride is a white, crystalline powder, stable in air but slowly affected by sunlight. It melts with decomposition at 204–208°C, 1 g dissolves in 5 ml of H_2O but is much less soluble in ethanol.

Vitamin B_6 is widely distributed in foodstuffs, the best sources being muscle meat, liver, green vegetables, whole grain cereals and especially their bran.

p-Aminobenzoic acid (synonyms: PABA, anti-gray hair vitamin)

It is customary to regard this chemical compound as of the vitamin B group. p-Aminobenzoic acid (PABA) is widely distributed in plants and animals, however, its activity has been interpreted only as far as microorganisms are concerned, these requiring it for their growth. It has also been observed that rats deprived of p-aminobenzoic acid contract gray hair and that chickens require this vitamin as a growth factor. There is no indication that PABA is indeed required or is of use to the human body. On the other hand, the fact that PABA is of utmost importance in the nutrition of many types of bacteria, among them the pathogenic types, gave a clue to the development of various so-called sulpha drugs, all of which act as antimetabolites, competing with PABA in the metabolic needs of the pathogenic bacteria, as already explained in Chapter 12.

$$NH_2\text{—}\langle\ \rangle\text{—}COOH \qquad\qquad NH_2\text{—}\langle\ \rangle\text{—}SO_2NH_2$$

p-aminobenzoic acid   p-aminophenylsulphamide
(PABA)   (anti-vitamin)

p-Aminobenzoic acid links the pterin to the glutamic acid in the important vitamin, *folic acid*, as shown in the next paragraph.

Folic acid (synonyms: vitamin B_c; vitamin M; pteroylglutamic acid)

Originally, this vitamin or its derivatives had been shown to prevent a special type of anaemia in chicks (vitamin B$_c$), to be needed by monkeys (vitamin M), and to be a growth factor of microorganisms, *Lactobacillus casei* and *Streptococcus lactis* R. Finally, in 1945, folic acid was found to be effective in bringing about, in certain cases, the regeneration of erythrocytes in man.

The molecule of folic acid consists of glutamic acid, *p*-aminobenzoic acid and a pteridine derivative, as follows:

p-aminobenzoic   pteridine derivative
acid

glutamic acid   "pteroyl"-residue
residue

pteroylglutamic acid

Folic acid derivatives appears to be coenzymes in reactions related to the formation and transfer of single carbon units.

Vitamin B$_{12}$ (synonyms: cyanocobalamin; anti-pernicious anaemia vitamin)

The anti-pernicious anaemia factor is vitamin B$_{12}$. This remarkable vitamin, which is apparently most important in building up the red cells in blood, is the newest addition to the family of vitamins. Vitamin B$_{12}$ appears to be involved in the activation of folic acid. It is thought to participate in nucleoprotein synthesis and to be related to keep sulfhydryl groups in their active form.

Vitamin B$_{12}$ was originally found in liver, but subsequently it was discovered in surprisingly large quantities in the fungi *Streptomyces griseus*, from which it is now manufactured for medicinal purposes.

Its chemical structure was not elucidated until 1955 when it was discovered by Sir ALEXANDER TODD and his collaborators[16]. This compound is unique in several respects: it has the largest molecular weight of any non-proteinic and non-polymeric substances, its empiric formula being $C_{63}H_{88}O_{14}N_{14}PCo$; it is the only vitamin known so far to contain a metal, that metal being cobalt. Vitamin B$_{12}$ is a dark-red, crystalline compound, soluble in water, it contains no nucleotides and is an hexacarboxylic acid:

References p. 219/220

vitamin B_{12}

The central portion is an hexacarboxylic acid built of four reduced substituted pyrrole rings with cobalt at the center. A cyanide group is attached to the cobalt. The second important residue is the benziminazole riboside, which is linked on one side to cobalt and on the other side through phosphoric acid and aminopropanol to one of the pyrrole rings. (It is most interesting to note that, while not so long ago the elucidation of such a complicated molecule would have taken many years, it was completed this time in a few months by three-dimensional projection of its electron densities after the results of the X-ray analysis had been calculated by the UNIVAC electronic computor of the University of California, in Los Angeles.)

Another crystalline form of this vitamin has been isolated from bacteria, in which the cyanide group is substituted by an hydroxyl, and named *hydroxocobalamine*, or vitamin B_{12b}.

Vitamin B_{12} darkens and becomes black at $212°C$ but does not melt even if heated up to $320°C$. Its aqueous solutions are very stable in the pH

ange of 4–7, however, exposure to sunlight brings about loss of the vitamin
potency.

Foods known to be the best sources for vitamin B_{12} are mammalian liver
and kidney, oysters and clams. They contain 0.5 γ or more per gram of dry
matter. Good sources are also beef, lamb, veal and poultry, milk and fish,
all containing between 3 and 10 γ per 100 g. Vegetables, grains, seeds and
yeast, in many cases, do not contain this vitamin: most investigators
maintain that vitamin B_{12} may be regarded as a substance produced by
microorganisms and blue and green algae, but not by higher plants.

Inositol and bios I

The following two compounds are usually considered to belong to the
group B vitamins. They are both known as growth factors for microorganisms.

It should be remembered that inositol, because of its widespread distribution in plants, was at one time considered to constitute the primary carbohydrate formed by the plant during photosynthesis (see Chapter 4).

Inositol, however, was found to be an effective growth promoting factor
for some strains of yeast, especially in combination with other vitamins of
the B complex.

Inositol is soluble in water, but insoluble in alcohol or ether. It is a sweet
substance with a melting point of 215–216°C. While its empirical formula is
that of a monosaccharide, $C_6H_{12}O_6$, it has a cyclic structure:

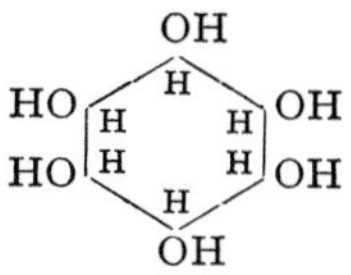

inositol

Inositol can appear in different geometrical isomers. However, of all these
forms, one is mostly widespread in nature, namely, *meso*-inositol:

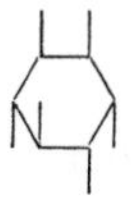

meso-inositol

In most cases, this is the only form which appears to be effective as a
growth promoting factor. Its physiological activity in man is unknown.

Inositol is also present in animal tissues, in wheat germ and in soy-beans, in phospholipids, *lipositols* (see Chapter 16). In addition, inositol is found in the brain tissue in a labile combination with a large molecule of protein.

Biotin (synonyms: vitamin H; bios II)

This is a growth factor required for the growth of yeast and certain other microorganisms. It is found only in small quantities in all animal tissues but is quite widely distributed in the plant kingdom and in yeast. Symptoms of deficiency in biotin, resulting in dermatitis, have been produced experimentally in animals and in man. It is presumed to be concerned as a coenzyme in certain carboxylation reactions.

Biotin is soluble in water and ethanol and is practically insoluble in organic solvents. In nature, it is mostly combined with a protein from which it can be easily separated by dialysis. The isoelectric point of biotin is pH 3–3.5. Its melting point is 230–232°C, and it is optically active: $[\alpha]_D = +92°$.

The structure of biotin has been elucidated by VIGNEAUD *et al.*[17] and found to consist of urea, thiophene and valeric acid:

$$
\begin{array}{c}
\text{O} \\
\parallel \\
\text{C} \\
\diagup\quad\diagdown \\
\text{HN}\qquad\text{NH} \\
|\qquad\quad| \\
\text{HC}\!-\!-\!-\!\text{CH} \\
|\qquad\quad| \\
\text{H}_2\text{C}\qquad\text{CH}\!-\!\text{CH}_2\!-\!\text{CH}_2\!-\!\text{CH}_2\!-\!\text{CH}_2\!-\!\text{COOH} \\
\diagdown\text{S}\diagup
\end{array}
$$

urea — thiophene — valeric acid

biotin

When raw egg white is fed to animals (including man), it exerts a toxic effect due to the protein, *avidin*, the so-called "egg white injury". Such injury is caused by the inactivation of biotin to an enzymatically unavailable biotin–avidin complex. The following foods are good sources of biotin[18]:

royal jelly,	1.70 γ/g;
liver,	0.96 γ/g;
chocolate,	0.32 γ/g;
roasted peanuts,	0.34 γ/g;
peas,	0.21 γ/g;
cauliflower,	0.17 γ/g;
lima beans,	0.098 γ/g;
whole wheat,	0.052 γ/g;
sea foods,	0.080 γ/g.

Vitamin C (synonyms: ascorbic acid, antiscorbutic vitamin)

As mentioned earlier, the history of this accessory food factor dates back to the 15th century without, of course, anyone being aware of the existence of a specific vitamin. However, while scurvy was first observed among seafarers and soldiers, large sections of the population, even in Northern Europe, suffered from a deficiency in vitamin C at times when no fresh fruits or vegetables were available in their diet.

Scurvy (scorbut) is characterized mainly by hemorrhagic conditions, by bleeding occurring especially in the gums and damage to capillaries. Wound healing is retarded. With children skeletal and teeth development are poor.

Curiously enough, most domestic animals, including dogs, hens and rats, are well capable of producing their own vitamin C. The only exceptions known so far are man, monkeys and guinea-pigs.

Vitamin C is widespread in the plant kingdom, but some fruits are exceptionally rich in it. Perhaps the richest fruit source of ascorbic acid is the West Indian cherry, other important sources are: rose hips, paprika, pine needles, guava (300 mg/100 g), black currant (210), parsley (190), broccoli (120), green pepper (120), and oranges (50 mg/100 g).

The isolation of vitamin C and the elucidation of its structure have been the work of many important scientists during comparatively recent times: ZILVA[19] performed the difficult task of concentrating the active principle from lemons, he also found that vitamin C was a strongly reducing substance. SZENT-GYÖRGYI[20] succeeded in crystallizing the vitamin, to which he assigned the name "hexuronic acid," with the chemical formula, $C_6H_8O_6$. KING[21], REICHSTEIN[22], HAWORTH[23] and others all contributed to our knowledge of the exact structure of vitamin C and succeeded in finding methods for its synthesis. This vitamin was finally named *ascorbic acid.*

$$CH_2OH \cdot CH \cdot OH \cdot CH \cdot C\!\!-\!\!OH$$

L-ascorbic acid

Ascorbic acid crystallizes in white, odorless plates, somewhat acid in taste, melting at 190–192°C, is exceedingly soluble in water (1 g in 3 ml) and is insoluble in organic solvents.

It is quite probable that in certain plant tissues ascorbic acid forms, *in situ*, a complex with protein, which is broken up by extracting the plant material with metaphosphoric or trichloracetic acid.

Ascorbic acid is optically active, $[a]_D^{20} = + 23°$, and may be regarded as a derivative of an hexose and, since carbon atoms 4 and 5 are asymmetric, it has four stereoisomers. The vitamin C with the highest potency is the L-ascorbic acid; its D-isomer, the *iso*ascorbic acid is only 1/5 to 1/20 as potent. All other hexuronic acids are devoid of all vitamin activity:

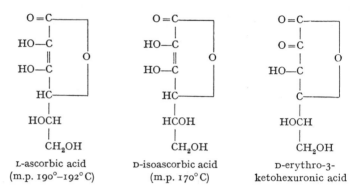

| L-ascorbic acid | D-isoascorbic acid | D-erythro-3- |
| (m.p. 190°–192° C) | (m.p. 170° C) | ketohexuronic acid |

Vitamin C is a monobasic acid with its lactone ring between the carboxyl group and carbon atom 4, while its exceptionally high reducing power is derived from the di-enolic configuration

$$
\begin{array}{c}
-\text{C—OH} \\
\parallel \\
-\text{C—OH}
\end{array}
$$

capable of giving, with alkalies, neutral water-soluble monometal salts without destroying the lactone ring.

This di-enolic configuration is the same functional group as is present in all *reductons*, as found by VON EULER[24]. When hexoses or pentoses are treated with strong alkalies a reducton is formed containing the same di-enol group (see Chapter 5). Reducton is a strongly reducing substance and is easily oxidized:

$$
\begin{array}{ccc}
\text{HC}\!=\!\!=\!\text{C—CHO} & \longrightarrow & \text{H—C—C—CHO} \\
\;\;|\quad\; | & & \quad\parallel\;\; \parallel \\
\;\;\text{OH}\;\;\text{OH} & & \quad\;\;\text{O}\;\;\;\;\text{O}
\end{array}
$$

hydroxyglycol-
aldehyde
(reducton)

The very same thing happens when ascorbic acid is oxidized and is thereby transformed into *dehydroascorbic acid*. However, this reaction is reversible and it is important to note that dehydroascorbic acid has also been proved to exert antiscorbutic action in the animal body.

$$CH_2OH \cdot CH \cdot OH \cdot CH \cdot C—OH \qquad\qquad CH_2OH \cdot CH \cdot OH \cdot CH \cdot C = O$$

L-ascorbic acid   dehydroascorbic acid

The complex, but so far unknown, mechanism of the action of vitamin C in the human body, apparently depends largely upon this reversible oxidation. Dehydroascorbic acid can be easily reduced to ascorbic acid, by H_2S for instance, but while ascorbic acid is more or less thermostable in the absence of oxygen, dehydroascorbic acid is much more thermolabile.

Oxidation of vitamin C takes place in the presence of molecular oxygen and is greatly accelerated even by traces of metals, especially copper. This oxidation is also catalyzed by the specific enzyme *ascorbinase* (*ascorbic acid oxidase*). Ascorbinase is one of the enzymes belonging to the group of *polyphenolases* (discussed in more detail in Chapter 19), and contains Cu as its prosthetic group.

The very first step in the oxidation of vitamin C in food products, such as fruit juices, involves the formation of hydrogen peroxide[25]:

$$
\begin{array}{c}
—C—OH \\
\| \\
—C—OH
\end{array}
+O_2 \longrightarrow
\begin{array}{c}
—C=O \\
| \\
—C=O
\end{array}
+H_2O_2 \qquad\qquad (1)
$$

However, even under completely anaerobic conditions and after complete inactivation of *ascorbinase*, the autoxidation of ascorbic acid proceeds slowly.

SZENT-GYÖRGYI[26] explains this phenomenon by the fact that all plant juices usually contain flavonoid substances (see Chapter 15), which are oxidized by the H_2O_2 (in the presence of the enzyme *peroxidase*) and thus the autoxidation of ascorbic acid continues so long as such flavone-oxides are available:

$$ \text{flavone} + H_2O_2 \xrightarrow{\text{peroxidase}} \text{flavone oxide} + H_2O \qquad\qquad (2)$$

and with a further molecule of ascorbic acid:

$$
\text{flavone oxide} +
\begin{array}{c}
—C—OH \\
\| \\
—C—OH
\end{array}
\longrightarrow
\begin{array}{c}
—C=O \\
| \\
—C=O
\end{array}
+ \text{flavone} \qquad\qquad (3)
$$

Flavonoids are very widely distributed in plants and it is most probable that this, indeed, is the possible mechanism of vitamin C oxidation under anaerobic conditions. A further discussion of these phenomena is given in Chapter 15.

The next steps concern the irreversible breakdown of dehydroascorbic acid with the total loss of vitamin C activity. In neutral media, the lactone ring of the dehydroascorbic acid is entirely destroyed within 10 minutes, if kept at 60°C. This breakdown is not an oxidative phenomenon and has been shown to take place also under anaerobic conditions:

$$CH_2OH \cdot CHOH \cdot CH \cdot C = O$$
$$O \! \bigg\langle \quad | \qquad \longrightarrow$$
$$C\!-\!C = O$$
$$\|$$
$$O$$

$$CH_2OH \cdot CHOH \cdot CH_2 \cdot C = O$$
$$|$$
$$HOOC \cdot C = O$$

dehydroascorbic acid   2-keto-3-ketohexuronic acid

Extensive changes, especially in color and flavor, occurring in fruit and vegetable products during storage, run parallel with the progressive decrease in the amount of ascorbic acid[27]. Darkening of citrus juices, for instance, during storage has been shown to occur after ascorbic acid has been totally and irreversibly oxidized[28]. In fact, one of the forms of browning of food products, as will be shown in Chapter 20, is the transformation of the 2-keto-3-ketohexuronic acid into furfural by dehydration and decarboxylation. The furfural so formed polymerizes and gives rise to dark colored products or it can enter into further combinations with amino acids, etc.

$$CH \cdot OH\!-\!CH_2$$
$$| \qquad |$$
$$CH_2 \quad O = C \cdot CO \cdot COOH \quad \longrightarrow$$
$$\diagdown OH$$

$$CH\!-\!CH$$
$$\| \quad \|$$
$$CH \quad C \cdot CHO$$
$$\diagdown O \diagup$$

2-keto-3-ketohexuronic acid   furfural

To prevent oxidation of vitamin C when dealing with foods containing it, several precautions must be strictly observed. In the first place, the enzyme *ascorbinase* should be inactivated; this is especially important when dehydrating fruits and vegetables, and it can be achieved by properly blanching such foods. Steam blanching is preferable to scalding in hot water since vitamin C is lost to a great extent during leaching in large quantities of water. Secondly, oxygen should be excluded as far as possible during the preparation and processing of food products: whenever possible, deaeration or exhausting of the food products should be carried out. Food products which are essential for their vitamin C content should be canned, if possible, in plain tin cans, where the reducing conditions help to prevent the autoxidation of ascorbic acid (see Chapter 15). In some cases, antioxidants can be used to prevent oxidation: it has been reported[29], as a result of a series of oxidation–reduction potential studies, that D-isoascorbic acid, the antiscorbutic activity of which is only one-twentieth that of L-ascorbic acid, is a strong antioxidant, for it oxidizes more rapidly than vitamin C in food products, thus protecting the latter from deterioration.

Taking all the above factors into consideration: absence of air, proper inactivation of *ascorbic acid oxidase*, freedom from traces of copper in

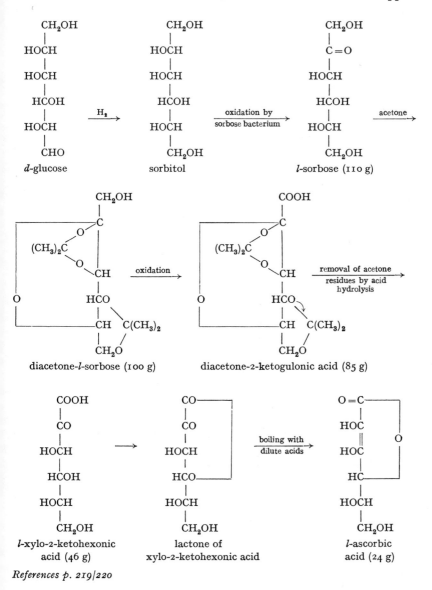

processing equipment, manufacturing conditions can be worked out under which the losses of vitamin C will be reduced to a mere minimum.

Several methods exist for preparing vitamin C synthetically. One technically possible and economically worthwhile method, now largely used in industry and yielding some 15 % of the original starting material, is that proposed by REICHSTEIN et al.[30]. Although, theoretically, the synthesis can begin with glucose, technically the process starts with L-sorbose, according to the scheme on p. 209.

Of some interest to food technologists is the process, proposed by ISBELL[31], which synthesizes ascorbic acid from galacturonic acid and uses beet pulp after sucrose extraction as the starting material. ISBELL hydrolyzed the pectin-rich beet pulp into Na-Ca-galacturonate obtaining 15 to 20 % of the weight of dry pulp. Further hydrogenation yielded over 90 % of sodium-L-galactonate and calcium-L-galactonate and, subsequently, L-galactono-γ-lactone. When oxidized, this latter compound yielded 25–30 % of 2-keto-L-galactonate. Finally, by lactonization and enolization, ascorbic acid was prepared with a yield of over 90 %. For this last step, ISBELL gives the following electronic interpretation:

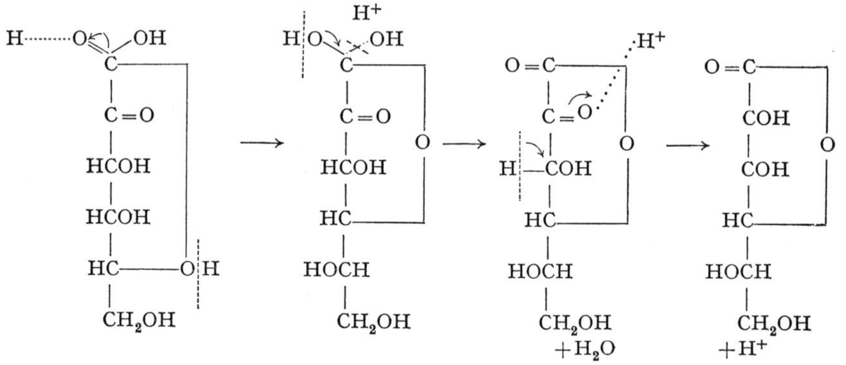

The estimation of vitamin C activity was, for a long time, performed by bio-assays with guinea pigs. TILLMANS[32] found a specific chemical method for the titration of ascorbic acid using 2,6-dichlorophenol indophenol, a blue substance which is specifically oxidized into its colorless leuco form.

Notwithstanding the fact that ascorbic acid has been the most studied vitamin, there are still many unsolved problems regarding its biogenesis, its functions in plants and in animals, the great variations of its content in different plants, as well as the diversity in the capability of animals to synthesize their own vitamin C. Even mechanisms connected with the activity of ascorbic acid are largely unsolved. While most other vitamins are required by man for his well-being in γ quantities, the daily requirements for ascorbic acid amount to 70–75 mg.

2,6-dichlorophenol indophenol

Furthermore, it is still unknown why one and the same variety of a given plant contains varied amounts of ascorbic acid, and even in different parts of one single fruit its content varies. It has been established, for instance, that in many fruits there exists a definite gradient of ascorbic acid which declines from the epicarp towards the endocarp: several varieties of Italian oranges tested showed[33] the following contents in mg per 100 g:

in the flavedo (yellow peelings),	175 –292	mg;
in the albedo (white peel),	86 –194	mg;
and in fruit flesh,	44.9– 73.2	mg.

A similar distribution of vitamin C has been found[34] in the lime (*Citrus limetta* Risso), while the guava grown in Israel showed[35] the following gradient relationship between the epicarp, the flesh and the center of the fruit—9:4:1.

It has been shown[36] that in bruised or cut portions of fruits or vegetables, the amount of vitamin C is greatly augmented after a few days. In sliced potatoes, for instance, the amount of vitamin C rises from 10.8 mg to 24.1 mg per 100 g in three days. This traumatic formation of ascorbic acid is considered to be a "defense mechanism".

Foods with a high content of vitamin C are best packed in tin cans because of the reducing conditions in the can. Recently MANNHEIM[37] conducted a storage study on pasteurized orange juice packaged in cans as well as in plastic bags made of Mylar polyethylene, cellophane polyethylene, saran and aluminium coated polyethylene and stored at room temperatures. While no significant decrease of ascorbic acid was observed in the juice packaged in cans, considerable losses were found in some of the plastic bags.

The vitamin D group (synonyms: anti-rachitic vitamin; ergocalciferol—D₂; cholecalciferol—D₃)

As early as 1838 rickets, a children's disease, called in some places "the English disease", was ascribed in France by JULES GUERIN as due to faulty diet. However, until about 1922 most of the prominent pediatricians in Europe and America were sceptical about the value of cod-liver oil in curing rickets.

Several facts emerged from mere observation and accumulation of data: the strata of population which suffered most from this disease were the poor sections of town dwellers whose children had very little opportunity to enjoy sunshine. But, even in sunshine-rich countries such as Egypt, rickets had been reported among the classes who dwelt with their children in slums away from the sun. In contrast to this, the Eskimos, who spend their child-hood mostly in dark huts during the long, arctic night, are free from rickets.

Today, the explanation for all these peculiar phenomena is simple: the Eskimo's diet is rich in fish-liver oils which contain sufficient anti-rickets vitamin; on the other hand, children who live in countries with abundant sunshine are exposed to the ultraviolet rays of the sun which are able to synthesize the anti-rickets vitamin in the children's own bodies.

Deficiency in anti-rickets vitamin causes insufficient deposition of mineral matter, calcium and phosphates, in the bones, which then become soft and apt to bend. The blood of a rickets patient is poor in these minerals and high in the enzyme *alkaline phosphatase*.

It has now been established that *ergosterol* found in yeast and fungi and *7-dehydrocholesterol* found in various fats and oils, are precursors of the anti-rickets vitamins. These two substances (and a few other sterols to a lesser extent) acquire antirachitic properties on irradiation by ultraviolet rays and the products so obtained are now called:

vitamin D_2 or *ergocalciferol*—by irradiation of ergosterol, and
vitamin D_3 or *cholecalciferol*—by irradiation of 7-dehydrocholesterol.

The following are the formulae of vitamins D_2 and D_3 and their precursors:

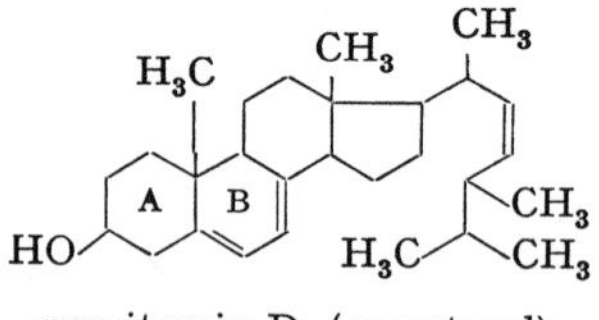

provitamin D_2 (ergosterol)

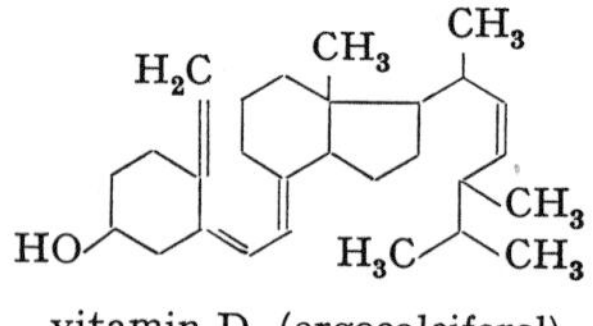

vitamin D_2 (ergocalciferol)

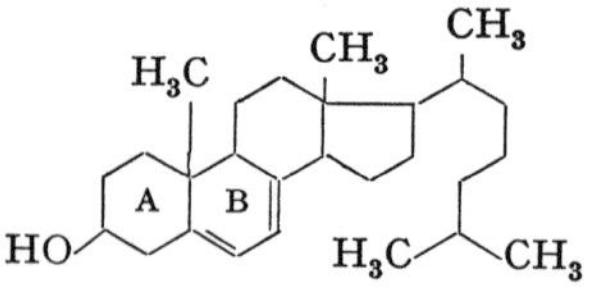

provitamin D_3 (7-dehydrocholesterol)

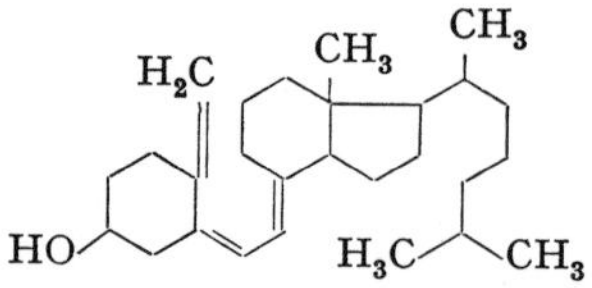

vitamin D_3 (chlolecalciferol)

When the provitamins are irradiated, the ring B opens at position 9,10.

Several other provitamins have been found in nature, all of them being sterols in which an hydroxyl is attached to carbon atom 3 and with a Δ5,7-dienic group. It will be noted that all these steroid compounds are very similar in their structure to terpenoids, which have been discussed in Chapters 3 and 17. It has recently been demonstrated that sterols, in a similar way to terpenoids, are biosynthesized in living organism from acetic acid. By administering isotopically labeled acetic acid to a rat and by studying the degradation products of the resulting cholesterol, it has been found that the intermediate substance is the triterpene *squalene*, which is apparently converted by several steps into a steroid. In the following structural formulae, the origin of the carbon atoms is shown by rings: the black dots represent the methyl group of acetic acid, while the white rings represent its carboxyl ($CH_3 \cdot \overset{\circ}{C}OOH$):

Squalene   Cholesterol

Although some details in this biosynthesis[38] are not yet fully clarified, there is no doubt that sterols, and among them the group of D vitamins, are all derivatives of isoprenoids and the primary substance from which they are synthesized, as in the case of terpenes, carotenoids, etc., is acetic acid *via* mevalonic acid and isopentenyl pyrophosphate, nature's active isoprene (see Chapter 17).

The accepted international unit of anti-rachitic vitamins is 0.025 γ of pure cystalline vitamins D_2 and D_3 and the preventive dose is considered to be 400 I.U. per day.

In contrast to all other vitamins, only very few foods contain the D vitamins. The richest sources are fish-liver oils (cod, halibut and tuna) and egg yolk. Most of the vegetable oils and animal fats, and consequently also milk, have only slight activity. Some fatty food products, such as margarine are now usually enriched artificially with vitamin D.

The vitamin E group (synonyms: tocopherols; anti-sterility vitamins)

The lack of these vitamins has been found to cause sterility in rats. While such a deficiency in a female rat can be restored by addition of vitamin E,

References p. 219/220

in the male rat the sterility condition becomes permanent and incurable. The effect of anti-sterility vitamins in other animals and in humans is still a matter of controversy. Claims have been made that cases of abortion in cattle could be cured by vitamin E.

Vitamin E was first discovered in 1922, and is found in lettuce and wheat germ, which are the best sources. Although vitamin E is soluble in oils, like vitamins A and D, no anti-sterility vitamin is found in fish-liver oil or in the other rich sources of fat-soluble vitamins.

In 1936, vitamin E was isolated in a pure state and found to be the closely related substances α- and β-tocopherol (from the Greek *tokos*—birth and *phero*—to bear, -*ol* indicating an alcohol). Since then, five more derivatives have been isolated from wheat germ oil, corn oil, soy-bean oil, etc. All tocopherols are derivatives of a 6-hydroxychroman with an isoprenoid side-chain in position 2, and they differ only in their substitution groups at carbon atoms 5, 7 and 8. The following are the structural formulae of the principal tocopherols:

α-tocopherol (5,7,8-trimethyltocol)

β-tocopherol (5,8-dimethyltocol)

γ-tocopherol (7,8-dimethyltocol)

δ-tocopherol (8-monomethyltocol)

In each case the isoprenoid side-chain is the same, and is very similar to that of phytol (see Chapter 2). The other three tocopherols are: $\epsilon = $ 5-monomethyltocol, $\xi = $ 5,7-dimethyltocol and $\eta = $ 7-monomethyltocol. The tocopherols found in blood plasma are apparently conjugated to a protein.

Small quantities of tocopherols are found in practically all vegetable oils, where they act as natural antioxidants. They are, however, largely removed during the preparation of edible oils, especially during the bleaching process (see Chapter 16). Even when left in the fats or oils, the tocopherols are destroyed as soon as the oils become rancid.

The mechanism of the oxidation of α-tocopherol has been shown[39] to follow the following scheme:

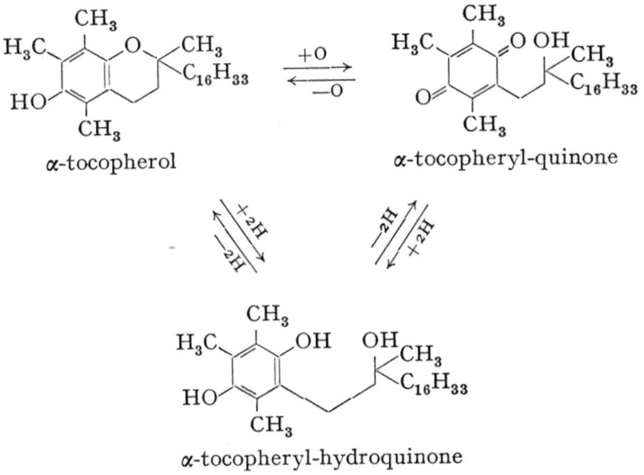

α-tocopherol α-tocopheryl-quinone

α-tocopheryl-hydroquinone

Apart from their ability to become easily oxidized, the tocopherols are otherwise very stable when foods are processed at high temperature (up to 200° C in the absence of oxygen) or when oils are treated with alkalis during neutralisation, or during their catalytic hydrogenation; they are, however, destroyed by ultraviolet rays.

In nature, all tocopherols are oils and it is impossible to crystallize them. Only the synthetic racemic form *dl*-α-tocopherol has been obtained as crystals. The I.U. is 1 mg of α-tocopherolacetate.

The vitamin K group (synonyms: "coagulation factor"; the "blood-clotting vitamin"; the antihemorrhagic factor)

These vitamins have been found in green plants only quite recently (1934) and were first isolated from alfalfa. Inadequate content of an enzyme, *prothrombin*, which is responsible for the quick clotting of the blood, causes hemorrhages. Addition of vitamin K restored the normal formation of prothrombin and prevented hemorrhages. This condition was first demonstrated in chickens by DAM AND SCHØNHEYDER of Denmark. Other animals, except birds, apparently do not require these vitamins for they are produced in the intestines by some microorganisms. DOISY and his coworkers, in the United States, isolated two substances from alfalfa, both derivatives of naphthoquinone, containing isoprenoid side-chains. The final structure of these vitamins was elucidated by contributions from FIESER, KARRER and other organic chemists. Both DAM and DOISY were jointly awarded the Nobel Prize in 1943. The chemical structure of these vitamins was established to be as follows:

vitamin K_1 (2-methyl-3-phytyl-1,4-naphthoquinone)

vitamin K_2 (2-methyl-3-difarnesyl-1,4-naphthoquinone)

It should be remembered that such a long isoprenic side-chain, phytol, as is present in the chlorophyll molecule, and difarnesyl makes the vitamins insoluble in water. The vitamins K_1 and K_2, therefore, are classed in the category of fat-soluble vitamins.

However, in 1940, DOISY synthesized two other substances, derivatives of naphthoquinone, *phthiocol* and 2-methyl-1,4-naphthoquinone, which was given the name *menadion*, both without the isoprenoid side-chain and having the full degree of vitamin K activity.

menadion (vitamin K_3)   phthiocol

In the absence of the side-chain, vitamin K_3 is better soluble in water and more easily assimilated by the body. The best sources for the natural vitamins K_1 and K_2 are alfalfa, spinach, cabbage, cauliflower and chestnuts. Fruits and cereals contain only very little vitamin K.

Vitamin K seems to have a general metabolic function. It is believed that, due to their quinone structure, K vitamins take some part in oxidation–reduction reactions, such as the reaction of oxidative phosphorylation in the chloroplasts of the green leaves for the generation of ATP.

Vitamin P (synonyms: permeability vitamin)

Various chemical and clinical observations made by RUSZNYÁK AND SZENT-GYÖRGYI[40] led them, in 1936, to assume that ascorbic acid (vitamin C) is accompanied in the plant cell by another important active factor, which is responsible for the state of permeability of the capillary walls and can prevent their fragility. The active substance isolated from lemon juice, called by these investigators, *citrin*, consisted of a mixture of several flavonoid glucosides, among them *hesperidin* and *eriodictin*. Some later tests reported that this vitamin P not only increases the capillary resistance, decreases the permeability of the blood vessels, and is valuable in the treatment of vascular purpura, but is also beneficial in the treatment of hemorrhagic nephritis of various origins.

The chemistry of the bioflavonoids will be discussed in detail in Chapter 15. Further work in this direction was not able to indicate which member of the citrin mixture is responsible for the vitamin activity. Moreover, some investigators came to the conclusion that experimental scurvy in animals is the symptom of mixed C and P avitaminosis, pure P avitaminosis having no clinical symptoms. Finally, when single bioflavonoids were isolated and purified, they were even less effective. All these flavonoids, in solution, appear to be in equilibrium with their open-chain chalcone (see p. 228).

SCARBOROUGH[41] is of the opinion that neither hesperidin nor its aglucone, *hesperitin*, fulfill the requirements of a vitamin. They may, however, be precursors of a more active substance, or may be involved in some yet unknown mechanism.

Other observers have demonstrated cases of scurvy in man, which were undoubtedly cured with pure synthetic vitamin C alone without any additional vitamin P. The discrepancies between the results obtained by various investigators led the International Committee on Vitamins to recommend, in 1950, that the use of the term "vitamin P" should be discontinued.

Use of vitamins in the food industry

In summarizing the descriptions given above of the individual vitamins, it is obvious that their presence in our diet is required not only in order to prevent specific disease but also to supply the body, in some cases, with the necessary prosthetic groups for the enzymes or otherwise to assist in the normal metabolic processes. A perfectly balanced diet could no doubt supply all these vitamins, however, two causes may interfere: the loss of vitamins which may occur during processing or storage of foods, and the fact that most people in the world do not adhere to a "balanced diet" either by force of circumstances and privation or by force of negligence and custom. During the short time since the isolation and synthesis of most of the vitamins, it has become possible to produce them synthetically, or to prepare them otherwise at comparatively low cost. Some of the manufacturers of food products are now practicing the restoration of the vitamins lost during processing by enrichment of their produce. In many countries such fortification is now required by law for certain staple foods.

It has already been mentioned that white bread baked from low-extraction flour is deficient in some vitamins, which are removed, in these cases, together with the wheat germ and the bran. Today, 90 % of the white bread (72 % extraction) sold in the United States is enriched by thiamine, riboflavin, niacin and iron, and in Britain the same 72 % extraction flour is similarly brought up in its vitamin content to the flour of 80 % extraction.

Other cereals, such as rice and corn (maize) both of which constitute the principal food of the major part of mankind, are also deficient in the important vitamins because the milling procedures cause the removal of the bran layers and the germ rich in these vitamins. Rice is now enriched to some extent in some Eastern countries, the Philippines, Japan, Thailand, as well as in Columbia and Venezuela. As far as maize is concerned, even the whole kernel is deficient in niacin, or its precursor tryptophan, and it should be supplemented.

Vitamins A, D, iron and sometimes also vitamins C and B_6 are added to milk, to butter and to margarine. The A and D enrichment of this latter is now required by most countries because margarine is often interchangeable with butter.

Nowadays, many fruit juices and fruit products are enriched by the addition of vitamin C, since this vitamin is required in rather large doses and since its preservation in the final drink is not easily attained.

Because vitamin B_6 has been found to be concerned with amino acid metabolism and synthesis of fats, as well as with a number of other important metabolic reactions, such as decarboxylation, this vitamin is now recommended as an additive to some staple foods: bread, milk and processed cereals.

A comprehensive review on the question of enrichment of foods by vitamins has recently been presented by HARRIS[42].

The action of vitamin C (sometimes in conjunction with citric acid) is not restricted to biological effects and is used as an antioxidant to improve the shelf life of different flavors. Flavoring ingredients containing aldehydes, ketones and keto esters are susceptible to oxidation and are apt to lose their characteristic flavor during storage. By being preferentially oxidized, ascorbic acid preserves the flavor of the product and prevents off-flavors. Moreover, the addition of vitamin C to frozen fruit packs delays browning, as explained in Chapter 20. It is also used as an antioxidant for fats, oils, aqueous oil emulsions and other food products.

REFERENCES

[1] Capt. LIND, *Treatise on Scurvy*, London, 1753.

[2] F. G. HOPKINS, *J. Physiol.*, 44 (1912) 425.

[3] G. ZIMMERMAN, *Biol. Abstr.*, 28 (1954) 8804.

[4] M. KAREL, Effects of packaging on maintenance of nutrients in food products, in R. S. HARRIS AND H. VON LOESECKE, *Nutritional Evaluation of Food Processing*, J. Wiley, New York, 1960.

[5] O. WARBURG AND W. CHRISTIAN, Über ein neues Oxydations ferment und sein Absorptionsspektrum, *Biochem. Z.*, 254 (1932) 438.

[6] R. KUHN *et al.*, Über Lactoflavin, den Farbstoff der Molke, *Ber.*, 66 (1933) 426, 522, 1435.

[7] P. KARRER *et al.*, Synthesen von Flavinen, IV, *Helv. Chim. Acta*, 17 (1935) 426, 522, 1435.

[8] A. D. HOLMES AND C. P. JONES, *J. Nutrition*, 29 (1945) 201.

[9] R. J. WILLIAMS *et al.*, *J. Am. Chem. Soc.*, 55 (1932) 2012.

[10] R. J. WILLIAMS, *Advances in Enzymol.* 3 (1943) 253.

[11] L. J. HARRIS, *Vitamins in Theory and Practice*, Cambridge Univ. Press, 1955.

[12] F. LYNEN, *Federation Proc.*, 12 (1953) 3, 683.

[13] J. GOLDBERGER *et al.*, *J. Am. Med. Assoc.*, 71 (1918) 944.

[14] M. E. PULLMAN *et al.*, *J. Biol. Chem.*, 206 (1954) 129.

[15] R. O. CRAVIOTO *et al.*, Increment of niacin content during the roasting of coffee, *Ciencia (Mex.)*, 15 (1955) 24.

[16] D. CROWFOOT HODGKIN, A. W. JOHNSON AND A. R. TODD, Structure of vitamin B_{12}, *Chem. Soc. (London) Spec. Publ. No. 3*, (1955) 109.

[17] V. DU VIGNEAUD *et al.*, *J. Biol. Chem.*, 140 (1941) 763.

[18] V. H. CHELDELIN AND R. J. WILLIAMS, *Univ. Texas Publ.*, 4237 (1942) 105.

[19] S. S. ZILVA, *Biochem. J.*, 17 (1923) 416.

[20] A. SZENT-GYÖRGYI, *Biochem. J.*, 22 (1928) 1387.

[21] W. A. WAUGH AND C. C. KING, *J. Biol. Chem.*, 97 (1932) 325.

[22] T. REICHSTEIN *et al.*, *Helv. Chim. Acta*, 16 (1933) 1019.

[23] W. N. HAWORTH, E. L. HIRST AND S. S. ZILVA, *J. Chem. Soc.*, (1934) 1155.

[24] VON EULER AND C. MARTIUS, Über Reduktion (Enol-Tartronaldehyd) und Askorbinsäure, *Ann. Chem.*, 505 (1933) 73.

[25] A. WEISSBERGER AND J. E. LuVALLE, Oxidation Processes; XVII, The Autooxidation of Ascorbic Acid in the Presence of Copper, *J. Am. Chem. Soc.*, 66 (1944) 700.

[26] A. SZENT-GYÖRGYI, *Studies on Biological Oxidation and Some of Its Catalysts*, Barth, Leipzig, 1937.

[27] H. G. BEATTIE, K. A. WHEELER AND C. S. PEDERSON, Changes occurring in fruit juices during storage, *Food Research*, 8 (1943) 395.

[28] J. J. HAMBURGER AND M. A. JOSLYN, Auto-oxidation of filtered citrus juices, *Food Research*, 6 (1941) 599.

[29] W. B. ESSELEN, JR., J. J. POWERS AND R. WOODWARD, d-Isoascorbic acid as an antioxidant, *J. Ind. Eng. Chem.*, 37 (1945) 295.

[30] T. REICHSTEIN, Synthese der D- und L-ascorbinsäure (C-vitamin), *Helv. Chim. Acta*, 16 (1933) 1019.
[31] H. S. ISBELL, *J. Research Natl. Bur. Standards*, 33 (1944) 45.
[32] J. TILLMANS, P. HIRSCH AND W. HIRSCH, Das Reduktionsvermögen pflanzlicher Lebensmittel und seine Beziehung zum Vitamin C, *Z. Untersuch. Lebensm.*, 63 (1932) 1, 21, 241, 267, 276; 65 (1933) 145.
[33] H. M. RAUEN, M. DEVESCOVI AND N. MAGNANI, The Vitamin C content of italian oranges and orange pulps, *Z. Untersuch. Lebensm.*, 85 (1943) 257.
[34] R. RIBEIRO et al., Vitamin C distribution in different parts of the lime, *Rev. fac. med. vet., Univ. Sao Paulo*, 2 (1942) 23.
[35] J. B. S. BRAVERMAN AND VERA IVANOVITZ (Technion, Haifa, Israel), unpublished data (1955).
[36] S. M. PROKOSHEV, Traumatic formation of vitamin C in sliced potatoes, *Biokhimiya*, 9 (1944) 36.
[37] H. C. MANNHEIM, A. I. NELSON AND M. P. STEINBERG, *Food Technol.*, 11 (1957) 421.
[38] A. TODD, New horizons in chemistry, *Nature*, 187 (1960) 819.
[39] W. H. HARRISON et al., *Biochim. et Biophys. Acta*, 21 (1956) 150.
[40] ST. RUSZNYÁK AND A. SZENT-GYÖRGYI, Vitamin P: Flavanols as vitamins, *Nature*, 238 (1936) 627.
[41] H. SCARBOROUGH, Observations on the nature of Vitamin P and the Vitamin P potency of certain foodstuffs, *Biochem. J.*, 39 (1945) 271.
[42] R. S. HARRIS, Supplementation of foods with vitamins, *Agr. Food Chem.*, 7 (1959) 88.

SELECTED BIBLIOGRAPHY TO CHAPTER 14

BROWN GENE M., Biosynthesis of water-soluble vitamins and derived coenzymes, *Physiol. Revs.*, 40 (1960) 331.
CLIFCORN, L. E., Factors Influencing the Vitamin Contents of Canned Foods, *Advances in Food Research*, 1 (1948) 39.
FELDBERG, C., Adequacy of Processed Cereals in Human Nutrition Chapter 23 in: S. A. MATZ, *The Chemistry and Technology of Cereals as Food ana Feed*, The Avi Publishing Co., Westport, 1959, chap. 23.
HARRIS, LESLIE J., *Vitamins in Theory and Practice*, Cambridge Univ. Press, 1955.
HARRIS, R. S., AND H. VON LOESECKE, *Nutritional Evaluation of Food Processing*, John Wiley & Sons, New York, 1960.
HARRIS, R. S. AND K. V. THIMANN, *Vitamins and Hormones*, 6 Vols., Academic Press, New York, 1943–1948.
ROSENBERG, H. R., *Chemistry and Physiology of the Vitamins*, Interscience, New York, 1945.
SEBRELL JR., W. H. AND R. S. HARRIS, *The Vitamins*, Vols. I–III, Academic Press, New York, 1954.
WILLIAMS, R. J. et al., *The Biochemistry of B-Vitamins*, Reinhold Publishing Co., New York, 1950.

CHAPTER 15

GLYCOSIDES – ANTHOCYANINS AND ANTHOXANTHINS

Chapters 2 and 3 were devoted to plant pigments, chlorophyll and the carotenoids, all soluble in oils or organic solvents, the *lipochromes*. These pigments are actually adsorbed on the chromoplasts. All other plant pigments are soluble in water and are found in the vacuolar sap of plant cells mostly in the form of glycosides. These glycosides are very widely distributed in the plant kingdom, and are responsible for the beautiful colors of many flowers and fruits. They consist of two major groups, the *anthocyanins* and the *anthoxanthins* or the *flavonoids*. Both groups are built of an aglucone which can be separated from the sugar moiety by enzymatic or acid hydrolysis. Apart from various substitutions, the aglucones of all these water-soluble plant pigments have the same carbon skeleton: C_6—C_3—C_6.

Anthocyanins

This group of glycosides was first studied by RICHARD WILLSTÄTTER, and more recently by Sir ROBERT ROBINSON[1]. When hydrolyzed, the anthocyanins result in a sugar and an aglucone, called *anthocyanidin*. The carbohydrate residue may be either an hexose such as glucose, or a galactose with or without an additional pentose, such as rhamnose.

The anthocyanidins are composed of a benzopyrylium nucleus and a phenol ring, the two together being called *flavylium*:

benzopyrylium nucleus phenol ring
trihydroxy-2-phenol benzopyrylium chloride
or trihydroxy flavylium chloride

It should be noted that this is an *oxonium* compound (in which the oxygen is four-valent) found in nature as a chloride. The positions at carbon atoms

3, 5 and 7 are taken up by hydroxyls, the sugar moiety in anthocyanins usually being attached to the hydroxyl at position 3. From this parent structural formula, all anthocyanidins are derived by diverse substitutions in the phenol ring B.

pelargonidin   cyanidin   delphinidin

All the names of anthocyanidins are derived from the names of flowers. Pelargonidin is found in the strawberry; cyanidin in the fig, almond, mulberry, sweet cherry and elderberry; delphinidin in pomegranate and eggplant.

KARRER showed a way of establishing the constitution of the anthocyanidins mentioned above. By treating them with a 10 % solution of berium hydroxide in an inert atmosphere, the pigment is broken up into phloroglucinol and a residual phenolic derivative:

pelargonidin   phloroglucinol   p-hydroxybenzoic acid

cyanidin   ⟶   "   +   protochatechuic acid

delphinidin ⟶   "   +   gallic acid

Further substitution of the hydroxyls in the phenol ring by methoxyl groups about a number of additional shades in these pigments. It is noteworthy that, while an addition of hydroxyl groups increases the blue hue, additional methoxyl groups bring about an increased red coloration (see formula on p. 223).

The anthocyanin pigments change their color easily at different pH values and hence can be used as indicators. Due to changes in pH in the plant sap, the flowers sometimes change their color at different times of the day. At

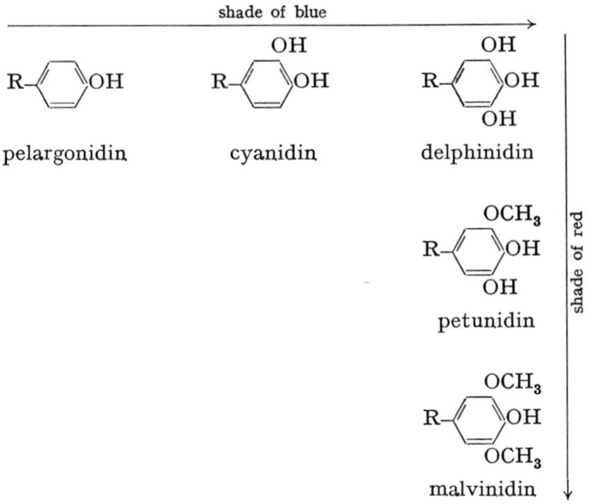
shade of blue
R
OH
pelargonidin
cyanidin
delphinidin
OCH_3
petunidin
malvinidin
shade of red

acid pH the anthocyanins are mostly red, while in alkaline solutions they change to blue, as for instance:

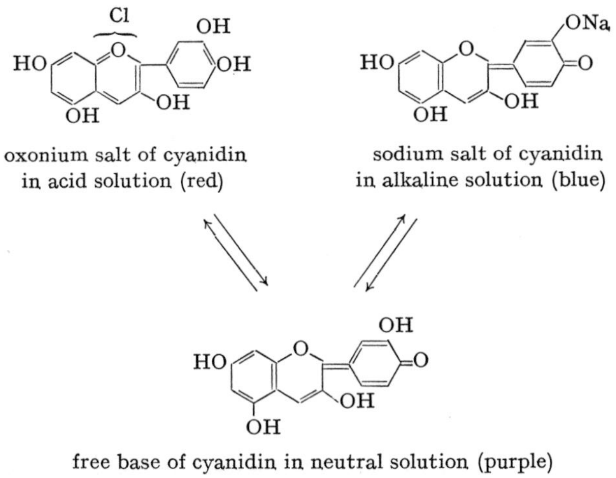
Cl
HO
OH
O
ONa
oxonium salt of cyanidin
in acid solution (red)
sodium salt of cyanidin
in alkaline solution (blue)
free base of cyanidin in neutral solution (purple)

The biosynthesis of anthocyanins in plants depends largely on the temperature as well as on light. The anthocyanin *betain* of the red cabbage, for instance, will develop at temperatures between 20 and 30° C, whereas at 10° C its formation is greatly hampered. In many cases their biosynthesis is regulated by the wavelength of light. In such fruits as apricots, peaches,

References p. 232/233

apples, pears and all deciduous fruits, the formation of anthocyanins is at its maximum at wavelengths of 3,600 to 4,500 Å, indicating that these pigments play some part in the absorption of sunlight in conjunction with the chlorophylls and the carotenoids.

Sulfur dioxide bleaches the anthocyanin pigments apparently by producing a change in the pH or by means of its strong reducing power.

The most serious problem which is posed by anthocyanin pigments in food technology is their ability to depolarize hydrogen when fruits containing these pigments are canned in tinned canisters. It is well known that a tinned steel can containing an acid fruit is exposed to the attack of fruit acids at the places where the tin coating is imperfect, even if such imperfections are microscopically small. This phenomenon is due to the establishment of an electrocouple created by the two metals and the acid, and causes the evolution of hydrogen *in statu nascendi*. However, due to the polarization effect, accumulation of hydrogen may decrease or even stop the corrosion of the can unless some depolarizing substance interferes. The presence of oxygen in the head space may have such a depolarizing effect. Unfortunately, the anthocyanins all act as depolarizers, *i.e.* they bind the evolved hydrogen, thus giving the corrosion the opportunity to proceed. At the same time, the anthocyanins are reduced at positions 2:3 of their molecule, which, of course, also causes a change in their color. Red cherries canned in such a way will often turn blue or purple or even colorless. Anthocyanin colored fruits should, therefore, be only canned in specially laquered tins.

Crude fungal enzyme preparations, from *Aspergillus niger*, presumably containing an enzyme *anthocyanase*, exert a significant decolorizing effect on the anthocyanins in berry fruits and in grapes. It has been suggested[2] that with the aid of such an enzyme it may be feasible to use the juice from red grapes for the production of white wines. This discoloration apparently involves the enzymatic hydrolysis of the anthocyanin into sugar and aglucone and a spontaneous transformation of the latter into colorless derivatives.

Anthoxanthins (flavonoids)

The other group of glycosides, the *anthoxanthins*, differ from the above only in the degree of oxidation of the aliphatic fragment in the C_6—C_3—C_6 skeleton. The aglucones of the anthoxanthins, therefore, consist of a benzopyrone nucleus:

γ-pyrone   parent structure of flavonoids

Apart from isoflavones and xanthones, the second phenol ring (B) in all other flavonoids is attached to the carbon atom in position 2, as in the anthocyanins. The following are the various types of flavonoids (R indicates the position of the sugar residue):

(1) flavones (positions 2:3 unsaturated)

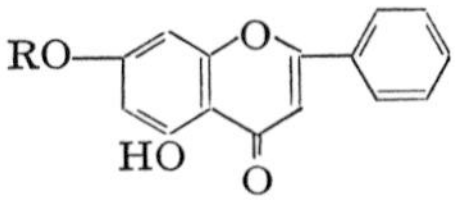

(2) flavonols (an additional OH at position 3)

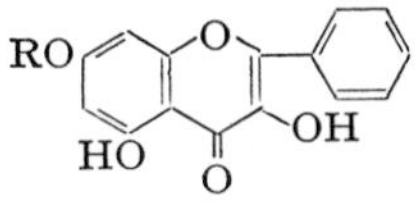

(3) flavanones (saturated at positions 2:3)

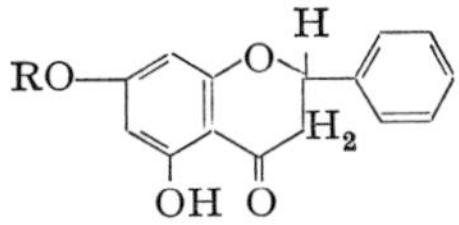

(4) flavanonols (position 3 saturated and extra hydroxyl group)

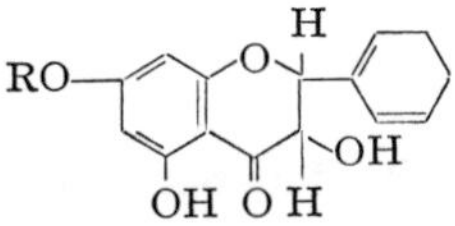

(5) isoflavones (phenol ring B at position 3)

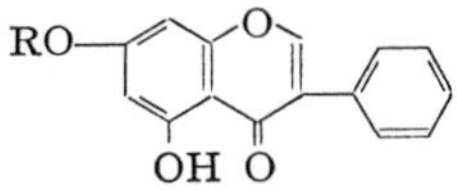

The mechanism of the biosynthesis of the flavonoids has not yet been elucidated. However, Sir ROBERT ROBINSON suggested the following scheme by which both anthocyanins and anthoxanthins may be derived from substances very widely distributed in nature, phloroglucinol, glyceraldehyde and catechol, (see formula on p. 226).

Although adequate information on the biosynthesis and the role played by both the anthocyanins and anthoxanthins is not yet available, some investigators are of the opinion that, just as the components of blood are important for animals, the sap-soluble glucosides should be expected to be of importance in the physiology of plants. Furthermore, all of these glucosides are characteristic of individual species of plants and are definitely controlled by specific genes present in these plants: it seems, therefore, that they should have important physiological significance.

As can be seen above, most of the flavonoids have their sugar moiety at-

phloroglucinol   glyceraldehyde   catechol

hypothetical intermediate

anthocyanidin   anthoxanthin

tached at position 7 of ring A, with the exception of flavonols in which the sugar is linked to the aglucone at position 3 of the aliphatic bridge. However, there is some divergence of opinion among various investigators on this point. BATE-SMITH[3] is of the opinion that the sugars *in situ* may be attached to different hydroxyl groups at positions 3, 4 or 7 or even at more than one point. Moreover, the sugar residue may be different in each case and linked in different sequences as disaccharides or trisaccharides. This opinion is based on the fact that when an extract of plant material is analyzed by paper chromatography, one finds numerous spots, all of which give typical reactions for flavonoid compounds; however, after being hydrolyzed with mineral acid, the same plant extract shows only one flavonoid spot, namely that of the aglucone.

On the other hand, NORDSTRÖM[4] claims that it is possible to make a fair estimate of the structure of unknown flavonoids in their naturally occurring mixtures by using a modern chromatographic technique. By introducing the value R_m, which is log $(1/R_f - 1)$, it is possible to deduce the number of (OH) groups in unknown aglucones and the number of sugar moieties in glycosides related to one known aglucone. Thereafter, the application of color reactions, on infrared and ultraviolet spectrophotometry on the spots of the chromatogram give, in many cases, an absolute characterization of the structure of the flavonoid.

The various flavonoids are generally very widely distributed in nature. In citrus fruits, for instance, in which some of them are found in quite appreciable amounts, their principal location is in the carpellary membranes, at the boundary between the albedo and the juice segments. HALL[5] believes that the flavonoid glycosides, which are only sparingly soluble in water, combine with the sugars in the plant to give glucose–glycoside complexes. These better soluble and easily hydrolyzable complexes may serve as an excellent medium for translocation of the carbohydrates photosynthesized in the chlorophyllous tissue to other portions of the plant where the sugars are stored or utilized.

The flavonoids are mostly levorotatory and can be hydrolyzed from the sugar moiety by the enzyme *emulsin*. The anthoxanthins can also form oxonium salts, however, these are generally unstable in water solutions.

A few examples of flavonoids will make matters clearer. The flavonol *rutin*, found in tea leaves and also in other plants, consists of the aglucone *quercetin* and a combination of two sugars, a pentose (rhamnose) and an hexose (glucose). The two sugars bound together are called *rutinose* and are linked to the aglucone in position 3, as is usual with most flavonols:

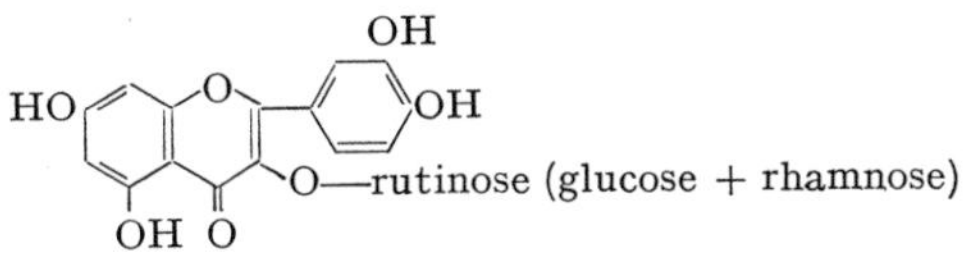

rutin

Note the unsaturated bond at position 2:3, which is capable of being easily reduced by adding hydrogen, to form a flavanone.

A quite similar aglucone, which is, however, a flavanone, is *eriodictyol*, the constituent of the glycoside *eriodictin*. Eriodictyol also has two hydroxyl groups in the B ring and can be converted into quercetin by amyl nitrite in the presence of hydrochloric and sulfuric acids, showing an example of converting, chemically, a flavanone into a flavonol:

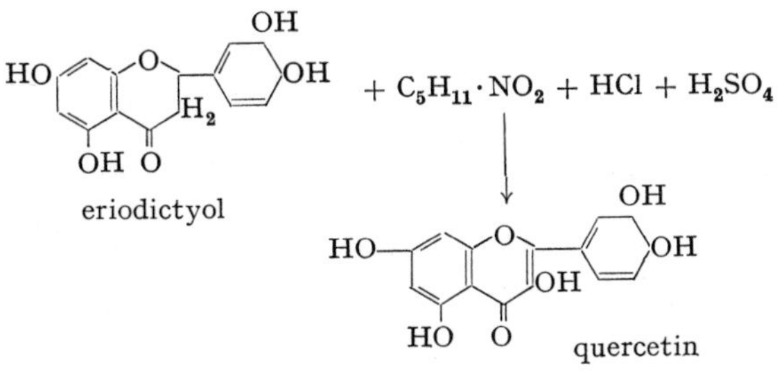

$+ C_5H_{11} \cdot NO_2 + HCl + H_2SO_4$

eriodictyol

quercetin

A very widely distributed flavanone is *hesperidin* (from the Greek *Hesperides*—citrus fruits) also containing the disaccharide rutinose (rhamnose + glucose) at position 7. Hesperidin is only slightly soluble in water and somewhat more so in alcohol. M.p. = 252°C. Its aglucone, *hesperitin*, melts at 227°C.

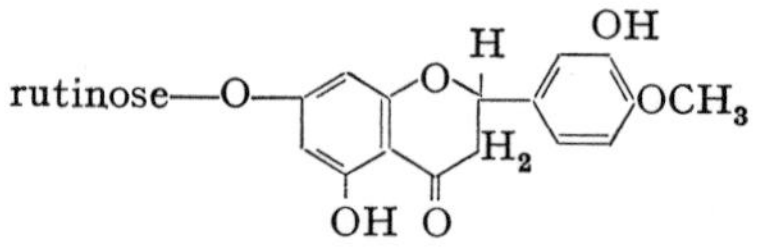

hesperidin

Hesperidin, and probably also all other flavonoids, is very soluble in alkali. At a pH 11 to 12, the inner ring is opened forming chalcones:

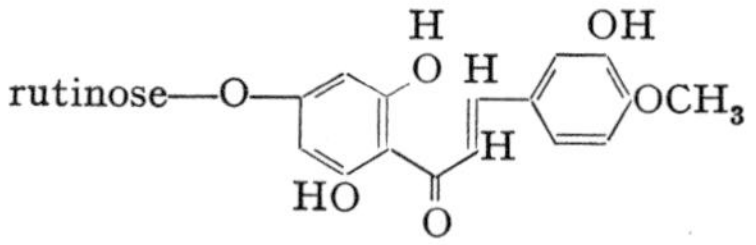

hesperidin chalcone

In contrast to anthocyanins, most of the flavonoids are colorless or only very slightly colored, however, their chalcones are yellow to strongly brown in color. There is ample reason to assume that in their chalcone form the flavonoids are salts of the corresponding alkali. At an acid pH the chalcones return to their former closed structure, thereby losing their color.

In order to isolate the chalcones, it is customary to methylate the newly formed hydroxyl in position 1. Such methylated chalcones are extremely soluble in water:

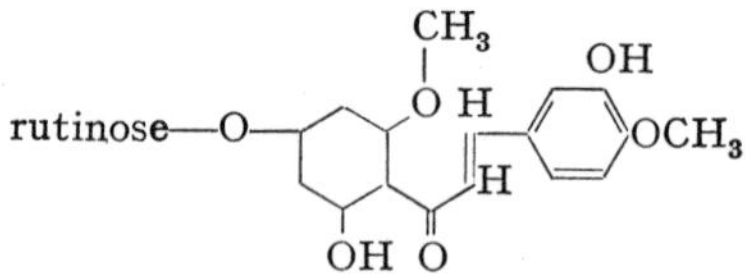

hesperidin methyl-chalcone

Like all other phenolic substances, the flavanoids are expected to be easily oxidized. The oxidation can take place at the various hydroxyl groupings, especially when two such hydroxyls are in *ortho* positions, and also at the double bond between carbon atoms 2 and 3, especially in the chalcones. The flavanoids could therefore be considered as antioxidants, however, a number of investigations did not exactly establish their effectiveness. It has also been mentioned in Chapter 14 that flavonoids may be involved in the auto-oxidation of vitamin C even under anaerobic conditions, as long as the oxidized form of the flavone is present in the substrate. There is some evidence[6] that the bioflavonoids in food products, such as fruit juices, are always in equilibria with their chalcones, this being the reason for their peculiar behavior towards oxidation.

Bioflavonoids

The name *bioflavonoids* has been used recently for some anthoxanthins which are believed to be of importance in biological processes in man.

In the previous chapter, mention was made of the vitamin P (permeability vitamin) which was considered to be the flavanone, hesperidin. When pure hesperidin was prepared, its vitamin activity was very much reduced. Later, vitamin P was considered to be a mixture of hesperidin, its chalcone and eriodyctin. LAVOLLAY[7] states that *epi*-catechin has been found, up to the present time, to have the most action on capillary resistance. The difficulties encountered in establishing the activity of this vitamin are of interest: conclusive evidence could be arrived at only by means of bio-assay, however, attempts to carry this cut met with great difficulties, for there is no criterion at present for compounding a completely flavone-free diet. Moreover, the methods of identification of the flavonoids are not sensitive enough and not specific.

Besides vitamin P activity, hesperidin in its phosphorylated form acts as an inhibitor of *hyaluronidase*, an enzyme which is engaged in the liquefaction of hyaluronic acid gel. This liquefaction is required before the spermatozoon can penetrate the ovum. Phosphorylated hesperidin can, therefore, probably be used to suppress fertility[8].

Bitter substances

One member of the flavonoid family, the glycoside naringin, found particularly in grapefruit and in sour oranges, is extremely bitter and imparts the specific bitterness to this fruit. Naringin (from the Sanskrit word *"naringi"* for orange), when pure, is a white crystalline glucoside discovered by DE VRY in 1857, soluble in alcohol, acetone and only to the extent of 1 part in 2,000 in water at 20°C. Its bitterness is even greater than that of quinine and it can be detected in dilutions of 1:50,000. When dried at 110°, it melts at 171°C, but when crystallized from water with its additional 6 molecules of water it melts at 83°C. When dissolved in ethanol, naringin is levorotatory, $[\alpha]_D^{18} = -65°,2'$. Its aglucone is called *naringenin* and the structural formula is as follows:

rutinose—O ... H / \ OH
H$_2$

OH O

naringin

The sugar moiety is attached at position 7 and can be hydrolyzed by boiling in mineral acid. If treated in the cold with alkali, it gives a chalcone but, if boiled with KOH, naringin is broken up into phloroglucinol and *p*-coumaric acid.

The highest concentrations of naringin in the fruit are in the carpellary membranes, and the beautiful star-like clusters of naringin crystals can be seen in the grapefuit during a freezing spell in the citrus-growing belt. On standing, grapefruit juice acquires even more bitterness, due to the fact that the naringin diffuses slowly from the pieces of carpellary membranes, on which it is adsorbed, into the juice.

Since the aglucone, naringenin, is not bitter, several attempts have been made to find a suitable enzyme in order to cleave the sugar moiety from the naringin. The well known β-glucosidase *emulsion* does not react with naringin but "pectinol", the commercial pectic enzyme preparation has been found to be active[9]. THOMAS, SMYTHE AND LABBEE[10], after screening a large number of microorganisms, succeeded in isolating an enzyme, which they called *naringinase* C, and which is capable of rapidly hydrolyzing naringin *in vitro* at pH 3.5 to 5.0 and at temperatures of 20–50° C. These investigators came to the conclusion that even partial hydrolysis of naringin, namely the removal of rhamnose giving *prunin* (naringin-7, β-glucoside), is quite sufficient for the debittering of natural grapefruit juices.

Apart from grapefruit (*C. decumana*), naringin is also responsible for the bitter taste of the sour orange (*C. aurantium*), however, most of the other varieties of citrus fruits contain no naringin and their bitterness is caused by quite another substance. The bitter principle of Navel and Valencia oranges has been isolated and identified by HIGHBY[11]. This substance is called *limonin*, with an empirical formula $C_{26}H_{30}O_8$, and a melting point of 290° C. Quite recently[12], the structure of limonin has been completely elucidated and found to be a triterpenoid of the following formula, containing two lactone rings which can be opened reversibly, a β-substituted furan ring, a ketonic oxygen atom, and two ethereal oxygen rings, (see formula on p. 231).

In many foods the bitterness is caused by quite different substances; thus, for instance, the bitterness of beer is caused by *tyrosol* and the bitterness of chocolate is due to the presence of *theobromine* and *caffeine*.

The bitter principle of olives, *oleuropein*, is a glucoside of caffeic acid esterified with a phenol, probably similar to chlorogenic acid[13].

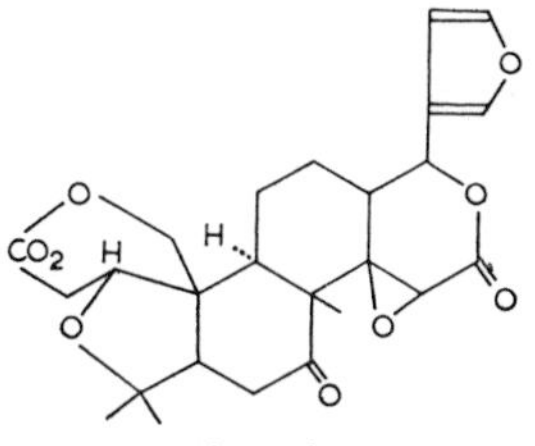

limonin

Apart from their pronounced bitter taste, it is believed that many flavonoids sometimes impart to various foods undesirable astringency.

Tannins

Closely related to the glucosides described above is a group of very complex substances, the *tannins*. Tannins are only a generic name covering a wide range of compounds widely distributed in nature. Some plants are very rich in tannins, especially in their bark and leaves, however, one can encounter these substances to a smaller degree in practically all plants. Oak galls contain as much as 80 % of their total solids as tannins. Tannin extracts have been used from time immemorial for tanning hides. In foods, such as tea or in some varieties of fruits, such as apples, pears, persimmons, dates, etc., even small amounts of tannins cause noticeable astringency.

There have been many different suggestions for grouping the numerous tannins, but no generally accepted classification exists so far. Some "simple" tannins are glucosides of digallic acid: gallotannin, for instance, is considered to be a pentadigalloyl-α-glucoside, probably of the following structure:

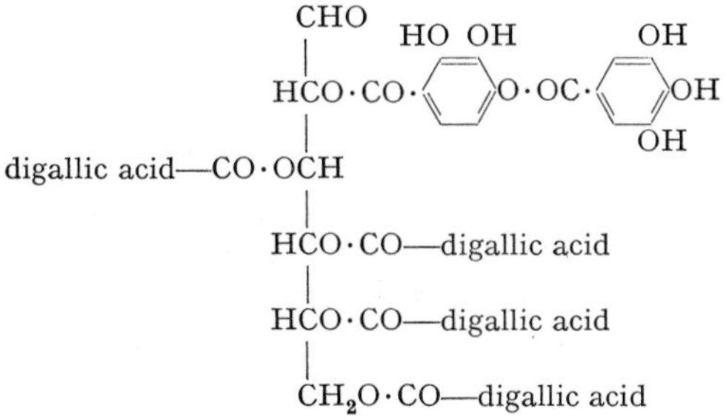

While such tannins are derivatives of pyragallol, there is another group called *phlobatannins*, which are based on catechol derivatives and which are more related to the anthocyanins and anthoxanthins. These tannins are widely distributed in plant material and in fruits and, on boiling with dilute acids, give brown to red amorphous water-insoluble substances.

The presence of small amounts of tannins in fruits and fruit products impart the quality of "possessing a body", however, larger amounts cause pronounced and undesirable astringency. On maturing the fruits lose an appreciable amount of their tannins (see Chapter 19).

probable formula of tea catechin

REFERENCES

[1] W. J. C. LAWRENCE, J. R. PRICE, R. M. ROBINSON AND R. ROBINSON, A survey of the anthocyanins, *Biochem. J.*, 32 (1938) 1661;
Distribution of the anthocyanins in flowers, fruits and leaves, *Trans. Roy. Soc. (London)*, B230 (1939) 149.

[2] H. T. HUANG, Decolorization of anthocyanins by fungal enzymes, *Agr. Food Chem.*, 3 (1955) 141.

[3] E. C. BATE-SMITH, Flavonoid compounds in foods, *Advances in Food Research*, 5 (1954) 267.

[4] C. G. NORDSTRÖM, Identification of flavonoid glycosides, as quoted in KARL PAECH, Colour development in flowers, *Ann. Rev. of Plant Physiol.*, 6 (1955) 273.

[5] J. A. HALL, Glucosides of the navel orange, *J. Am. Chem. Soc.*, 47 (1925) 1191.

[6] ANINA YARON AND J. B. S. BRAVERMAN, *Studies in the Auto-oxidation of Ascorbic Acid*, in the press.

[7] J. LAVOLLAY, J. L. PARROT AND J. SEVESTRE, On the nature of Vitamin P, *Compt. rend.*, 217 (1943) 540.

[8] B. F. SIEVE, A new antifertility factor, *Science*, 116 (1952) 373.

[9] S. V. TING, Enzymatic hydrolysis of naringin in grapefruit, *J. Agr. Food Chem.*, 6 (1958) 546.

[10] D. W. THOMAS, C. V. SMYTHE AND M. D. LABBEE, Enzymatic hydrolysis of naringin, the bitter principle of grapefruit, *Food Research*, 23 (1958) 591.

[11] R. H. HIGHBY, The bitter constituents of Navel and Valencia Oranges, *J. Amer. Chem. Soc.*, 60 (1938) 3013.

[12] D. H. BURTON, E. J. COREY AND O. JEGER, The constitution of limonin, *Experientia*, 16 (1960) 41.

[13] W. V. CRUESS AND J. SUGIHARA, The oxidase of the olive, *Arch. Biochem.*, 16 (1948) 39.

SELECTED BIBLIOGRAPHY TO CHAPTER 15

BATE-SMITH, E. C., Flavonoid compounds in foods, *Advances in Food Research*, 4 (1954) 262.

BATE-SMITH, E. C., Astringency in foods, *Food*, 23 (1954) 124.

GEISSMAN, T. A., Anthocyanins, chalcones, aurones, flavones and related water soluble plant pigments, in K. PAECH AND M. V. TRACY, *Modern Methods of Plant Analysis*, Vol. 3, Springer, Berlin, 1955, p. 450.

GEISSMAN, T. A. AND E. HINREINER, Theories of the biogenesis of flavonoid compounds, *Botan. Rev.*, 18 (1952) 77.

JOHNSON, G., M. M. MAYER AND D. K. JOHNSON, Isolation and characterization of peach tannins, *Food Research*, 16 (1951) 169.

KWIETNY, A. AND J. B. S. BRAVERMAN, Critical evaluation of the cyanidin reaction for flavonoid compounds, *Bull. Research Council Israel*, 7C (1959) 187.

LOVALLAY, J. *et al.*, *Qualitas Plantarum et Materiae Vegetabiles*, 3/4 (1958) 508.

MAYER, F., The chemistry of natural coloring matters, *Ann. Rev. Biochem.*, 21 (1952) 472.

ROBINSON, G. M. AND R. ROBINSON, A survey of anthocyanins, *Biochem. J.*, 28 (1934) 1712.

SECHARDI, T. R., Biochemistry of natural pigments, *Ann. Rev. Biochem.*, 20 (1951) 487.

Sunkist Growers, Coop. Citrus Growers of California and Arizona, *Analytical Methods for the Citrus Bioflavanoid Products*, 1956.

VAN RIJN, J. J. AND H. DIETERLE, *Die Glykoside*, Bornträger, Berlin, 1931.

YANG, H. Y. AND W. F. STEELE, Removal of excess anthocyanins by enzymes, *Food Technol.*, 12 (1958) 517.

CHAPTER 16

LIPIDS

Definition and occurrence

Of the three most important nutrients, carbohydrates, proteins and edible fats, the latter belong to a large class of very diverse substances called *lipids*. They can be classified into three main groups, their common property being the fact that all contain fatty acids—mostly long, straight hydrocarbon chain, saturated or unsaturated, with a carboxyl group ending:

(a) *Fats and oils*—consisting of triglycerol esters of fatty acids (designated here by F_1, F_2 and F_3) of the following general formula, which easily undergo saponification (alkaline hydrolysis) whereby glycerol and fatty acids are obtained:

$$
\begin{array}{ccccc}
\text{CH}_2\text{OOCF}_1 & & \text{CH}_2\text{OH} & & \text{F}_1\cdot\text{COOH} \\
| & & | & & \\
\text{CH}\cdot\text{OOCF}_2 & \xrightarrow{\text{alkali}} & \text{CH}\cdot\text{OH} & + & \text{F}_2\cdot\text{COOH} \\
| & & | & & \\
\text{CH}\cdot\text{OOCF}_3 & & \text{CH}_2\cdot\text{OH} & & \text{F}_3\cdot\text{COOH} \\
\text{fat or oil} & & \text{glycerol} & & \text{fatty acids}
\end{array}
$$

(b) *Waxes*—consisting of fatty acids esterified by monohydric long-chain alcohols, such as melyssil alcohol, $(\text{C}_{30}\text{H}_{61}\text{OH})$, in beeswax.

(c) *Phospholipids*—complex compounds in which glycerol or other alcohols are esterified partly by fatty acids and partly by phosphoric acid and by basic nitrogenous compounds.

Lipids generally dissolve readily in organic solvents, such as ether, acetone, alcohols, chloroform, CS_2 and petroleum ether. The fractions extracted by these solvents may, naturally, contain other compounds, such as terpenes, sterols, pigments and other non-saponifiable material. Saponification is, therefore, applied to separate them from the major lipid-fraction.

Lipids occur in all parts of plants and animal tissue; however, they are mostly found in specific fat tissues, seeds and some fruits:

in green leaves—to the extent of 0.4–5 % of the total dry substance, which, in itself, is quite an appreciable amount;

in fruits—sometimes as much as 50 % in olives, 20 % in avocadoes, in coconut, etc.;

in seeds and nuts—as an important reserve material in cottonseed, sunflower, ricinus, soy-bean, palm nut, nutmeg, linseed, peanut, etc.;
  in animals—body fats, butter, wool fat, herring oil, cod-liver oil, etc.

Fatty acids

The fatty acids are divided into two groups, those that are saturated and those that are unsaturated. They can be readily separated by the difference in the solubility of their lead (Pb) salts in 95 % ethyl alcohol. Saturated fatty acids precipitate as solid white powders, while the unsaturated acids remain in solution. Another distinction between the two groups is their reaction with iodine: iodine added to an unsaturated fatty acid combines with the carbons at the double bond to the extent of two atoms of iodine to each unsaturated bond. The iodine number serves as an indication of the degree of unsaturation of a triglyceride.

$$R—CH=CH—R'+I_2 \xrightarrow{\text{HgCl}_2} R—CHI—CHI—R'$$

Saturated fatty acids. These are normal straight-chain acids with an even number of carbon atoms from C_2 to C_{26}. Those with fewer than 12 carbon atoms are volatile, *i.e.* they can be steam distilled. The most widely distributed in nature are palmitic, lauric and stearic acids. Fatty acids with a higher number of carbon atoms, C_{28}–C_{38}, are found mainly in waxes. A list of some of the fatty acids, indicating their main sources is given below:

butyric acid	$CH_3(CH_2)_2 \cdot COOH$,	in butter;
caproic acid (hexanoic),	$CH_3(CH_2)_4 \cdot COOH$,	in coconut, palm oil;
caprylic acid (octanoic),	$CH_3(CH_2)_6 \cdot COOH$,	in coconut, palm oil;
capric acid (decanoic),	$CH_3(CH_2)_8 \cdot COOH$,	in coconut, palm oil;
lauric acid (dodecanoic),	$CH_3(CH_2)_{10} \cdot COOH$,	in coconut;
myristic acid (tetradecanoic),	$CH_3(CH_2)_{12} \cdot COOH$,	in nutmeg;
palmitic acid (hexadecanoic),	$CH_3(CH_2)_{14} \cdot COOH$,	in plant and animal fats;
stearic acid (octadecanoic),	$CH_3(CH_2)_{16} \cdot COOH$,	in plant and animal fats;
arachidic acid (eicosanoic),	$CH_3(CH_2)_{18} \cdot COOH$,	in peanut oil;
lignoceric acid (tetracosanoic),	$CH_3(CH_2)_{22} \cdot COOH$,	in peanut oil;
cerotic acid (hexacosanoic),	$CH_3(CH_2)_{24} \cdot COOH$,	in wool fat.

As exceptions to the above, small amounts of saturated straight-chain fatty acids with an odd number of carbon atoms (C_5 to C_{17}) and a variety of branched-chain fatty acids, having either an even or an odd number of carbon atoms, have been isolated from several sources.

References p. 251

Unsaturated fatty acids. The majority of oils from plant sources contain unsaturated fatty acids. This group also consists, generally, of straight-chain fatty acids with an even number of carbon atoms from C_{10} to C_{24}. The possibilities for isomers existing among them are large due to: (a) the number of unsaturated double bonds (mono-, di-, tri- and tetraethenoid) present; (b) their position in the chain; (c) the possibility of *cis* or *trans* configurations.

Here are a few of the most important unsaturated fatty acids and their sources:

oleic acid (octadeca-9-enoica), $CH_3(CH_2)_7 \cdot CH = CH \cdot (CH_2)_7 \cdot COOH$, in olive oil;

linoleic acid (octadeca-9,12-dienoic), $CH_3 \cdot (CH_2)_4 CH = CH \cdot CH_2 \cdot CH = CH(CH_2)_7 \cdot COOH$
in linseed oil and soy bean oil.

linolenic acid (octadeca-9-12-15-trienoic)

arachidonic acid (eicosa-5-8-11-14-tetraenoic)

According to world statistical figures, two of the unsaturated fatty acids, oleic and linoleic, account for 34 % and 29 %, respectively, of all the edible oils produced by man annually, as against only 11% for palmitic acid, a saturated fatty acid.

Isomerization of fatty acids

From the structure of both saturated and unsaturated fatty acids, it is evident that there can be three possible types of isomerism in these compounds:

(a) the single isomerism of a straight chain *versus* a branched chain, as, for instance, in butyric and isobutyric acids:

$$CH_3 \cdot CH_2 \cdot CH_2 \cdot COOH \qquad \begin{matrix} CH_3 \\ \\ CH_3 \end{matrix} \!\! \diagdown \!\! \diagup CH \cdot COOH$$

butyric acid   isobutyric acid

(b) isomerism caused by the position of the double bond in the long chain of an unsaturated fatty acid, as for instance in oleic acid and isooleic acids:

$$\Delta^{9:10} \text{ oleic acid} \; -CH_3 \cdot (CH_2)_7 CH = CH(CH_2)_7 \cdot COOH$$

$$\Delta^{12:13} \text{ isooleic acid} \; - \; CH_3(CH_2)_4 CH = CH(CH_2)_{10} \cdot COOH$$

In the case of more than one unsaturated double bond, this type of isomerization can give two distinct kinds of systems, conjugated and non-conjugated:

$$-C = C - C = C - \qquad\qquad -C = C - C - C = C-$$

conjugated   non-conjugated

(c) the third type of isomerization which can occur in unsaturated fatty acids is *cis-trans* geometrical configurations, such as in the C_{18} fatty acid:

$$CH_3(CH_2)_7 \cdot CH \qquad\qquad CH_3(CH_2)_7 \cdot CH$$
$$\|\qquad\qquad\qquad\qquad\quad \|$$
$$HOOC \cdot (CH_2)_7 \cdot CH \qquad\qquad CH \cdot (CH_2)_7 \cdot COOH$$

oleic acid (*cis*)   elaidic acid (*trans*)

In nature, most unsaturated fatty acids occur mainly in the *cis*-form, while only traces of *trans*-forms have been detected in natural lipids. However, these forms have been found in relatively large amounts in the body fats of ruminants as well as in natural lipids which have been subjected to hydrogenation.

Recently, it has been established that certain unsaturated fatty acids mainly linoleic acid with two double bonds, cannot be synthesized by the animal body fast enough. These have now been termed *"essential fatty acids"*.

Lately, there has been some speculation in medical circles on whether or not the essential fatty acids are able to prevent the accumulation of excessive cholesterol in the human blood. Closely related to such findings, it has been shown that certain groups of the population who have never used hydrogenated fats (such as margarine, containing mostly saturated fatty acids) in their diet but only liquid, unsaturated oils, have a very low incidence of atherosclerosis. These findings will have to be substantiated by further research, but if found true, they may have an important influence on the present methods of processing oils and their hydrogenation and refining.

Properties

Some of the oils have the property of forming a hard, solid film on drying in the air. Such oils are called *"drying oils"* and are used in the manufacture of paints and varnishes. These oils, *i.e.* linseed oil, contain a large number of unsaturated fatty acids. Other oils, *"non-drying oils"*, do not dry on standing and do not form hard films, an example of these being olive oil. The industry has also distinguished a third group, the *"semi-drying oils"*, such as cottonseed oil, which form films very slowly.

As in the case of some proteins, fatty acids can also form thin films on the surface of water. Such films behave as monomolecular layers the thickness of which corresponds to the length of a single fatty acid chain. At interfaces between water and some organic solvent the polar carboxyl group of the fatty acid will be attracted by water, while the long, non-polar hydrocarbon moiety will dissolve in the organic solvent. In pure water, however, a drop of fatty acid placed on the surface will tend to spread until it attains the

thickness of a single molecule, since the attraction between the non-polar
hydrocarbon moieties of the fatty acid molecules is much stronger than their
affinity for water. This property presents a possibility for calculating the

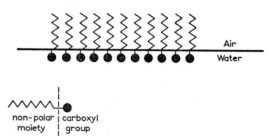

Fig. 40. Orientation of oil molecules on the surface of water.

cross-sectional dimension of a single fatty acid molecule by measuring the
area of the monomolecular film when subjected to a pressure sufficient to
align the hydrocarbon chains parallel to one another.

Fats and oils

It is merely an accepted convention to designate by the name "fats" only
these glycerides which will solidify at ordinary room temperature, while the
name "oils" is assigned to all others, which will remain liquid in these
circumstances. The structures of the component fatty acids are really the determining factor: the more saturated the fatty acids, the higher the melting
point of the fat. All natural fats and oils are mixtures of triglycerides in
which the three fatty acids esterifying the glycerol usually differ from each
other: nature's principle in this case is maximum heterogeneity of the fatty
acids (F) and the glycerol (G):

$$GF_1F_2F_3$$

Less common is the combination in which two fatty acids are identical—
$GF_1F_1F_2$. The case in which all three hydroxyls are esterified by the same
fatty acid is very rare indeed. Due to the great similarity in the solubilities of
these mixed tri-glycerides, it is extremely difficult to fractionate them as
separate entities, and it is, therefore, obvious that they can vary considerably
with respect to the nature and arrangement of their constituent fatty acids.
For the characterization of the natural fats and oils a number of physical and
chemical methods exist by which fair estimates can be made of their identification. All these methods are well presented in many of the recently published treatises on fats and oils. A good description relating to food products
is given by MEYER[1].

Biosynthesis

There is ample evidence that triglycerides are synthesized in the plant direct-ly from carbohydrates. In walnuts and almonds it has been shown that carbo-hydrates disappear at the same rate as the oils are formed. This does not mean that it is a direct transformation. In fact, in pecan nuts the disappearance of sugars corresponds to only 5 % of the oil formed, which means that there may be other sources in the plant from which triglycerides are synthesized.

In contrast to the above, it can be observed in many cases that the oils are formed at the place where they are finally stored. Such is the case, for instance, in olives where oil continues to form even after they have been plucked from the tree; the same phenomenon happens in linseed.

The third interesting fact with regard to the biosynthesis of oils is that they usually form during a rather short period of growth—over a short span of about two weeks the oil content may rise from 2 % to 30 % and more—and that during this period the respiration of the plant is accelerated to a considerable extent[2].

Furthermore, it is most interesting to note that, while the fruit or the seeds are maturing, the degree of unsaturation of the fatty acids becomes greater. Linseed oil, for example, 8 to 10 days after flowering of the plant, shows in the seeds an iodine number of 100, while after maturing it will reach 200. This occurrence is further substantiated by the fact that these lipids, being semi-solid at the beginning, become quite fluid as maturation progresses.

During formation of oils from carbohydrates a compound rich in oxygen is transformed into one poor in oxygen. Respiration going on in the meantime will be characterised by a definite CO_2 production accompanied by a relative small O_2 uptake. The respiratory quotient (R.Q.), $CO_2:O_2$, will be higher than 1.

Indeed, the respiratory quotient in ricinus, almonds and olives, during the peroid of oil formation, attains the figure of 1.5. The graph shown in Fig. 41 clearly shows how the respiration quotient rises during the period of lipid formation.

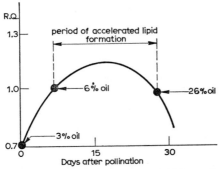

Fig. 41. The change of the R.Q. during lipid formation in plants.

References p. 251

The path of biosynthesis of lipids has been finally shown[3] to start with acetate and with the active participation of Coenzyme A and ATP*.

Acetylcoenzyme A (CoA) adds CO_2 with the help of a biotin-containing enzyme and malonyl-CoA is formed. The reaction depends upon ATP supply. This malonyl-CoA contains an active CH_2 group reacting easily with an other acyl-CoA and forming after decarboxylation a β-keto-acid. After

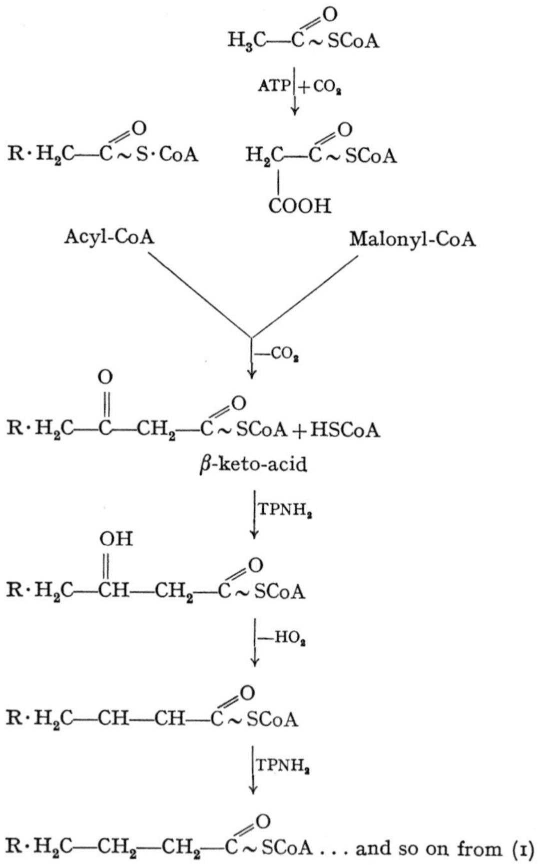

$$H_3C—C \overset{\diagup O}{\sim} SCoA$$

$$ATP | + CO_2$$

R·H$_2$C—C$\overset{\diagup O}{\sim}$S·CoA   H$_2$C—C$\overset{\diagup O}{\sim}$SCoA

COOH

Acyl-CoA   Malonyl-CoA

(1)

$$—CO_2$$

$$R·H_2C—\overset{O}{\overset{\|}{C}}—CH_2—C \overset{\diagup O}{\sim} SCoA + HSCoA$$

β-keto-acid

$$TPNH_2$$

$$R·H_2C—\overset{OH}{\overset{\|}{C}H}—CH_2—C \overset{\diagup O}{\sim} SCoA$$

$$—HO_2$$

$$R·H_2C—CH—CH—C \overset{\diagup O}{\sim} SCoA$$

$$TPNH_2$$

$$R·H_2C—CH_2—CH_2—C \overset{\diagup O}{\sim} SCoA \dots \text{ and so on from (1)}$$

reduction, dehydratation and further reduction (inversion of the β-oxidation of fatty acids) an acyl compound is formed with two CH_2 groups more than that which reacted with the malonyl-CoA.

---

* Anyone interested in the intermediate metabolism of fatty acids and oils in animals and human beings is referred to the excellent textbook by FRUTON AND SIMMONDS[4].

Manufacture of edible oils

The extraction of edible oils from various sources has lately undergone many changes. While pressing of the oil-rich material was, until recently, the main method of extraction, today most modern plants use solvent extraction. Olive oil is still the principal oil which is extracted by pressing in expellers or hydraulic presses, the first pressing, the so-called "virgin oil", having a bland flavor, while subsequent pressings produce lower grades of oil.

Most other oils are extracted nowadays by countercurrent extraction with such solvents as light petroleum fractions, benzene, carbon disulfide, etc. The seeds are usually pretreated by passing them through hot rolls where they are flaked. Heating denatures the proteins present and facilitates the release of oil. In this form, the flakes move in a continuous stream countercurrent to the solvent so that the oil-rich solvent meets the fresh incoming material, while fresh solvent meets the practically exhausted flakes. The solvent is then recovered from the remaining oil by distillation and is returned to the process. The exhausted seeds (the "oil-cake") are used as a protein-rich animal feed. Solvent extraction of oil seeds tends to remove relatively large proportions of non-lipid components from the seeds.

The next steps in the manufacture of edible oils are concerned with refining the crude oil. These include steam and alkali refining, deodorization and bleaching. The crude oils often contain large amounts of free fatty acids, non-saponifiable lipids, pigments and natural anti-oxidants, such as tocopherols. The lower free fatty acids, being volatile by steam, can be removed by steam distillation under vacuum, while the remaining fatty acids are converted by means of sodium or potassium hydroxides into soaps and removed by centrifugation or by settling. In order to remove excessive coloration, most oils are bleached by filtration with adsorbents such as activated carbon, kieselguhr, Fuller's earth, etc. Some vegetable oils, particularly cottonseed, peanut and soy-bean oils have quite unpleasant odors and flavors which are usually removed by a deodorization procedure; this consists of heating the oil to 200–250°C under reduced pressure (about 1–6 mm Hg) and stripping it with steam to remove the volatiles which cause the objectionable odor.

All these procedures do not adversely affect the composition of the edible oils, except for the fact that vitamin E, a mixture of tocopherols which is a natural antioxidant present in the oils, is largely removed. The effect of processing on the composition of oils has been ably discussed by FEUGE[5].

Hydrogenation or "hardening of oils"

As mentioned before, natural vegetable oils are usually liquid at ordinary room temperature because they contain a large proportion of unsaturated fatty acids in their triglycerides. However, it was shown, long ago, that if these could be converted into saturated fatty acids the oils would become plastic fats. Such plastic fats are frequently applied as margarine and shortenings in households and in the baking industry. SABATIER was the first to show that vegetable oils could be hydrogenated by gaseous hydrogen in the presence of a catalyst such as metallic nickel. This process is the essential unit operation used both in the manufacture of margarine and other shortenings. Both nutritionally and in appearance, there is very little difference today between butter and margarine, especially when the latter is fortified by vitamins D and carotene.

Commercial hydrogenation is usually carried out in large vessels under a pressure of 2–10 atmospheres and at temperatures between 110° and 190°C with finely divided suspensions of nickel at concentrations of 0.03–0.10% based on the weight of oil. The reaction is halted when the product has reached an iodine number in accordance with the desired consistency of the fat.

During this reaction hydrogen is added to the double bonds of the hydrocarbon chains of the unsaturated fatty acid groups in the tri-glyceride molecules, so that linolenic acid may be converted into linoleic or isolinoleic acid, linoleic to oleic acid and oleic into stearic acid. However, it has been shown that the double bonds farthest removed from the ester linkage are more reactive than those nearest to it. Moreover, the hydrogenation reaction tends to be selective in the sense that the greater the degree of unsaturation of a fatty acid group the greater is its tendency to add hydrogen. As a consequence of this selectivity, a fatty acid, such as linoleic, for instance, having two double bonds will tend to be hydrogenated before an oleic acid group, attached to the same glyceride, because it has only one double bond[6].

Hydrogenation may also improve the keeping qualities of oils because it makes them more resistant to oxidation and, therefore, to rancidity. The carotenoids to which the color of natural oils is mainly attributed are also hydrogenated, thereby losing their conjugated nature and, therefore, also their color. The color of margarine is thus restored by the addition of carotene.

In addition to the considerations mentioned earlier regarding the nutritional requirements of human beings for "essential fatty acids" (all of which happen to be unsaturated, while hydrogenated fats are not), one must also remember that hydrogenation brings about some transformation of the naturally occurring *cis* isomers to *trans* isomers. Much research is needed to decide whether such transformations are of consequence in our diet.

Enzymatic cleavage and oxidation

The deesterification of triglycerides is also catalyzed by the enzyme *lipase*. This enzyme is apparently present in all oil-containing seeds. The rate of the catalytic action of lipase is different in various oils. It is not specific and can catalyze the breakdown of glycerol triacetate as well as that of ethyl butyrate, *i.e.* a triglyceride esterified by a non-fatty acid and also an ester of a simple monohydric alcohol and a fatty acid.

One must assume therefore that *lipase* is a mixture of several unidentified enzymes, contained also in different parts of the digestive tract.

The tendency of fats and oils to become rancid is a phenomenon well known since ancient times. Rancidity is a general name by which spoilage of lipids is designated, be it caused by long storage, by microbial action or by oxidation. This proneness to oxidation is easily explicable when one takes into account the presence of long, unsaturated hydrocarbon chains. *In situ*, such oxidation is catalyzed by the enzyme *lipoxidase*.

Lipoxidase has been crystallized from soy-beans; it is found in many higher plants and reacts, in the presence of oxygen, with long-chain fatty acids containing two or more double bonds to form short-chain fatty acids. It was believed that this oxidative breakdown involved the intermediate formation of peroxides:

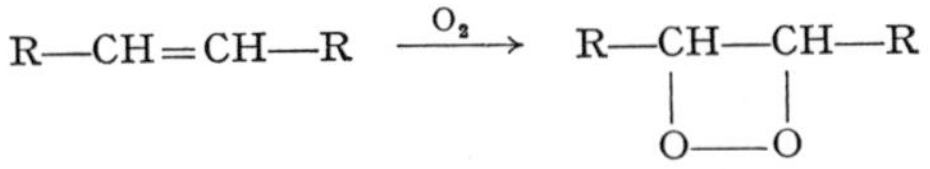

$$R\text{---}CH\text{==}CH\text{---}R \xrightarrow{\text{O}_2} R\text{---}\underset{\underset{\displaystyle O\text{---}O}{|}}{CH}\text{---}\underset{\underset{}{|}}{CH}\text{---}R$$

Such a peroxide formed by the action of the enzyme lipoxidase could, according to this theory, activate a secondary non-enzymatic oxidation, such as, for instance the oxidation of carotene. This may be the reason why the presence of *lipoxidase* is such an important factor in the breakdown of carotene in dehydrated fruits and vegetables. As an example, one may cite the action of *lipoxidase* in fresh alfalfa grass which destroys the carotene when the grass is dried in air (see Chapter 3).

The above theory was based on the supposition that the amount of unsaturated fatty acids in the oxidized oil constantly decreases, while the amount of peroxides formed increases. In point of fact, this has not been proved and such peroxides have not been demonstrated in oxidized oils.

Recent investigations in this field have shown that the mechanism of oxidation of fatty acids includes formation of an hydroperoxide which contains the unchanged double bond. Auto-oxidation of all unsaturated compounds is explained today by the formation of free radicals at the α-methylenic group. According to this mechanism[7] the oxidation proceeds as a chain reaction by detaching an hydrogen atom from the α-methylenic group, as shown in the following scheme for a fatty acid with two double bonds.

These become conjugated during the oxidation reaction. The changes can be easily traced in the ultraviolet range of 232 mμ for hydroperoxides and at 268–270 mμ for secondary oxidation products.

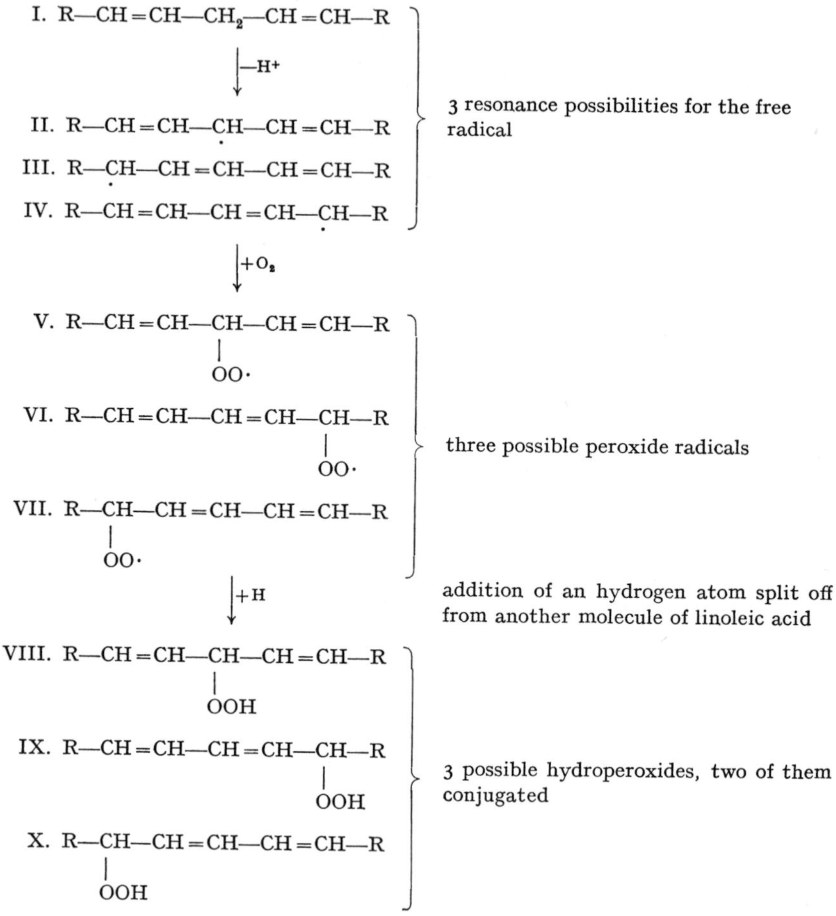

I. $R—CH=CH—CH_2—CH=CH—R$

$\downarrow$ —H+

3 resonance possibilities for the free radical

II. $R—CH=CH—\overset{\cdot}{C}H—CH=CH—R$

III. $R—\overset{\cdot}{C}H—CH=CH—CH=CH—R$

IV. $R—CH=CH—CH=CH—\overset{\cdot}{C}H—R$

$\downarrow$ +O$_2$

V. $R—CH=CH—\underset{\underset{OO\cdot}{|}}{C}H—CH=CH—R$

VI. $R—CH=CH—CH=CH—\underset{\underset{OO\cdot}{|}}{C}H—R$

VII. $R—\underset{\underset{OO\cdot}{|}}{C}H—CH=CH—CH=CH—R$

three possible peroxide radicals

$\downarrow$ +H

addition of an hydrogen atom split off from another molecule of linoleic acid

VIII. $R—CH=CH—\underset{\underset{OOH}{|}}{C}H—CH=CH—R$

IX. $R—CH=CH—CH=CH—\underset{\underset{OOH}{|}}{C}H—R$

X. $R—\underset{\underset{OOH}{|}}{C}H—CH=CH—CH=CH—R$

3 possible hydroperoxides, two of them conjugated

Recent investigations have shown that linoleic acid contained upon oxidation at least 90 % of conjugated hydroperoxides and that most of them were *cis–trans* isomers.

When more than one double bond is present the fatty acid can form a number of such configurations, *i.e.*, *cis–cis*, *cis–trans*, *trans–trans* or *trans–cis*, etc. Linoleic acid, for example, which has the formula

$$CH_3—(CH_2)_4—CH=CH—CH_2—CH=CH—(CH_2)_7—COOH$$

can have four possible *cis–trans* stereoisomers:

(1) 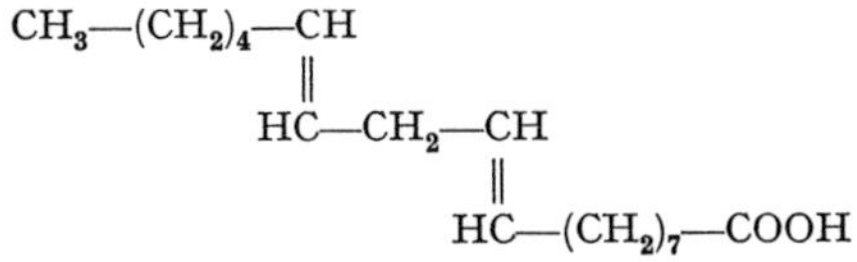 CH_3—$(CH_2)_4$—CH
$\parallel$
HC—CH_2—CH   (*trans–trans*)
$\parallel$
HC—$(CH_2)_7$—COOH

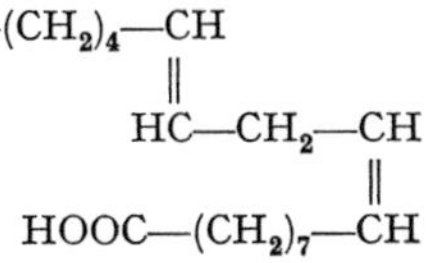

(2) CH_3—$(CH_2)_4$—CH
$\parallel$
HC—CH_2—CH   (*trans–cis*)
$\parallel$
HOOC—$(CH_2)_7$—CH

(3) 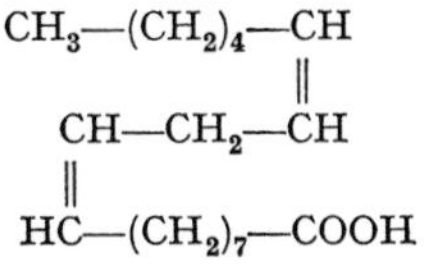 CH_3—$(CH_2)_4$—CH
$\parallel$
CH—CH_2—CH   (*cis–cis*)
$\parallel$
HC—$(CH_2)_7$—COOH

(4) 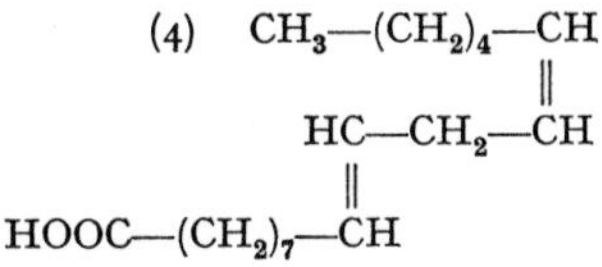 CH_3—$(CH_2)_4$—CH
$\parallel$
HC—CH_2—CH   (*cis–trans*)
$\parallel$
HOOC—$(CH_2)_7$—CH

Similarly, eleostearic acid, which occurs in Chinese wood oil, and which has three double bonds, has eight possible stereoisomeric configurations.

The oxidation of unsaturated compounds is preceded by a so-called *induction period* during which the amount of hydroxyperoxides is still small and, therefore, the rate of oxidation is slow. By adding peroxides or a quantity of already rancid oil, the rate of oxidation will be considerably accelerated since the rancid oil will supply free radicals which will cause the oxidation of many new chains.

The presence of heavy metals brings about the disruption of peroxides and the creation of new free radicals and consequently leads to accelerated rates of oxidation. Many organic peroxides are able to remove electrons from, or donate electrons to, metallic cations in accordance with their redox potential power:

$$Cu^+ + ROOH \longrightarrow Cu^{2+} + R-O:^- + \cdot OH$$

$$Cu^{2+} + ROO:^- \longrightarrow R-OO\cdot + Cu^+$$

In contrast to metals, antioxidants are compounds which are able to prevent or at least to retard oxidation.

References p. 251

Antioxidants

One may assume *a priori* that because an oxidative system requires the presence of all three components, enzyme, oxygen and substrate, it would be sufficient to inactivate the enzyme or to eliminate oxygen. In practice, however, inactivation of the enzymes is sometimes undesirable, and complete elimination of oxygen by such means as deaeration, exhausting, etc. is impossible. In such cases, the only recourse is the use of *antioxidants*. They are widely used to prevent rancidity of oils and fats caused not only by enzymes but also by free radicals which bring about very undesirable changes in the palatability of food products in which oils or shortenings take part, as well as the oxidative changes taking place in essential oils terpenoids and other aromatic compounds (see Chapter 17).

In most cases, antioxidants are nothing more than substances with preferential ability to oxidize, *viz.*, certain compounds which will oxidize prior to the substances that are being protected. A great number of natural products have been known to exert antioxidation activity, for instance, the already mentioned tocopherols. Tocopherols are now prepared synthetically and can be used to the extent of 0.01 % in many oil-containing food products (potato chips, salted nuts, breakfast cereals, peanut butter, shredded coconut, etc.) in order to prevent rancidity.

Of the many other natural antioxidants, mention should be made of the bark of Douglas fir, the fruit of Osage orange, rosemary and sage. Various spices are also known to exert antioxidant properties. CHIPAULT[8] surveyed the action of 32 spices in simple oil-in-water emulsion systems which were found to protect the emulsions against oxygen absorption. In most cases, the spices were more effective in emulsions than in ordinary oils, however, the degree of their effectiveness was different in various substrates. Cloves turned out to be most effective in emulsions. Other spices with a high degree of antioxidant activity were: allspice, cardamon, cassia, cinnamon, ginger, mace, nutmeg, oregano, black pepper, rosemary, sage, savory, thyme and turmeric.

The first commercial natural antioxidants used in the United States were *lecithin* and *gum guaiac* (0.005 %). Later, industrial chemicals took their place, the most active among them was *propyl gallate* (0.06 %). In more recent times *butylated hydroxyanisol* (BHA) has come into use, although it imparts some phenol flavor to oils at the high temperatures used in frying, as well as *nordihydroguaiaretic acid* (NDGA). The latest antioxidant very widely used is *butylated hydroxytoluene* (BHT), which has no undesirable flavor and is not toxic. This substance is also known by the name di-*tert*-butyl-*p*-cresol (DBPC) or 2,6-di-*tert*-butyl-4-methylphenol.

Mixtures of several antioxidants sometimes have a better effect, apparently because of some coaction or *synergistic effect*. Often a mixture of antioxidants with some *sequestering agents* is desirable, such as citric or phosphoric acids, which have the property of binding even trace quantities of metals. Some metals such as Fe and Cu are known to accelerate greatly the oxidation reactions and their traces can reduce the shelf life of food products by as much as 50 %. Sequestering agents have the ability to chelate with these metals and to inhibit their action. Sometimes sugars also exert a synergistic action in preventing oxidation, and it may be noted that sucrose often has a better effect than glucose or invert sugar (used, for instance, in sweet biscuits).

Antioxidants of another type, such as *santoquin* (6-ethoxy-1,2-dihydro-2,2,4-trimethylquinoline) are used to prevent the oxidation of carotenoids in various cattle fodders, such as alfalfa meal. For use in fruit products, antioxidants should be easily soluble in water. Today, excellent antioxidants such as ascorbic acid are produced synthetically in bulk and at very low prices. Ascorbic acid prevents oxidation and therefore also discoloration in meat products, salmon, mushrooms, cabbages and many canned fruit products.

Besides sulfur dioxide and the sulfites, which are very effective antioxidants and which have already been discussed above, a number of substances containing sulfur have been suggested for preventing oxidation, among these the amino acids cysteine and cystine, glutathione, as well as thiocarbamide, sulfonamides and even pineapple juice because of its high content of naturally occurring sulfhydryl compounds.

Recently, new modes of usage for the antioxidants have been suggested. It is now usual to impregnate the packaging material with antioxidants instead of admixing them with the product itself. The wax wrapping paper for bread, cheeses, coffee, etc. are often impregnated with antioxidants.

Of the various substances proposed as antioxidants, hydroquinone and catechol must be classed as harmful and deleterious and should not be used[9].

Waxes

As mentioned before, waxes are a type of lipid, in which the fatty acids are esterified by higher monohydric alcohols rather than by glycerol. These alcohols contain from 24 to 36 carbon atoms. Natural waxes are mixtures of many such esters and often contain unesterified alcohols, ketones and hydrocarbons having an odd number of carbon atoms.

Waxes are widely distributed in nature, both in plant and animal material. They can be classified into three distinct groups:

(a) those forming the leaf-cuticle;

(b) those forming the fruit-cuticle—both types are found on the external surfaces, where they serve as a protective coating and prevent undue evaporation of moisture;

(c) those which are distributed in the cells of the plants.

References p. 251

Some important natural waxes are: *beeswax*—secreted by the honeybee and containing, among other constituents, palmitic and cerotic acids and melissyl alcohol; *carnauba wax*—which coats the leaves of the carnauba palm, and which contains even higher alcohols and fatty acids; *lanolin*—a waxy material obtained from wool; *spermaceti*—found in the head of the sperm whale and containing cetyl and oleyl alcohols and palmitic acid;

As a rule, the waxes are solids with melting points between 60° and 80°C; they are more resistant to saponification than fats and oils, and are also less susceptible to auto-oxidation.

Phospholipids

This third group of lipids are fat-like substances containing fatty acids, phosphoric acid and a nitrogenous base, all of which are esterified by a polyhydroxyl alcohol, either glycerol or inositol. Accordingly, the phospholipids themselves are divided into three sub-groups: phosphatidic acids, phosphatides and lipositols.

In the *phosphatidic acids*, two hydroxyls of the glycerol are bound to fatty acids while the third is bound to phosphoric acid:

$$CH_2 \cdot O \cdot F_1$$
$$CH \cdot O \cdot F_2$$
$$CH_2 \cdot O \cdot PO_3H_2$$

In the plant, mainly in the cytoplasm, the phosphatidic acids are bound to cations such as K, Mg and Ca.

The *phosphatides* contain, in addition to the above, a nitrogenous base connected to the phosphoric acid. Choline is found in lecithin while ethanolamine or serine is present in cephalins. *Lecithin* is found in various animal tissues, in egg yolk and in soy-beans. Soy-beans lecithin is produced commercially and is mainly used as an excellent emulsifying agent in many food products.

$$CH_2\text{—}OOC \cdot F_1$$
$$CH\text{—}OOC \cdot F_2$$

(fatty acids moieties may be either saturated or unsaturated)

$$CH_2\text{—}O\text{—}\overset{\overset{O}{\|}}{P}\text{—}O \cdot CH_2CH_2N^+(CH_3)_3$$
$$\underset{O^-}{|}$$

— choline and phosphoric acid moiety

lecithin

Lecithins from various sources contain different saturated or unsaturated fatty acid groups. As shown above lecithin is a *zwitterion*, a dipolar ion in which a negative charge on the phosphoric acid residue is neutralized by a positive charge on the quaternary nitrogen of choline. The outstanding characteristic of the lecithins is their high chemical reactivity: they are easily oxidized or hydrolyzed, and easily combine with a number of other substances such as proteins and carbohydrates.

Cephalins are other phosphatides found in egg yolk and also in many animal tissues, particularly in brain tissue. Cephalins contain oleic and stearic acids as the only fatty acids, and ethanolamine $(NH_2 \cdot CH_2 \cdot CH_2OH)$ as the nitrogenous basic constituent instead of choline:

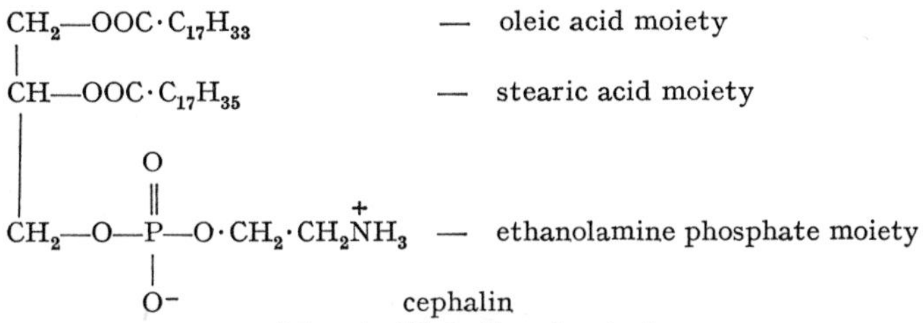

$$CH_2\!-\!OOC \cdot C_{17}H_{33} \qquad -\text{ oleic acid moiety}$$
$$CH\!-\!OOC \cdot C_{17}H_{35} \qquad -\text{ stearic acid moiety}$$
$$CH_2\!-\!O\!-\!\overset{\overset{\textstyle O}{\|}}{P}\!-\!O \cdot CH_2 \cdot CH_2\overset{+}{N}H_3 \quad -\text{ ethanolamine phosphate moiety}$$
$$\underset{O^-}{|}$$

cephalin
(phosphatidyl ethanolamine)

A second cephalin has been isolated from brain tissue which contains the amino acid serine,

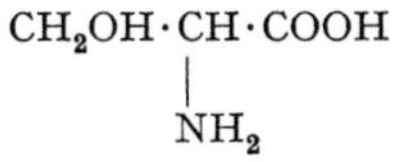

$$CH_2OH \cdot CH \cdot COOH$$
$$\underset{NH_2}{|}$$

in place of ethanolamine. Cephalins are thought to play a part in the process of blood clotting.

The third sub-group of the phospholipids are the *lipositols*. Here the place of glycerol is taken by inositol. Lipositols have been found in soy-beans as well as in nerve tissue.

One such lipositol has been found to be an alcohol-insoluble phospholipide which gives, on hydrolysis, equimolar portions of glycerol, a fatty acid, and inositol *meta*-diphosphate:

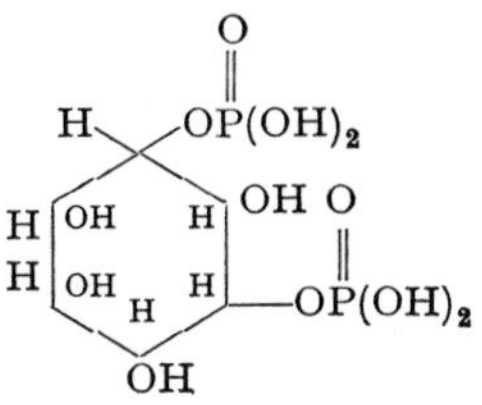

inositol meta(diphosphate)

Enzymatic cleavage of phospholipids

An example of the enzymatic breakdown of phospholipids is given by the following scheme which represents the successive cleavage of lecithin. At least four different enzymes take part: *lecithinase A*, which removes the middle fatty acid; *lecithinase B*, which can remove both fatty acids; *choline phosphatase*, which hydrolyzes the link between choline and phosphoric acid; and, finally, *glycerophosphatase*, which splits off phosphoric acid from glycerol.

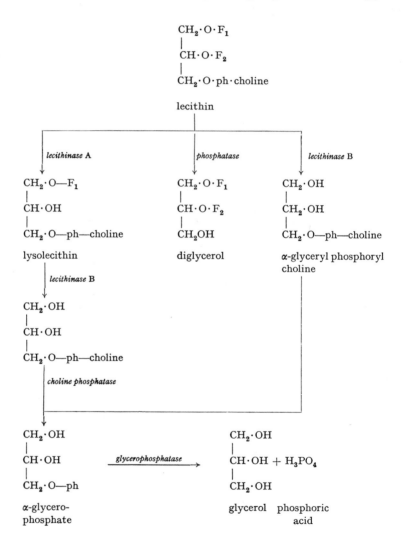

REFERENCES

[1] LILIAN H. MEYER, *Food Chemistry*, Reinhold Publishing Co., New York, 1960.
[2] J. BONNER, *Plant Biochemistry*, Academic Press, New York, 1950.
[3] E. R. STADTMAN AND H. A. BARKER, *J. Biol. Chem.*, 191 (1951) 365.
[4] J. S. FRUTON AND SOFIA SIMMONDS, *General Biochemistry*, 2nd edn., John Wiley & Sons, New York, 1958.
[5] R. O. FEUGE, Effect of processing on composition of edible oils, in R. S. HARRIS AND H. VON LOESECKE, *Nutritional Evaluation of Food Processing*, John Wiley & Sons, New York, 1960.
[6] A. E. BAILEY, *Industrial Oil and Fat Products*, Interscience Publishers, New York, 1951.
[7] R. T. HOLMAN, *Progress in the Chemistry of Fats and Other Lipids*, 2 Vols., Pergamon Press, London, 1954.
[8] J. R. CHIPAULT, G. R. MIZUNO AND W. O. LANDBERG, Antioxidant properties of spices in oil-in-water emulsions, *Food Research*, 20 (1955) 443.
[9] A. J. LEHMAN, O. G. FITZHUGH, A. A. NELSON AND G. WOODWARD, The pharmacological evaluation of antioxidants. *Advances in Food Research*, 3 (1951) 197.

SELECTED BIBLIOGRAPHY TO CHAPTER 16

BAILEY, A. E., *Industrial Oil and Fat Products*, Interscience Publishers, New York, 1945.
BATEMAN, A., Olef in Oxidation, *Quart. Revs. (London)*, 8 (1954) 308.
DEUEL, H. J., *The Lipids*, Interscience Publishers, New York, 1951.
DEVINE, J. AND P. N. WILLIAMS, *The Chemistry and Technology of Edible Oils and Fats*, Pergamon Press, New York, 1961.
GREEN, D. E., The Synthesis of Fat (review), *Sci. American*, (Feb. 1960) 46.
HILDITCH, T. P., *The Chemical Constitution of Natural Fats*, 2nd edn., Chapman and Hall, London, 1947.
LOVERN, J. A., *The Chemistry of Lipids of Biochemical Significance*, Methuen and Co., London, 1955.
MARKLEY, K. S., *Fatty Acids*, Interscience Publishers, New York, 1947.
TROTMAN-DICKENSON, A. F., *Free Radicals*, Methuen and Co., London, 1959.

CHAPTER 17

ESSENTIAL OILS

Ein köstlicher, teurer Schatz

CONRAD GESNER, 1555

Occurrence

The essential oils, those odoriferous substances found in practically every plant, are very numerous and widely distributed in many different parts of the same plant: in the roots, stem, leaves, flowers and fruits.

Here are a few examples of such essential oils listed according to their source:

in roots—licorice, caradamum, asparagus oil;

in stem—turpentine;

in leaves—mint, geranium oil, eucalyptus oil;

in flowers—jasmin, neroli oil, rose oil;

in fruits—orange and lemon oils, bergamot oil, essences of strawberries, grapes, etc.

It is interesting to note that, when one plant has essential oils in several parts of it, they always differ in their constitution; thus, for instance, an orange tree has essential oils in its flowers (oil of neroli), in its young leaves and twigs (oil of petitgrain), in the yellow peel (flavedo), in its fruits (oil of orange) and, finally, a specific aroma in the orange juice—all of these are quite different in odor and in their chemical composition.

In some fruits the aromatic material may be actually dissolved in the juice, however in many cases in fruits and in the leaves, the essential oils are secreted in numerous tiny oil sacs or glands located in the epicarp adjacent to the chromoplasts. These glands or canal-like intercellular receptacles are ductless and have no walls of the usual type in the cells, but are bounded by the debris of degraded tissues.

The physiological function of essential oils in plant metabolism is still obscure. While the odoriferous principle in the leaves or flowers can be assumed to be useful in attracting insects to the pollen, no such property can be ascribed to the oil present in other parts of the plant. The oil may possibly act as a protection against insect attack. For the moment, however, there is no definite proof for either theory and the only alternative that remains is to regard essential oils, as many other secondary products, anthocyanins, alkaloids, tannins, etc., as waste products of plant metabolism.

All essential oils contain, for the most part, volatile mixtures of terpenes, sesquiterpenes, alcohols, aldehydes, ketones, acids, esters, along with some non-volatile residues consisting of camphors and other waxy materials.

Structure

Some aromatic components of essential oils, aldehydes and esters, have a straight-chain structure. However, the greater part of most essential oils belongs to the class of terpenoids, of which the simplest members are terpenes of the general formula $C_{10}H_{16}$. RUZICKA[*] was the first to emphasize the biogenetic relationship of the terpenoids to isoprene.

According to RUZICKA, most terpenes and many other natural products may be regarded as multiples of the unsaturated aliphatic hydrocarbon, C_5H_8, having the following structure:

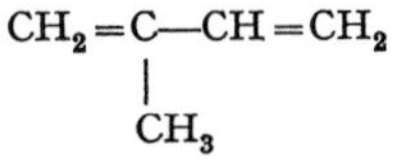

$$CH_2 = C - CH = CH_2$$
$$|$$
$$CH_3$$

isoprene

In fact, dipentene, the racemic form of limonene, is obtained synthetically by dimerization of isoprene, after heating it at about 300°C.

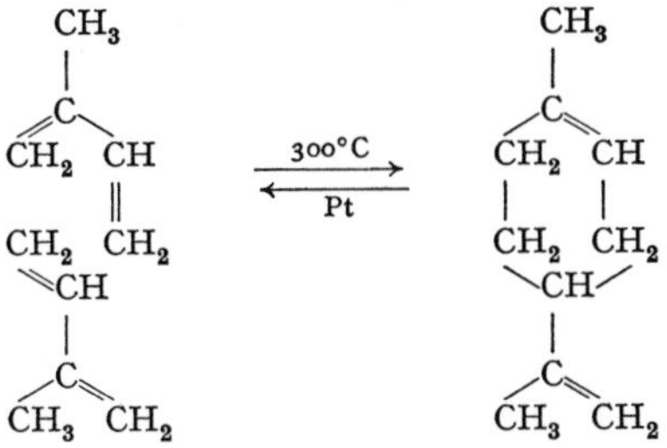

two molecules   dipentene
of isoprene

Conversely, isoprene is formed when limonene or dipentene vapors are passed over red-hot platinum wire. (The yield is particularly good when

---

[*] Swiss Federal Institute of Technology, Switzerland. Nobel Prize laureate.

References p. 268

dipentene vapors are diluted with nitrogen or are passed over the catalyst at low pressure.)

Accordingly, RUZICKA emphasized the biogenetic relationship of the terpenoids and showed that, so far as their carbon skeleton is concerned, they could, in general, be regarded as made up of 2, 3, 4, 6 and 8 units of isoprene usually joined head to tail but sometimes head to head (see isoprene rule, Chapter 3):

isoprene (C_5H_8)

monoterpenes ($C_{10}H_{16}$)
(hydrocarbons, alcohols, aldehydes)

sesquiterpenes ($C_{15}H_{24}$)
(ketones and acids)

diterpenes ($C_{20}H_{32}$)
(phytol, vitamin A)

triterpenes ($C_{30}H_{48}$)
(resins)

tetraterpenes ($C_{40}H_{64}$)
(carotenoids)

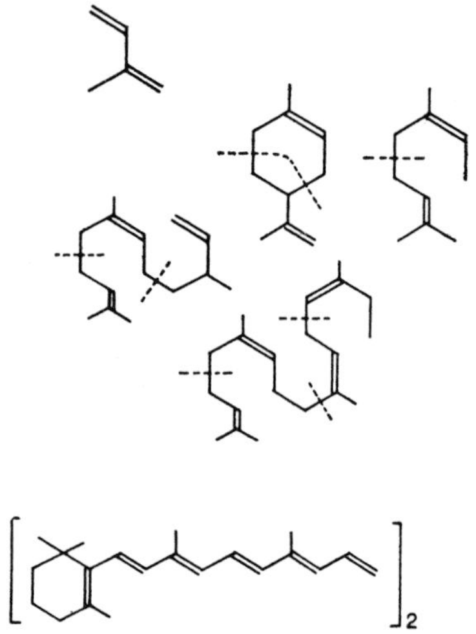

The isoprene hypothesis is more striking when one considers that phytol, carotenoids (see Chapter 3), rubber, as well as squalene and sterols (see Chapter 14) may all be regarded as derivatives of isoprene. This hypothesis also supports the opinion that the essential oils are formed during photosynthesis in the epidermal cells of fruits and leaves, and that they are not waste products of the general metabolism of the plant.

Biosynthesis

However, isoprene, as such, has never been shown to exist in the plant tissue. In looking for suitable precursors, a great number of theories have been advanced from time to time in order to find a structural unit responsible for the biogenesis of all the products mentioned above.

One of the theories suggested is that essential oils are derivatives of primary substances created during photosynthesis, such as, for instance, the amino acid leucine, which can easily undergo deamination and decarboxylation and can be converted into isoamyl alcohol, in itself an odoriferous substance having an isoprenic configuration:

$$CH_3—CH \cdot CH_2 \cdot CH \cdot COOH \qquad \xrightarrow[-CO_2]{NH_3} \qquad CH_3—CH \cdot CH_2 \cdot CH_2OH$$

$$\underset{CH_3}{|} \qquad \underset{NH_2}{|}$$

$$\underset{CH_3}{|}$$

leucin

isoamyl alcohol

The most attractive theory regarding the formation of the essential oils in the plant and the actual precursor of the terpenes has been proposed by READ[1] who considered as the key substance the acyclic alcohol, geraniol, $C_6H_{18}O$, or its stereoisomer, nerol; both compounds are widely distributed in the plant kingdom, either in the free state or as esters of acetic or other acids. READ proposed they might be formed by condensation of acetone and acetaldehyde according to the following series of reactions:

$$\underset{CH_3}{\overset{CH_3}{>}}CO + CH_3 \cdot CHO \xrightarrow{-H_2O} \underset{CH_3}{\overset{CH_3}{>}}C=CH—CHO$$

acetone acetaldehyde

β-methyl crotonaldehyde

Two molecules of β-methyl crotonaldehyde would give upon condensation:

$$CH_3 \cdot C=CH \cdot CHO + CH_3 \cdot C=CH \cdot CHO \xrightarrow{-H_2O} CH_3 \cdot C=CH—CH=CH—C=CH \cdot CHO$$

$$\underset{CH_3}{|} \qquad \underset{CH_3}{|} \qquad\qquad \underset{CH_3}{|} \qquad\qquad \underset{CH_3}{|}$$

3,7-dimethyl octa-2,4,6-triene-1-al

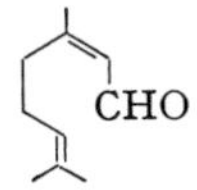

$\Big| +2H$

citral

$$CH_3—C=CH—CH_2—CH_2—C=CH \cdot CHO$$

$$\underset{CH_3}{|} \qquad\qquad\qquad \underset{CH_3}{|}$$

citral $(C_{10}H_{16}O)$

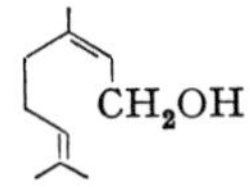

$\Big| +2H$

geraniol

$$CH_3—C=CH—CH_2—CH_2—C=CH \cdot CH_2OH$$

$$\underset{CH_3}{|} \qquad\qquad\qquad \underset{CH_3}{|}$$

geraniol

Geraniol could then easily undergo cyclization by dehydration to limonene:

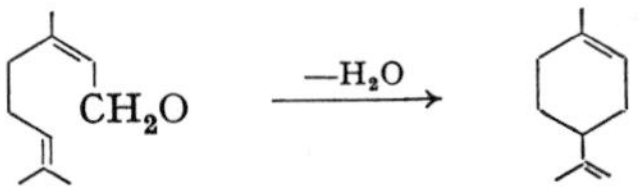

$\xrightarrow{-H_2O}$

geraniol

d-limonene

To account for the adoption of geraniol as the key substance in the formation of all terpenes, READ pointed out that geraniol possesses an unusual
molecular structure, since it contains a primary alcohol group activated by
an α,β-ethylenic linkage

$$HC=CH \cdot CH_2OH$$
$$|$$
$$CH_3$$

situated in close proximity to a second active group

$$CH_3 \cdot C = CH—,$$
$$|$$
$$CH_3$$

also containing an ethylenic linkage. Owing to the large mobility of this
grouping, geraniol can be regarded as the parent substance of a great variety
of cyclic terpenes and related bodies, the joint occurrence of which has been
observed in plant products.

READ was not far from the truth for, by means of recent isotopic studies,
it has now been ascertained that *acetic acid* is actually the primordial substance which is first converted by several steps to the six-carbon compound,
mevalonic acid (see Chapter 3).

Through its phosphate ester, mevalonic acid is converted to isopentenyl
pyrophosphate, which has been isolated from biological systems. Isopentenyl pyrophosphate is, in fact, the active isoprenoid compound from
which all terpenoids stem[2]:

$$CH_3 \cdot C(OH) \cdot CH_2 \cdot CH_2OH \longrightarrow$$
$$|$$
$$CH_2COOH$$

mevalonic acid

$$CH_2 = C—CH_2 \cdot CH_2O \cdot \overset{\overset{O}{\|}}{\underset{OH}{P}} \cdot O \cdot \overset{\overset{O}{\|}}{\underset{OH}{P}}—OH$$
$$|$$
$$CH_3$$

isopentenyl pyrophosphate

Isopentenyl pyrophosphate can isomerize to β,β-dimethylallyl pyrophosphate and, in fact, the two isomers may exist in equilibrium:

$$\overset{CH_2}{\underset{CH_3}{>}}C—CH_2CH_2O \cdot \overset{\overset{O}{\|}}{\underset{OH}{P}}—O—\overset{\overset{O}{\|}}{\underset{OH}{P}}—OH \quad \rightleftarrows \quad \overset{CH_3}{\underset{CH_3}{>}}C=CH \cdot CH_2O \cdot \overset{\overset{O}{\|}}{\underset{OH}{P}}—O—\overset{\overset{O}{\|}}{\underset{OH}{P}}—OH$$

isopentenyl pyrophosphate　　　　　　　　β,β-dimethylallyl pyrophosphate

Reaction between the two forms will give geranyl pyrophosphate and on reaction with yet another molecule *farnesyl pyrophosphate* may be obtained. In fact, such intermediates as farnesyl pyrophosphate have been isolated, and the various routes for the biosynthesis of the whole range of terpenoids are now quite clear:

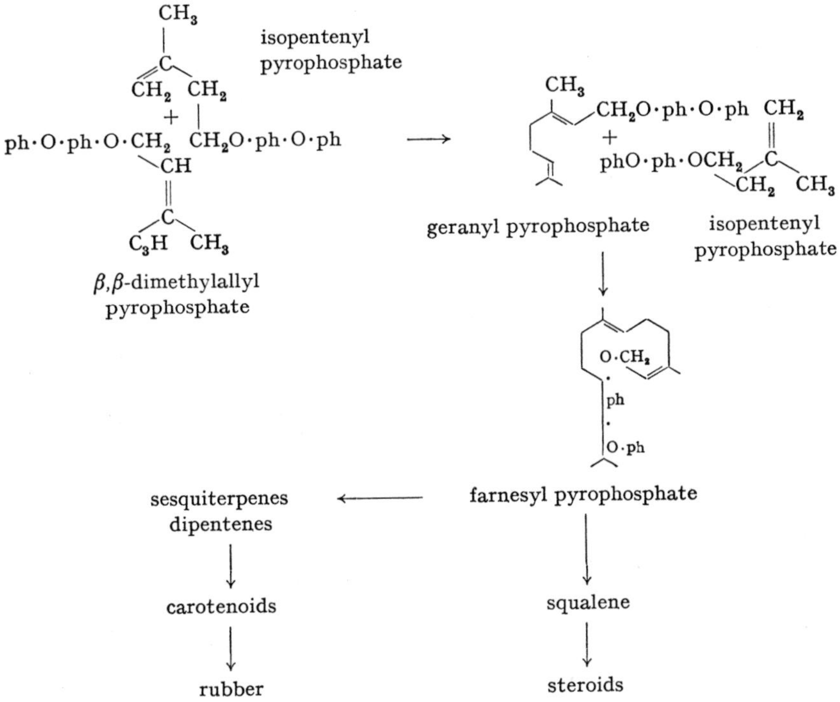

Further details regarding this scheme in connection with the biosynthesis of carotenoids and of the steroids from squalene are given in the appropriate chapters, 3 and 14.

Monoterpenes

The essential oils found in nature are mixtures of a number of monoterpene hydrocarbons of the general formula, $C_{10}H_{16}$, hydrocarbons ($C_{15}H_{24}$) sesquiterpenes, both of which serve primarily as carriers for the more important classes of *oxygenated compounds* (alcohols, aldehydes, ketones, acids and esters) which, although present in much smaller quantities, are usually the bearers of the characteristic odor of the oil in question. All mono- as well as sesquiterpenes are volatile when distilled by steam.

References p. 268

A few of the simplest monoterpenes, such as *myrcene* (from oil of bay) and *ocimene* have acyclic aliphatic structures and contain three double bonds:

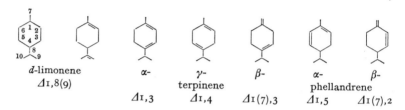

myrcene   ocimene

The bulk of the monoterpene hydrocarbons, however, have a ring formation with two double bonds and may be grouped under the general name of *menthadienes*:

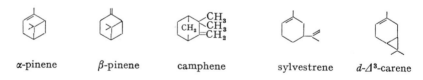

d-limonene   α-   γ-   β-   α-   β-

Δ1,8(9)   terpinene   phellandrene

         Δ1,3 Δ1,4 Δ1(7),3 Δ1,5 Δ1(7),2

d-Limonene constitutes over 90 % of orange oil, and its levorotatory modification occurs in Finland turpentine oil, American peppermint oil, etc. γ-Terpinene and α-phellandrene, which are easily oxidized into a ketone, are found in lemon oil.

The above are strikingly similar in structure except for the position of the double bonds. The following are some monoterpene hydrocarbons which have odd structures:

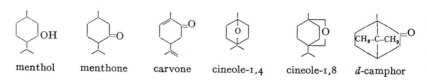

α-pinene   β-pinene   camphene   sylvestrene   d-Δ^3-carene

Pinene exists in two optically active modifications. Its α-isomer is the principal constituent of turpentine and is found also in neroli oil. Its presence in lemon oil, if detected, shows that this oil has been adulterated with turpentine.

Examples of the cyclic oxygenated hydrocarbons are:

menthol   menthone   carvone   cineole-1,4   cineole-1,8   *d*-camphor

Menthol is the main constituent of mint oil, carvone is found in caraway and *d*-camphor in *Cinnamomum camphore*. The two cineoles and the carvone are products of the oxidation of some of the cyclic hydrocarbons, as will be shown later.

The monoterpenes fraction boils over a range 170–200°C at atmospheric pressure.

Sesquiterpenes

The higher-boiling fractions of many essential oils, those boiling over the range of 250° and 280°C at atmospheric pressure consist of sesquiterpene hydrocarbons with the general formula $C_{15}H_{24}$. They are widely distributed in nature but have been investigated only to a limited extent. The sesquiterpenes have a density of approximately 0.90, their viscosity is higher than that of monoterpenes and have only a faint odor. The structures of a few sesquiterpenes have been shown below:

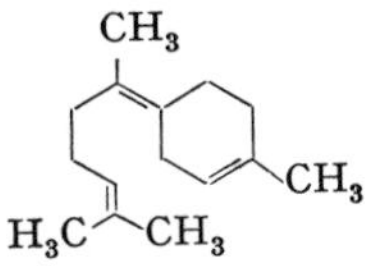

γ-bisabolene 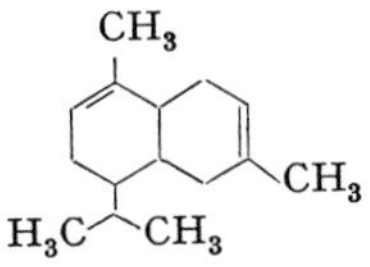   cadinene 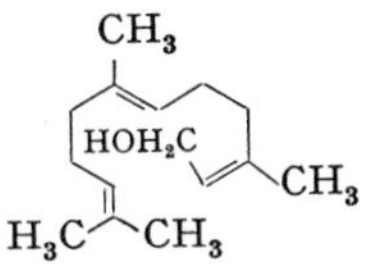   farnesol

γ-Bisabolene, is found in bergamot oil, and cadinene, which is its cyclic isomer (with two rings) is found in the oil of guayule and other plants. The sesquiterpene, farnesol, which is an alcohol, appears to be widely distributed and *is found in small amounts in many essential oils and is considered now to be an important intermediate in the formation of all terpenoids* (see above).

Celery oil contains another sesquiterpene, β-selinene, and eucalyptus oil— α-eudesmol—both of them having curious isoprenoid structures:

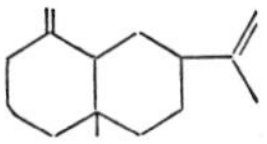

β-selinene 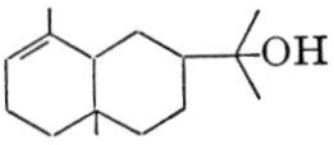   α-eudesmol

Oxygenated terpenes

As already mentioned, the principal bearers of the specific odors of the essential oils are the oxygenated compounds. These are mostly aliphatic alcohols, aldehydes, etc., and may be regarded as derivatives of the aliphatic monoterpenes, ocimene and myrcene.

References p. 268

The most important alcohols are:

| linalool | geraniol (*trans*) | nerol (*cis*) | *d*- and *l*- citronellol | α-terpineol |

d-Linalool occurs in sweet oranges, and its acetate ester is very prominent in bergamot and other oils. Geraniol and nerol are merely *trans* and *cis* configurations of the same alcohol, the first being the main constituent of geranium oil and the second that of the oil of orange blossoms (neroli). Both geraniol and nerol undergo ring closure on acid treatment to yield 1,8 terpine hydrate. The rate of this reaction indicates whether the substance in question is geraniol or nerol: a *cis*-configuration (nerol) will close more rapidly:

| nerol | α-terpineol | 1,8-terpine |

Citronellol is a very widely distributed alcohol, which has the odor of roses and is almost always accompanied by geraniol. Since it has an asymmetric carbon atom, it exists in two optically active modifications. While *d*-citronellol occurs in lemon oil, its levorotatory isomer is found in rose oil, both enantiomorphic forms being found in geranium oil.

α-Terpineol is a solid substance, which has a closed ring structure and is optically active. Terpineol can be prepared from limonene by hydrobromination and substitution of the Br by an hydroxyl group:

| *d*-limonene | limonene monobromide | α-terpineol |

Commercially α-terpineol is prepared from α-pinene by the action of H_2SO_4 in acetic acid.

In the high boiling fraction of neroli oil, an aliphatic sesquiterpene alcohol is found. It possesses only a faint odor but is capable of fixing other perfumes:

$$\overset{\displaystyle OH}{\underset{\displaystyle }{}}$$

$$CH_3\!-\!\underset{\underset{\displaystyle CH_3}{|}}{C}\!=\!CH\cdot CH_2\cdot CH_2\cdot \underset{\underset{\displaystyle CH_3}{|}}{C}\!=\!CH\cdot CH_2\cdot CH_2\cdot \overset{\overset{\displaystyle OH}{|}}{\underset{\underset{\displaystyle CH_3}{|}}{C}}\cdot CH\!=\!CH_2$$

or in short:

nerolidol

Still more important are the terpene aldehydes which are very widely distributed in essential oils and are greatly valued because they possess characteristic odors and flavors. In fact, the aldehyde value of most of the essential oils is the major determination made when appraising their quality. The most recognized aldehydes are α- and β-citrals, and d- and l-citronellals:

α-citral (*trans*)	β-citral (*cis*)	citronellal	methyl- anthranilic acid	methyl- anthranilic acid methyl ester

Citral is widely distributed in nature; it is an important constituent of many essential oils, particularly lemon oil and lemon grass oil. In all these, citral appears as a mixture of the two stereoisomers, α-citral (*trans*) and β-citral (*cis*). Citral can be prepared synthetically from methyl heptenone and ethyl chloroacetate using Zn as a catalyst. If citral is condensed with acetone in the presence of weak alkalis, pseudoionone is formed, which, when heated with dilute H_2SO_4, gives a mixture of α- and β-ionone, a synthetic perfume with the odor of violets[3].

Citronellal, another aliphatic unsaturated aldehyde, has one double bond and, since it has one asymmetric carbon atom, appears in two stereoisomeric configurations, d- and l-.

Methyl anthranilic acid and its methyl ester, although not terpenoids are of extreme importance as odoriferous substances and occur as the different flavors of certain fruits, such as grapes.

It must be pointed out that along with terpene alcohols and aldehydes, which all have an isoprenic structure, a number of normal straight-line compounds are found in many essential oils. Thus, for instance, there is *n*-nonyl alcohol, $CH_3 \cdot (CH_2)_7 \cdot CH_2OH$, which usually appears as an ester of caprylic acid, and *n*-decyl aldehyde, $CH_3 \cdot (CH_2)_8 \cdot CHO$, which is the principal aldehyde found in the peel oil of oranges.

Stearoptenes

A considerable quantity of a non-volatile residue is obtained after steam distillation of all natural essential oils. Moreover, similar wax-like substances separate from the oils on prolonged standing. These residues are called *stearoptenes*. They are soft, wax-like more or less slimy masses. Although much work has been done on their composition and, in some instances, pure substances have been isolated, there is still much work to be done for the elucidation of their characteristics and especially on their tendency to form precipitates. Some of the stearoptenes are probably derivatives of flavanoid substances which are usually present in the plant tissues in close proximity to the oil-containing sacs or glands. Some others are apparently esters of lipids and certain monohydric alcohols, such as xanthophyls.

Citropten, identical with *limettin*, has been isolated from lemon oil, it is a derivative of coumarin (benzo-α-pyrone) and its structure shows a resemblance to the flavanoids:

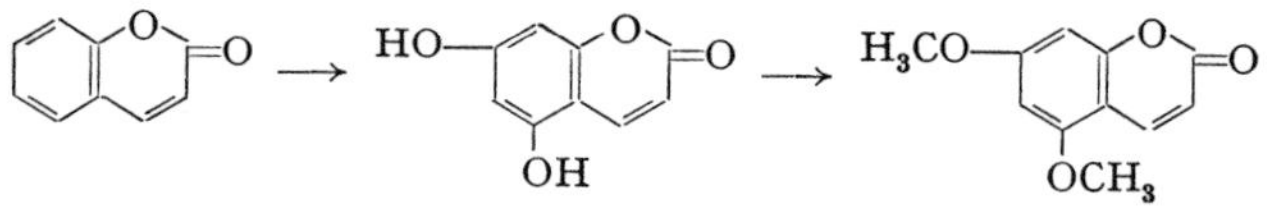

coumarin   dihydroxycoumarin   citroptene

Bergaptene is a stearoptene found in bergamot oil to the extent of 5 %. It crystallizes in fine white needles, m.p. 188°C. The composition of other stearoptenes has not been sufficiently studied; some of them seem to contain sterols.

Transformation of terpenes

Most of the aliphatic monoterpenes can readily close their ring to become cyclic terpenes, as shown above, during the cyclization of geraniol into limonene. However, such reactions are not reversible. The following is an example of such transformations in peppermint and spearmint oils (according to KREMERS[4]):

Another type of transformation in essential oil constituents occurs when these are distributed in an aqueous solution. Such is the case, for instance, when *d*-limonene, which constitutes the bulk of orange oil, is present in orange juice. In such case the essential oil will undergo an acid catalyzed hydration–dehydration with a resulting off-flavor[5]. This has also been attributed to the conversion of citral to *p*-cymene as well as to the oxidation of *d*-limonene to carvone and carveole[6].

The analytical procedures employed in the appraisal of various essential oils are fully described in a number of important treatises[7,8]. Recoverable oil in canned juices, as well as in many oil-containing plant materials, can be successfully determined by a simple oil separatory trap, described by the U.S.D.A.[9] (Fig. 42).

References p. 268

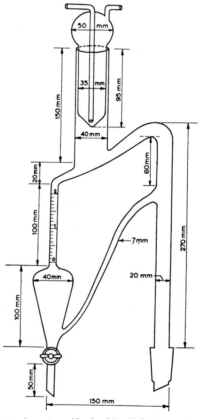

d-limonene($[\alpha]_D = 106°$)

1,4-terpin   terpinolene($\alpha = 0°$) α-terpineol($[\alpha]_D = 100°$)   1,8-terpin

$+H_2O$ $-H_2O$ $+H_2O$

$-H_2O$ $-H_2O$

1,4-cineole($\alpha = 0°$) α-terpinene($\alpha = 0°$)   1,8-cineole($\alpha = 0°$)

Fig. 42. Essential oil separatory trap (devised by U.S. Dept. Agr., Marketing Service).

Extraction of essential oils

In many cases the crude essential oils are still extracted by steam distillation, mostly with primitive equipment in their native places of origin. The plant materials, such as menth, geranium, rose, etc., are distilled with water usually in copper vessels and the distillate is collected from the condensers, the oil phase being subsequently separated from the water and filtered off. When the essential oil in question is liable to suffer from high temperatures, a vacuum is applied.

However, many essential oils do not lend themselves to steam distillation and in such cases methods using various organic solvents are used. The extraction of essential oils from flowers, such as jasmin and cassia are usually performed by means of diffusion, percolation or maceration with solvents such as petroleum ether, the solvent being subsequently distilled off *in vacuo* at a low temperature. The solvents will in these cases naturally extract a number of other substances in addition to the essential oils, *e.g.* lipids, sterols, pigments, etc., and very often the resulting products are quite solid (called "concretes").

Another process used for the extraction of essential oils from flowers is *enfleurage*, which consists in spreading the flowers upon a neutral, purified fat which slowly absorbs the essential oil. This method of preparation is used in various cream pomades and lotions.

A number of essential oils used in flavoring food products, especially citrus fruit oils, are so delicate that none of the above methods can be successfully used. These oils are pressed by hand or by various, so called "cold-press" methods making use of the fact that the essential oils secreted in the glands or sacs of the plant tissue are maintained under a certain turgor pressure. When the glands are ruptured mechanically the oil will eject with considerable force to a relatively great distance. The extraction of the essential oils in these cases consists, usually, in piercing or rupturing the oil glands and collecting the oils in the form of water emulsions, which are then separated by centrifuging.

Terpeneless oils

As has been pointed out earlier most essential oils are mixtures of oxygenated compounds, which are the principal odoriferous agents, with terpenes and sesquiterpenes, which are hydrocarbons but which have no aroma of their own. Moreover, these terpenes differ greatly from the oxygenated compounds in their solubility, being very poorly soluble in weak alcohols; they also oxidize into oxides and peroxides and are apt to polymerize. It has, therefore, always been the aim of the manufacturer of flavoring extracts to recover the valuable portion of the essential oils, *i.e.*

the oxygenated compounds, in some sort of "concentrated form". This process, consisting primarily in the elimination of the less odorous terpenes, is called *deterpenation* and the resulting oxygenated compounds—*terpeneless oils*.

There are three main methods for the deterpenation of essential oils: (1) by fractional distillation *in vacuo*[10]; (2) by counter-current fractional distribution using different solvents[11]; and (3) by chromatographic separation in columns containing silica gel or other adsorbing material[12]. All these are described in detail in the references mentioned.

Aroma recovery

Many operations, applied in food processing, cause considerable losses in flavor and especially in aroma. Such losses are caused in the first place during the blanching of vegetables and fruits. While blanching by steam or scalding by hot water are mainly required in order to inactivate the enzymes, which might otherwise have a deleterious effect on the foods during subsequent operations and storage, at the same time blanching may cause substantial losses in aroma due simply to the fact that the odoriferous substances are distilled off during this process.

Even more important are the losses in aroma sustained during concentration and dehydration, for, no matter how low the temperature maintained during these processes of evaporating water, the volatile constituents will always tend to be removed first and be lost from the food. This is the major reason why most concentrated juices and dehydrated fruits and vegetables retain very little of their fresh odor and flavor.

Several methods are applied in the food industry to overcome these difficulties:

(a) In some cases, such as in the case of concentrating strawberry or grape juices, it is possible to strip off the aroma during evaporation by collecting the first fraction, rich in aroma substances, and returning this fraction back to the concentrates. A practical method has been elaborated in the Eastern Regional Research Laboratories of the U.S. Department of Agriculture[13] and is now successfully used in many countries (see Fig. 43).

(b) Aroma-recovery by distillation is, however, not always possible. In the case of citrus juices, for instance, the aroma is of such a delicate nature that it is soon broken down, due most probably, to reactions such as ACHD (acid catalyzed hydration–dehydration) described above. In such cases, "cut back" methods are generally used, whereby the prepared concentrates are rediluted to some extent with fresh, untreated juices possessing their full flavor and aroma. The resulting mixture is then frozen to a solid cake and stored at $-18°C$ ($0°F$) until it is consumed. Frozen orange concentrate which has now attained widespread recognition is produced by such pro-cedure[14].

(c) An ideal method of preserving the aroma in concentrated juices would be, of course, concentration by freezing out the water. Even thermodyna-mically this process is more attractive, since while the evaporation of 1 litre

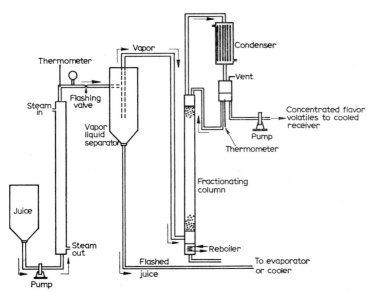

Fig. 43. Aroma recovery apparatus (according to Eastern Regional Research Labora-tories, U.S. Dept. Agr.).

of water requires about 560 calories, its conversion into ice requires only 80 calories. However, concentration by freezing has met so far with difficulties of its own[3] and with a few exceptions has not yet been used extensively in the food industry.

(d) The possibility that the aroma of some foods is derived from certain flavor precursors, which are activated by specific enzymes in order to form the desired aroma, has led HEWITT[15] to the idea that it might be more desirable to plan the processing treatment with the intent of securing the maximum survival of the precursor than to plan for maximum flavor survival. With this in mind, the authors patented a process for adding an enzyme preparation to a dehydrated vegetable, devoid of any flavor, but still containing the precursor, whereby the aroma and flavor would be restored. When a tasteless, odorless enzyme preparation from white mustard seeds (belonging to the same *Brassica* family as the treated vegetables) was

References p. 268

added to reconstitutee (formerly dehydrated) watercress or cabbage, the typical odor and taste were restored in a few minutes.

(e) In addition to natural flavors, the food industry the world over uses a great number of artificial flavorings, which are not the subject of this book. Their composition, preparation and use have been discussed by MEMORY[16].

REFERENCES

[1] F. M. READ, *J. Soc. Chem, Ind.*, 48 (1929) 786.
[2] A. TODD, New horizons in chemistry, *Nature*, 187 (1960) 819.
[3] J. B. S. BRAVERMAN, *Citrus Products*, Interscience Publishers, New York, 1949.
[4] R. E. KREMERS, *J. Biol. Chem.*, 50 (1922) 31.
[5] J. S. BLAIR *et al.*, Acid catalyzed hydration—dehydration, *Food Research*, 17 (1952) 235.
[6] W. L. STANLEY, Chemistry of volatile citrus flavors, *Chemistry of Natural Food Flavors Symposium*, Quartermaster Food and Container Institute, Chicago, 1957, p. 102.
[7] E. GILDEMEISTER, *Die Aetherischen Öle*, Schimmel & Co., Leipzig, 1928.
[8] E. GUENTHER, *The Essential Oils*, 6 Vols., D. Van Nostrand Co., New York, 1948.
[9] *United States Standards for Grades of Canned Orange Juice*, Effective March 13, 1956.
[10] J. B. S. BRAVERMAN, *Citrus Products—Chemical Composition and Chemical Technology*, Interscience Publishers, New York, 1949.
[11] W. J. D. VAN DIJEK AND A. H. RUYS, *British Pat. No. 355,294, U.S.Pat. No. 2,023,109.*
[12] J. G. KIRSHNER AND J. M. MILLER, *Ind. Eng. Chem.*, 44 (1952) 318.
[13] R. K. ESKEW, Preparation and applications of flavor concentrates from deciduous fruits, *Chemistry of Natural Food Flavors Symposium*, Quartermaster Food and Container Institute for the Armed Forces, Chicago, 1957, p. 113.
[14] D. K. TRESSLER AND M. A. JOSLYN, *The Chemistry and Technology of Fruit and Vegetable Juice Production*, Avi Publishing Co., New York, 1954.
[15] E. J. HEWITT, D. A. M. MACKAY, K. KONIGSBACHER AND T. HARRELSTROM, The role of enzymes in food flavors, *Food Technol.*, 10 (1956) 487; 13 (1959) 128; *U.S.Patent No. 2,924,521* (Feb. 3, 1960).
[16] J. MEMORY, *Food Flavorings*, Avi Publishing Co., Westport, Conn., 1960.

SELECTED BIBLIOGRAPHY TO CHAPTER 17

GILDEMEISTER E. AND F. HOFFMAN, *The Volatile Oils*, 3 Vols., J. Wiley and Sons New York, 1913.
GÜNTHER, E., *The Essential Oils*, 6 Vols., Van Nostrand Co., New York, 1948–1952.
KIRCHNER, J. G., The chemistry of fruit and vegetable flavors, *Advances in Food Research*, 2 (1949) 259.
Flavor Research and Food Acceptance, symposium sponsored by ARTHUR D. LITTLE, Inc., Reinhold Publ. Co., New York, 1958.
MAYO P. DE, *Mono- and Sesquiterpenoids*, Interscience Publ., New York, 1959. System of nomenclature for terpene hydrocarbons, *Am. Chem. Soc.*, (1955).
Chemistry of Natural Food Flavors Symposium, Quartermaster Food and Container Institute for the Armed Forces, Research and Develop. Command, May, 1957.
SIMONSEN, J. L., *The Terpenes*, 5 Vols., Cambridge Univ. Press, 1947–1952.
STOLL, A AND E. SEEBECK, Concerning alliine, the precursor of garlic oil, *Helv. Chim. Acta*, 31 (1948) 1432.

CHAPTER 18

PLANT ACIDS AND RESPIRATION

Respiration is combustion

ANTOIN LAVOISIER, 1789

Aliphatic plant acids

Of all the numerous acids found in plants, only a few aliphatic acids have special physiological significance, some are monocarboxylic, others are di- and tricarboxylic acids:

I. monocarboxylic acids:

(a) with two carbon atoms: $CH_3 \cdot COOH$—acetic acid

(b) with three carbon atoms: $CH_3 \cdot CO \cdot COOH$—pyruvic acid

II. dicarboxylic acids:

(a) with two carbon atoms:

$$\begin{array}{l} COOH \\ | \qquad \text{oxalic acid} \\ COOH \end{array}$$

(b) with four carbon atoms:

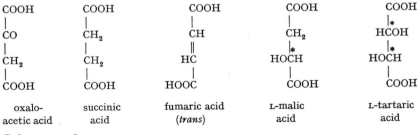

| oxalo-acetic acid | succinic acid | fumaric acid (*trans*) | L-malic acid | L-tartaric acid |

(c) with five carbon atoms:

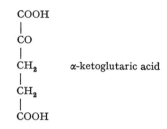

III. tri-carboxylic acids—with six carbon atoms:

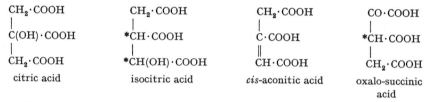

CH$_2$·COOH	CH$_2$·COOH	CH$_2$·COOH	CO·COOH
C(OH)·COOH	*CH·COOH	C·COOH	*CH·COOH
CH$_2$·COOH	*CH(OH)·COOH	CH·COOH	CH$_2$·COOH
citric acid	isocitric acid	cis-aconitic acid	oxalo-succinic acid

All these acids are widely distributed in nature:

oxalic acid—often constitutes upto 50 % of the total soluble solids in plant leaves in the form of its calcium salt, Ca-oxalate;

citric acid—which is not optically active, constitutes over 60 % of the total soluble solids in the juice of lemons and limes;

isocitric acid—with two asymmetric carbon atoms, was found relatively recently and has not been sufficiently studied; its *d*-isomer is found in blackberries;

malic acid—optically active, is very widely distributed in the plant kingdom and found in its *l*-configuration in many fruits (mainly in apples);

succinic acid—is widely distributed, however, only in small quantities;

fumaric acid—is found in nature only in the *trans* form—the *cis* form is named maleic acid and is not found in plants;

tartaric acid—which can give 4 stereoisomers, is found in nature only in its *l*-configuration; it constitutes the principal acid in grapes.

All of these aliphatic acids, except oxalic and tartaric acids, take part in the respiration cycle.

Aromatic plant acids

In addition to the aliphatic acids, there are a large number of aromatic acids which are found in the plant kingdom, however, in much smaller quantities. Some of the aromatic acids are found in their free state, such as benzoic acid ($C_6H_5 \cdot COOH$) in cranberries; some others in the form of esters, such as salicylic acid ($C_6H_4 \cdot (OH) \cdot COOH$), which is found as a methyl ester in plums and the acacia flowers. Other aromatic acids are linked with sugars as glycosides and are found in the form of gums. Oil of cinnamon, for instance, contains *cinnamic acid* and *o-* and *p-coumaric acids* (*or o-, p-hydroxy-cinnamic acids*):

cinnamic acid　　　　o-coumaric acid　　　　p-coumaric acid

Caffeic acid is found in coffee beans and digitalis; *gallic acid* in tannins, and *protocatechuic acid* is found in peas and gall nuts. There is no doubt that the sources of the last-mentioned three aromatic acids are the anthocyanidins and the flavanoids (see Chapter 15).

caffeic acid　　　　gallic acid　　　　protocatechuic acid

Potatoes and many other vegetables contain a widely distributed compound called *chlorogenic acid*, which is an ester of quinic acid (acting as alcohol) and caffeic acid. It exists in a number of isomeric forms depending on which hydroxyl group of quinic acid takes part in the ester link.

chlorogenic acid

Recent developments in chromatographic techniques have given better possibilities for identifying and separating the acids in plant tissues and food products when they are present in low concentrations, these being difficult to find by the old classical methods. HULME[1], investigating the changes in the total acids in Bramley's Seedling apples during storage, found *quinic* and *shikimic* acids which are evidently much more widely distributed in plant tissues than has previously been recognized. These two aromatic acids are apparently biosynthesized from glucose[2] and take part in metabolic processes as precursors of aromatic amino acids.

shikimic acid   quinic acid

Various food products contain some of these acids and many more, such as amino acids and others, all of which, no doubt, contribute to a great extent towards the taste and flavor of these foods. Although organic acids were found and their structure elucidated a long time ago, their physiological significance has been established only recently. In 1937, KREBS' AND JOHNSON showed the part played by aliphatic acids in the respiration of both plants and animals.

Acidity and sour taste

The mechanism of the accumulation of organic acids in fruits, and possible relationship of this mechanism to maturity is not clear. Normally, the per cent acid in a fruit juice decreases as the fruit matures; however, the quantity of the juice increases during maturation and it may well be that the absolute amount of acid per single fruit remains constant during its development, and that its percentage in the juice only appears to diminish because of the increase in the quantity of juice itself[3]. For example, a lemon which contains at the beginning of the season some 30 % juice of 7 % acidity—*i.e.* 2.10 g acid per 100 g fruit—will, at the end of the season, contain approximately 35 % juice with only 6 % acidity—*i.e.* the same amount of acid per 100 g of fruit as earlier in the season. This view has been supported by SINKLER[4, 5] in a study of the organic acids present in grapefruit.

While discussing the subject of acidity, it may perhaps be appropriate to discuss the question of the sour taste, which is of much importance to food producers.

Of the five senses in man's possession, those of taste and smell are the least exact; at least they are not easily measurable. Furthermore, these two senses are so closely allied that it is difficult to ascertain which is affected by a given stimulus. Of the two, the sense of smell is the more selective and is capable of greater variations. It is generally supposed that we judge the flavor of our food more by its odor than by its taste, for during swallowing, the passage to the respiratory channel is closed by the epiglottis, and immediately after swallowing, a gust of air is expelled, which as it passes the olfactory nerve, carries the odor and thereby permits us to discern the flavor.

Odor, therefore, contributes greatly to flavor which is in turn closely related to vision. For instance, flavors are difficult to judge when food is tasted in darkness or under lights of unnatural colors. Similarly when one watches a lemon being cut ones mouth waters. The understanding of such behavior lies, however, in the province of psychology, which is scarcely within the scope of this book.

Compounds which cause us to detect sourness in foods are mainly organic acids: lactic, tartaric, malic, malonic, oxalic, acetic, etc., as well as phosphoric acid and the acid salts.

There are three major methods for comparing the sourness or acidity of solutions: (1) comparing very weak acid solutions so that they barely differ from distilled water (threshold method); (2) comparing solutions of equal taste intensity but differing in concentration; and (3) comparing solutions of equal concentration in a scale of somewhat different tastes (like acetic and tartaric acids).

The main difficulty in all of these methods is that they are subjective and tests must consequently be made by a large number of individuals. The old proverb *de gustibus non est disputandum* appears to hold strongly in this case. The difficulty is still greater when high concentrations have to be evaluated. Whereas in tasting weak concentrations our selectivity may appear sufficient, it is of no practical use for acids at greater concentrations: one can, for example, easily distinguish between a juice of about 1 % acidity and one of 1.5 %, but one can scarcely discern between two solutions of 25 % and 30 % acidity. It is, therefore, obvious that in studying this effect only weak solutions should be used.

The physico-chemical properties of a compound depend largely on its chemical structure. Just as color depends on chemical structure, so too do taste and odor. However, the relationship between these senses and the chemical structure is little understood. Of the four basic tastes (*i.e.* salt, sweet, sour and bitter) the acid taste is best defined. Its intensity is roughly dependent on the concentration of hydrogen ion present. RICHARDS[6] showed in 1898 that while qualitatively this is correct, from the quantitative point of view, the hydrogen-ion concentration is not the sole decisive factor concerned in the sour taste. It is true, however, that mineral acids, whose degree of dissociation is much greater than that of the organic acids, seem more sour to the palate. Furthermore, when a mineral acid is neutralized the sour flavor disappears; so complete is this disappearance that one can use the taste as an exact indicator for titrating an acid and for determining the end point with considerable precision.

However, in comparing the sour taste of acids with their dissociation constants quantitatively, many inconsistencies are found. KASTLE[7], for instance, has shown that a solution of acetic acid will taste more sour than an HCl solution of the same molar concentration, although the hydrogen ion concentration of the HCl is higher. In other words, various acid solutions of equally sour taste intensity do not possess equal concentrations of hydrogen ions, as would be expected. If, on the other hand, acid solutions of equal pH are compared, little ionized organic acids will generally taste more sour than completely ionized mineral acids. Such examples are numerous in actual practice in the food industry. HARVEY AND FULTON[8] tested 30 varieties of tomatoes the pH of which fell between 4.15 and 4.5 and found that their taste differed enormously, although their pH differed only little.

RICHARDS tried to explain these discrepancies by suggesting that the very act of tasting removes the dissociated part of the acid and so leaves room for further dissociation. The reason why weak organic acids taste more sour than mineral acids of the same pH is due to the buffering action of the saliva and consequent maintenance of $[H^+]$ at high level longer than in the case of H^+Cl^-, etc.[9].

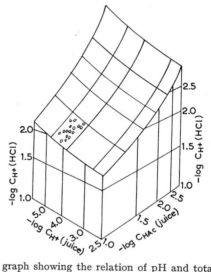

Fig. 44. Three-phase graph showing the relation of pH and total acidity to the taste of solutions (according to HARVEY).

Other investigators have obtained additional data showing that the degree of sourness is due also to factors other than free hydrogen ions. BREMOND[10] has shown that the sour taste of wines is determined more by the total titrable acidity than by pH: on aging, wines deposit a precipitate of cream of tartar, thus reducing their total acidity and degree of sourness without materially changing the pH value. Other investigators have looked for a different manifestation of the sour taste. RENQUIST is of the opinion that a definite relation exists between the coefficients of diffusion of various acids, and that there is some connection between the sour taste and the surface tension of acid solutions. Apparently, surface tension plays a certain role in this respect in "aromatic" acids such as acetic or tartaric.

HARVEY[11], in making an extensive study of the acid taste in fruit juices, chose hydrochloric acid as a standard for comparison: at a concentration of 0.025 N this acid is harmless to taste and is practically completely (97 %) dissociated, *i.e.* the hydrogen-ion concentration practically corresponds to the total titrable acidity. By choosing various buffers, HARVEY obtained solutions of equal pH although widely different in total titrable acidity. Lastly, he prepared, from acetic acid and sodium acetate, solutions of equal total acidity and different pH. Comparing these solutions with one another and with the chosen standard, and plotting the results of these tests on tri-dimensional Cartesian coordinates, HARVEY found that the sour taste is a function of two variables, pH and total acidity, as shown in Fig. 44. Later HARVEY confirmed these results by comparing various fruit and vegetable juices.

PAUL[12], using the method of dissociation constants, also compared various acid solutions with HCl and found that on the basis of taste the acids should be arranged as shown in Table IX, which does not agree with their dissociation constants.

TABLE IX

Compound	K
Carbonic acid (CO_2)	$3.04 \cdot 10^{-7}$
Acetic acid (CH_3COOH)	$1.82 \cdot 10^{-5}$
Lactic acid ($CH_3CH(OH)COOH$)	$1.38 \cdot 10^{-4}$
Hydrochloric acid (HCl)	∞
Tartaric acid ($COOH \cdot CH(OH) \cdot CH(OH) \cdot COOH$)	$9.7 \cdot 10^{-4}$

In this Table IX carbonic acid is the least and tartaric the most sour. These investigators, therefore, came to the same conclusion as the workers previously cited—namely, that the sour taste is affected not only by the cations but also by the nature of the anions, as well as by the undissociated molecules of the acid in question.

In conclusion it might be stated that sourness of various food products depends not only on the acids present and their degree of dissociation but also on the buffering systems of the particular food as well as on the presence

References p. 285

of flavorful substances and the rates of their diffusion into the taste receptors etc. Moreover the buffering action of saliva, mentioned before, should be taken into consideration.

Plant respiration

The two metabolic processes in the living cell (in animals, plants and in microorganisms) which are engaged in exploiting the energy contained in its food are fermentation and respiration. While fermentation (Chapter 6) results in products still rich in energy, respiration results in total breakdown of the carbohydrate into the simple oxides, CO_2 and H_2O, of very low potential energy. The substrates for this breakdown under aerobic conditions are simple hexoses, or other organic compounds, acids, fats, etc. The overall reaction of respiration for hexoses can be summarized as follows:

$$C_6H_{12}O_6 + 6\,O_2 = 6\,CO_2 + 6\,H_2O$$

Here, the "respiratory quotient" (*R.Q.*), *i.e.*, the ratio of the number of moles of CO_2 produced to the number of moles of O_2 taken up, will be equal to 1:

$$R.Q. = \frac{6\,CO_2}{6\,O_2} = 1$$

In the case of the oxidation of malic acid, for instance, which is richer in oxygen than an hexose, the *R.Q.* will be larger than 1:

$$C_4H_6O_5 + 3\,O_2 = 4\,CO_2 + 3\,H_2O$$

$$R.Q. = \frac{4\,CO_2}{3\,O_2} = 1.33$$

In the case of lipids, which are poorer in oxygen, the *R.Q.* is less than 1. By convention, the value for mixed fats is assumed to be 0.7.

It has now been established that both fermentation and respiration share a common stage, which is anaerobic, up to the point of formation of pyruvic acid. Thereafter, alcoholic fermentation continues under anaerobic conditions while respiration requires oxygen. Aerobic conditions are, in fact, required also by some other types of fermentations, such as citric acid formation by *Aspergillus niger*. On the other hand, lactic acid bacteria do their work under anaerobic conditions.

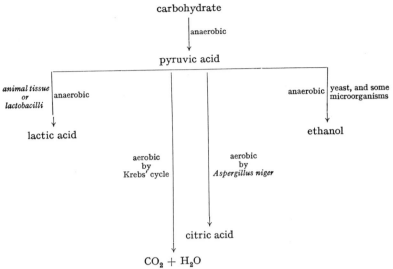

scheme showing the different paths for the breakdown of carbohydrates
by way of pyruvic acid

The tricarboxylic acid or KREBS' cycle

The respiration process begins with the condensation of pyruvic acid with
oxaloacetic acid (from the end of the cycle—see scheme below) to form citric
acid by dehydrogenation and decarboxylation. In fact, there are two steps
involved here:

(1) In the first step, *Coenzyme* A (CoA) and the DPN take part. CoA is engaged
in decarboxylation of the pyruvic acid and itself binds the remaining acetyl
group, while the DPN performs the dehydrogenation and is thereby reduced:

$$\text{HS}-\overline{\text{CoA}} + \text{CH}_3\text{CO}\cdot\text{COOH} + \text{DPN} \longrightarrow \text{CH}_3\text{CO}-\text{S}-\overline{\text{CoA}} + \text{CO}_2 + \text{DPN}\cdot\text{H}_2$$

CoA   Acetyl CoA

(2) In the second step, it has been convincingly demonstrated that a so-
called " condensing enzyme" catalyzes the reaction between oxaloacetic acid
and the acetyl–Coenzyme A complex to form citric acid:

$$
\begin{array}{c}
\text{CH}_2\cdot\text{COOH} \\
| \\
\text{CO}\cdot\text{COOH}
\end{array}
+ \text{acetyl–CoA} \xrightarrow[\substack{\text{condensing} \\ \text{enzyme}}]{+\text{H}_2\text{O}}
\begin{array}{c}
\text{CH}_2\cdot\text{COOH} \\
| \\
\text{C(OH)}\cdot\text{COOH} \\
| \\
\text{CH}_2\cdot\text{COOH}
\end{array}
+ \text{Coenzyme A}
$$

oxaloacetic acid   citric acid

(3) The citric acid formed in this way is held in equilibrium with its isomer isocitric acid and the aconitic acid through the enzyme *aconitase*:

$$
\begin{array}{c}
\text{CH}_2 \cdot \text{COOH} \\
| \\
\text{C(OH)} \cdot \text{COOH} \\
| \\
\text{CH}_2 \cdot \text{COOH} \\
\text{citric acid}
\end{array}
\quad
\underset{+\text{H}_2\text{O}}{\overset{-\text{H}_2\text{O}}{\rightleftarrows}}
\quad
\begin{array}{c}
\text{CH}_2 \cdot \text{COOH} \\
| \\
\text{C} \cdot \text{COOH} \\
\| \\
\text{CH} \cdot \text{COOH} \\
\textit{cis}\text{-aconitic acid}
\end{array}
\quad
\underset{-\text{H}_2\text{O}}{\overset{+\text{H}_2\text{O}}{\rightleftarrows}}
\quad
\begin{array}{c}
\text{CH}_2\text{COOH} \\
| \\
\text{CH} \cdot \text{COOH} \\
| \\
\text{CH(OH)COOH} \\
\text{isocitric acid}
\end{array}
$$

(4) In the next step, isocitric acid loses 2H to a *dehydrogenase* containing TPN to form oxalosuccinic acid:

$$
\begin{array}{c}
\text{CH}_2 \cdot \text{COOH} \\
| \\
\text{CH} \cdot \text{COOH} + \text{TPN} \\
| \\
\text{CH(OH)} \cdot \text{COOH} \\
\text{isocitric acid}
\end{array}
\quad
\overset{-2\text{H}}{\rightleftarrows}
\quad
\begin{array}{c}
\text{CH}_2\text{COOH} \\
| \\
\text{CH} \cdot \text{COOH} + \text{TPNH}_2 \\
| \\
\text{CO} \cdot \text{COOH} \\
\text{oxalosuccinic acid}
\end{array}
$$

(5), (6) The oxalosuccinic acid is further decarboxylated in two stages, first into α-keto-glutaric acid and then to succinic acid, by the action of Coenzyme A and DPN. This step conforms again to an oxidative decarboxylation in which TPP and probably thioctic acid too takes part.

$$
\begin{array}{c}
\text{CH}_2\text{COOH} \\
| \\
\text{CH} \cdot \text{COOH} \\
| \\
\text{CO} \cdot \text{COOH} \\
\text{oxalo-} \\
\text{succinic acid}
\end{array}
\quad
\underset{\substack{\textit{oxalosuccinic} \\ \textit{carboxylase}}}{\overset{-\text{CO}_2}{\rightleftarrows}}
\quad
\begin{array}{c}
\text{CH}_2 \cdot \text{COOH} \\
| \\
\text{CH}_2 \\
| \\
\text{CO} \cdot \text{COOH} + \text{HS} \cdot \overline{\text{CoA}} \\
\text{α-keto-} \\
\text{glutaric acid}
\end{array}
\quad
\overset{-\text{CO}_2}{\underset{+\text{DPN}}{\longrightarrow}}
\quad
\begin{array}{c}
\text{CH}_2 \cdot \text{COOH} \\
| \\
\text{CH}_2 \\
| \\
\text{CO} - \text{S} \cdot \overline{\text{CoA}} \\
\text{succinyl-CoA}
\end{array}
\quad
\overset{\text{GDP}}{\underset{+\text{H}_3\text{PO}_4}{\longrightarrow}}
\quad
\begin{array}{c}
\text{COOH} \\
| \\
\text{CH}_2 + \text{HS} \cdot \overline{\text{C}} \\
| \quad\quad + \text{GTP} \\
\text{CH}_2 \\
| \\
\text{COOH} \\
\text{succinic acid}
\end{array}
$$

The forming of succinic acid is probably coupled with a phosphorylating mechanism when the energy is transferred with a phosphoric acid residue to form guanosine triphosphate (GTP) from guanosine diphosphate (GDP).

(7) The oxidation is continued by means of *succinic acid dehydrogenase* which splits off 2H from succinic acid only to attach it to a flavoprotein, thereby forming fumaric acid:

$$
\begin{array}{c}
\text{CH}_2 \cdot \text{COOH} \\
| \\
\text{CH}_2\text{COOH} \\
\text{succinic acid}
\end{array}
+ \text{FAD}
\quad
\overset{\substack{\textit{succinic acid} \\ \textit{dehydrogenase}}}{\rightleftarrows}
\quad
\begin{array}{c}
\text{HC} \cdot \text{COOH} \\
\| \\
\text{HOOC} \cdot \text{CH} \\
\text{fumaric acid}
\end{array}
+ \text{FAD} \cdot \text{H}_2
$$

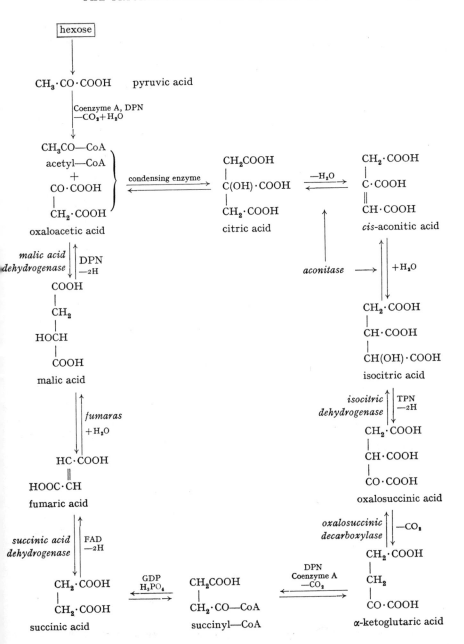

Fig. 45. Tricarboxylic acid or KREBS' cycle.

This reaction can be easily inhibited by malonic acid whose structure is somewhat similar to that of succinic acid, having only three carbon atoms instead of four ($HOOC \cdot CH_2 \cdot COOH$). In this case, malonic acid acts as an antimetabolite.

(8) In the next step, fumaric acid is hydrated into malic acid, this reaction being catalyzed by the enzyme *fumurase*:

$$
\begin{array}{ccc}
\begin{array}{l} HC \cdot COOH \\ \parallel \\ HOOC \cdot CH \end{array} & \xrightarrow[\longleftarrow]{\textit{fumarase} + H_2O} & \begin{array}{l} CH \cdot (OH) \cdot COOH \\ | \\ CH_2 \cdot COOH \end{array} \\
\text{fumaric acid} & & \text{malic acid}
\end{array}
$$

(9) The last step in the respiration cycle consists again of the dehydrogenation of malic acid by means of DPN, converting it to oxaloacetic acid, which is now ready to accept a further molecule of acetyl-CoA and to start the cycle anew:

$$
\begin{array}{l} CH(OH) \cdot COOH \\ | \\ CH_2COOH \end{array}
+ DPN
\xrightarrow{-2H}
\begin{array}{l} CO \cdot COOH \\ | \\ CH_2COOH \end{array}
+ DPNH_2
$$

Enzymes of the respiration cycle

Decarboxylation. In the first step of the respiration cycle, decarboxylation takes part by means of Coenzyme A. The prosthetic group active in this enzyme works together with that catalyzing the decarboxylation of pyruvic acid during fermentation under anaerobic conditions *i.e.* with the thiamine pyrophosphate (co-*carboxylase*)—the phosphorylated vitamin B_1. This reaction can also take place *in vitro* by means of ground plant tissues and works equally well with all α-keto aliphatic acids, such as pyruvic, α-keto-glutaric and oxalosuccinic acids, according to the general scheme:

$$
R\!-\!CO \cdot COOH \xrightarrow[\textit{carboxylase}]{} RCHO + CO_2
$$

During fermentation, pyruvic acid is decarboxylated to acetaldehyde according to the following scheme:

$$
\begin{array}{l} CH_3C \cdot COOH \\ \parallel \\ O \end{array}
\longrightarrow
\begin{array}{l} CH_3CH + CO_2 \\ \parallel \\ O \end{array}
$$

The so-called *Coenzyme A* (see page 196) is widely distributed in nature and plays a decisive role in many metabolic processes.

The mechanism of decarboxylation of oxalosuccinic acid into α-keto-glutaric acid is a matter for speculation. Some authorities are of the opinion that this step is performed by a similar enzyme, as in the case of pyruvic acid during fermentation, namely, *oxalosuccinic carboxylase*, in which the prosthetic group is the phosphorylated thiamine (vitamin B_1). Other investigators[13] suggest that this step is not catalyzed by a separate *decarboxylase* but proceeds *via* the mediation of *isocitric dehydrogenase* itself; in other words, this isocitric enzyme has a double function of both dehydrogenation and decarboxylation. After this, the next decarboxylation of α-keto-glutaric acid into succinic acid is again tackled by *Coenzyme A*.

Dehydrogenation. The enzymes catalyzing the dehydrogenation reactions in the KREBS' cycle apparently also differ in nature: while the first stage during pyruvic acid decarboxylation by Coenzyme A is carried out in the presence of a *dehydrogenase* containing DPN, the dehydrogenation of isocitric acid into oxaloacetic acid is catalyzed by TPN.

Finally, DPN-linked *malic acid dehydrogenase* yields oxaloacetic acid. In the dehydrogenation of succinic acid into fumaric acid, another enzyme is involved, which is apparently the FAD. For a summary of these enzymes see also Chapter 19.

Phosphorylation. A phosphorylation step, with the aid of GDP, is also involved in this cycle, namely in the decarboxylation of α-keto-glutaric acid into succinic acid by Coenzyme A. The GDP seems to be in equilibrium with the adenylic acid system of ADP.

HANS KREBS received the Nobel prize in 1953 in physiology for his work in elucidating the respiration cycle[14]. The above schemes have been supplemented by the results obtained by other investigators since the first publications of KREBS[15].

The accumulation of specific individual acids in certain fruits, such as citric acid in various citrus fruits, or malic acid in apples and pears, is explained by probable interference in the various enzymatic systems engaged in the respiration cycle. This may be due to the presence of a substance, which plays the role of an antimetabolite and which interferes with the activity of a certain enzyme, or it may be due to the weaker activity of one enzyme than of an other.

Evolution of CO_2 during storage of fruits and vegetables and the diminution of malic acid in stored apples, for instance, can, of course, be explained by their continued respiration after picking. It must be pointed out that the acids in plant tissues are usually combined with various cations and, in such a state, they create buffers, which protect the plant from excessive shocks that can be caused through sudden changes in pH. The plant receives its cations from the soil and most of them are bound to organic acids (57–73 %), as shown by BARTHOLOMEW AND SINCLER (see Ref. 15), thus one can explain the transfer of the cations in plants. The mechanism of metabolic transformations of aliphatic acids in plants, and especially in various fruits, is still a matter for conjecture.

Of special interest are experiments[16] which show diurnal variations in the levels of malic and citric acids as against starch in excised leaves. In the dark, the acid level rises with a concomitant fall in the starch content, while during the day, when photosynthesis is in progress, the opposite occurs (Fig. 46).

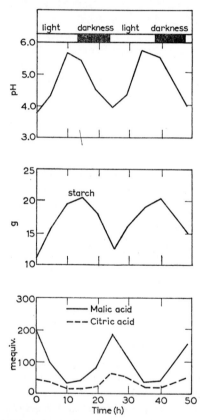

Fig. 46. Diurnal variations of organic acids, starch and pH in excised leaves (according to H. B. VICKERY, *Plant Physiol.*, 27 (1952) 9).

The pentose oxidation cycle

The anaerobic breakdown of carbohydrates during fermentation and the aerobic pathway during respiration which begins with pyruvic acid proceed mainly according to the EMBDEN–MEYERHOF pathway followed by the KREBS tricarboxylic acid cycle. The EMBDEN–MEYERHOF scheme is the exclusive route during fermentation as well as during the conversion of glycogen into pyruvic acid in animal muscle. The KREBS' cycle is probably responsible for 90 % of the carbohydrate metabolism during respiration. Nevertheless, it is of importance to mention that additional metabolic pathways have been recently shown to exist in plants, in some animal tissues and in several types of microorganisms. One of such alternative routes recognized only recently by HORECKER[17, 18] in 1953 is the so-called "pentose-cycle", which involves the oxidation of glucose 6-phosphate to 6-phosphogluconic acid and the conversion of the latter into pentose phosphate. This HORECKER–WARBURG–DICKENS route (see also the Calvin cycle, Chapter 4) bears considerable likeliness to the dark reaction in photosynthesis, but in reverse.

It has been known for some time that an enzyme *glucose-6-phosphate dehydrogenase*, which contains TPN, is capable of catalyzing the oxidation of D-glucopyranose-6-phosphate into 6-phosphogluconic acid. As a first step gluconolactone is received. This hydrolyses spontaneously to 6-phosphogluconic acid. The β-keto-acid produced after further dehydration is easily decarboxylised. An enzyme, named *6-phosphogluconic acid dehydrogenase*, found in *Escherichia coli*, is capable of catalyzing the oxidative decarboxylation of this acid to form D-ribulose 5-phosphate:

$$
\begin{array}{llll}
\text{CHO} & \text{COOH} & \text{COOH} & \\
\text{HCOH} & \text{HCOH} & \text{HCOH} & \text{CH}_2\text{OH} \\
\text{HOCH} \xrightarrow[\text{TPNH}_2]{\text{TPN}} & \text{HOCH} \xrightarrow{-2\text{H}} & \text{C}=\text{O} \xrightarrow{-\text{CO}_2} & \text{C}=\text{O} \\
\text{HCOH} & \text{HCOH} & \text{HCOH} & \text{HCOH} \\
\text{HCOH} & \text{HCOH} & \text{HCOH} & \text{HCOH} \\
\text{CH}_2\text{O}\cdot\text{PO}_3\text{H}_2 & \text{CH}_2\text{O}\cdot\text{PO}_3\text{H}_2 & \text{CH}_2\text{O}\cdot\text{PO}_3\text{H}_2 & \text{CH}_2\text{O}\cdot\text{PO}_3\text{H}_2
\end{array}
$$

glucose 6-phosphate   6-phosphogluconic acid   6-phospho-3-keto gluconic acid   ribulose 5-phosphate

The oxidation of glucose into gluconic acid can be effected also by means of a microbial *glucose oxidase* (see Chapter 20).

The pentose so obtained forms an equilibrium between xylulose-5-phosphate and ribose 5-phosphate. These two pentoses are transformed by means of the enzyme *transketolase* into a triose and a seven carbon compound, glyceraldehyde 3-phosphate and sedoheptulose 7-phosphate, respectively. The dihydroxy-acetone portion of the sedoheptulose is easily cleaved by another enzyme, *transaldolase*, and transferred to the glyceraldehyde to form an hexose, while the remaining 4-carbon sugar (erythrose 4-phosphate) combines further with a pentose, as shown in Fig. 47 (see also page 42).

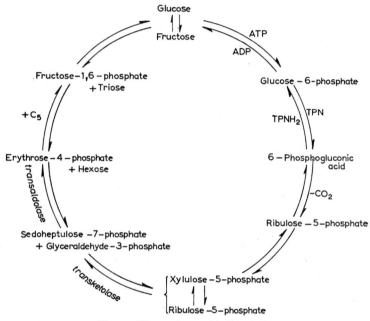

Fig. 47. The pentose oxidation cycle.

The overall reaction of hexose oxidation *via* the pentose cycle can be summarized as follows:

$$6C_6 + 6O_2 \longrightarrow 6C_5 + 6CO_2 + 6H_2O$$

$$4C_5 \longrightarrow 2C_6 + 2C_4$$

$$2C_5 + 2C_4 \longrightarrow 2C_6 + 2C_3$$

$$2C_3 \longrightarrow C_6$$

In other words, only one hexose molecule out of every 6 entering the cycle is changed into 6 CO_2 and 6 H_2O, the remaining 5 molecules enter the cycle again.

REFERENCES

[1] A. C. HULME, Some aspects of the biochemistry of apple and pear fruits, *Advances in Food Research*, 8 (1958) 329.

[2] B. D. DAVIS, *Harvey Lectures*, 50 (1956) 230.

[3] J. B. S. BRAVERMAN, *Citrus Products*, Interscience Publishers, New York, 1949.

[4] E. T. BARTHOLOMEW AND W. B. SINKLER, *The Lemon Fruit*, Univ. of Calif. Press, 1951.

[5] W. B. SINKLER, *The Orange*, Univ. of Calif. Press, 1961.

[6] T. W. RICHARDS, The relation of the taste of acids to their degree of dissociation, *Am. Chem. J.*, 20 (1898) 121.

[7] J. H. KASTLE, On the taste and affinity of acids, *Am. Chem. J.*, 20 (1898)466.

[8] R. B. HARVEY AND R. R. FULTON, Relation of pH and total acidity to the taste of tomatoes, *Fruit Products J.*, 14 (1935) 238.

[9] STEVENS, *Handbook of Experimental Psychology*, John Wiley, New York, 1951, p. 1148.

[10] E. BREMOND, *Contribution à l'Etude Analytique et Physico-chimique de l'Acidité des Vins*, Algeria, 1937.

[11] R. B. HARVEY, The relation between the total acidity, the concentration of hydrogen ion and the taste of acid solutions, *J. Am. Chem. Soc.*, 42 (1920) 712.

[12] TH. PAUL, Physikalische-chemische Untersuchungen über die Säure Geschmacks-empfindung, *Z. Electrochem.*, 27 (1921) 539.

[13] S. OCHOA, in J. B. SUMNER AND K. MYRBÄCK, *The Enzymes*, Academic Press, New York, 1952, chap. 72.

[14] H. A. KREBS, *Advances in Enzymol.*, 3 (1943) 191.

[15] H. A. KREBS AND W. A. JOHNSON, *Enzymologia*, 4 (1937) 148.

[16] H. B. VICKERY, *Plant Physiol.*, 27 (1952) 9.

[17] B. L. HORECKER, A new pathway for the oxidation of carbohydrate, *Brewers Dig.*, 28 (1953) 214.

[18] B. L. HORECKER, J. HURWITZ AND A. WEISSBACH, Xylulose-5-phosphate and the formation of sedoheptulose-7-phosphate with liver transketolase, *J. Am. Chem. Soc.*, 78 (1956) 692.

SELECTED BIBLIOGRAPHY TO CHAPTER 18

BENNETT-CLARK, T. A., Organic acids in plants, *Ann. Rev. Biochem.*, 18 (1949) 639.

BONNER, J., *Plant Biochemistry*, Academic Press, New York, 1950.

CHAPTER 19

BIOLOGICAL OXIDATION — ENZYMATIC BROWNING

Types of oxidation

In the previous chapter, we discussed the respiration mechanism of the living cell in accordance with the KREBS' cycle. Before we approach the question of the various oxidation phenomena in the plant material detached from its living source or in the ruptured cell, it seems appropriate to summarize the different types of oxidation reactions. In general, there are three forms of oxidation:

(a) The direct combination of molecular oxygen with another atom, let us say the combustion of coal in air with the production of carbon dioxide:

$$C + O_2 \rightarrow CO_2$$

The same type of oxidation is also found in some enzymatic reactions under aerobic conditions where the enzyme transfers the hydrogen acquired from the substrate directly to molecular oxygen. An example of such an enzyme, an *"aerobic" dehydrogenase*, is, for instance, the *Schardinger* enzyme (*xanthine oxidase*). This enzyme is a metalloprotein containing iron and molybdenum as well as FAD as the prosthetic group. The *Schardinger* enzyme will catalyze the direct oxidation of a great number of aldehydes into the corresponding acids as well as xanthine and hypoxanthine into uric acid (see Chapter 12).

(b) The second type of oxidation is *anaerobic oxidation*, or rather dehydrogenation. A number of substances are known which can act as hydrogen acceptors in the absolute absence of oxygen. One such substance is methylene blue, which is capable of adding hydrogen, thereby going over to its colorless leucoform. THUNBERG elaborated a method using a special reaction vessel (the THUNBERG tube) in which anaerobic oxidation can be demonstrated and measured (Fig. 48). The substrate together with methylene blue (MB) in an appropriate buffer are placed in the tube, while the enzyme is placed in a separate arm, which forms part of the hollow stopper. After closing the tube it is completely evacuated and the enzyme is then poured into the tube where it combines with the substrate. If the enzyme catalyzes the oxidation reaction the methylene blue will decolorize to become MBH_2. For example:

$$CH_3 \cdot CH_2OH + MB \quad \underset{\textit{reductase}}{\overset{\textit{dehydrogenase}}{\rightleftarrows}} \quad CH_3CHO + MBH_2$$

    ethanol   methylene   acetalde-   reduced
               blue   hyde   leucoform

The rate of the reaction can be measured with a stopwatch if the concentrations of the substrate and the enzyme are known.

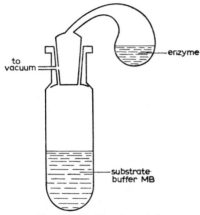

Fig. 48. The Thunberg tube.

It is not always easy to see how such oxidation reactions can proceed without oxygen. How, for instance, can glyceraldehyde acquire oxygen under anaerobic conditions to be oxidized into glyceric acid? Such oxidation reactions are explained by the presence of even small amounts of an hydrate of the substrate, in this case, aldehyde hydrate:

$$
\begin{array}{ccc}
\text{CHO} & \overset{\text{HO}\diagdown \diagup \text{OH}}{\text{CH}} & \text{COOH} \\
| & | & | \\
\text{CH} \cdot \text{OH} + \text{H}_2\text{O} \longrightarrow & \text{CH} \cdot \text{OH} + \text{MB} \longrightarrow & \text{CH} \cdot \text{OH} + \text{MBH}_2 \\
| & | & | \\
\text{CH}_2\text{OH} & \text{CH}_2\text{OH} & \text{CH}_2\text{OH} \\
\text{glycer-} & \text{aldehyde} & \text{glyceric} \\
\text{aldehyde} & \text{hydrate} & \text{acid}
\end{array}
$$

Similar reactions of oxidative decarboxylation have been described on page 159 in Chapter 12. All these reactions are possible under anaerobic conditions, due to hydration of the substrate, but they also require an hydrogen acceptor, such as MB above. However, in most biochemical reactions, it is the enzymes, the *dehydrogenases*, which play the role of hydrogen acceptors. These so-called "anaerobic" *dehydrogenases*, such as DPN or TPN are hydrogen acceptors, and are readily reduced to $DPNH_2$ or $TPNH_2$. We have met with such reactions in the previous chapters. The dehydrogenation step of succinic acid into fumaric acid in the KREBS' cycle is one example:

$$
\begin{array}{l}
CH_2 \cdot COOH \\
| \qquad\qquad + DPN \rightleftarrows \\
CH_2 \cdot COOH
\end{array}
\qquad
\begin{array}{l}
CH \cdot COOH \\
\| \qquad\qquad + DPNH_2 \\
HOOC \cdot HC
\end{array}
$$

$$\text{succinic acid} \qquad\qquad\qquad \text{fumaric acid}$$

A similar reaction is the oxidation of lactic acid, during the glycogen metabolism, in the human body, into pyruvic acid:

$$CH_3 \cdot CHOH \cdot COOH + DPN \rightleftarrows CH_3CO \cdot COOH + DPNH_2$$
$$\text{lactic acid} \qquad\qquad\qquad \text{pyruvic acid}$$

However, the small quantity of the enzyme must have a large turnover and the $DPNH_2$ cannot react directly with molecular oxygen and therefore, before this can occur, several steps must take place. First, these reduced anaerobic *dehydrogenases* exchange their hydrogen with other enzymes, namely flavoproteins (FP), such as those containing FMN or FAD:

$$DPNH_2 + FMN \rightleftarrows DPN + FMNH_2$$

In these interchanges $DPNH_2$ and $TPNH_2$ are the substrates of the flavoproteins (FP). At this stage, there is a switch from hydrogen transfer to electron transfer, as will be explained presently.

(c) The third form of oxidation is "electron transfer". In the reaction of zinc metal with copper sulfate, for instance, the atom of zinc is said to be "oxidized" by losing two electrons and the cupric ion is reduced to the Cu atom by accepting two electrons:

$$Zn + Cu^{2+}SO_4^{2-} \longrightarrow Zn^{2+}SO_4^{2-} + Cu$$

$$\text{or:} \quad Zn - 2e^- \longrightarrow Zn^{2+} \quad \text{and} \quad Cu^{2+} + 2e^- \longrightarrow Cu$$

A similar situation exists in the last step of biological oxidation. *Cytochrome c reductase* is an example of these enzymes, which are classed as *electron carriers*. The molecular weight of cytochrome *c* is only 13,000, comprising about 50 to 100 amino acids, and being a rather small protein, it is difficult to call it an enzyme. Its prosthetic group is a metalloporphyrin (see formula in Chapter 12, page 158) containing iron. The action of cytochrome *c* may be presented as follows:

$$\text{cytochrome } c \text{ Fe}^{3+} \quad \underset{-e^-}{\overset{+e^-}{\rightleftarrows}} \quad \text{cytochrome } c \text{ Fe}^{2+}$$

One can perceive now the last stage of the anaerobic oxidation reactions described above. The $FMNH_2$ which has received its hydrogen from $DPNH_2$ transfers its electrons to cytochrome *c* which, in turn, is oxidized by molecular oxygen, thereby forming a molecule of water. This oxidation of cytochrome *c* is catalyzed by yet another enzyme, *cytochrome reductase*. The following scheme, using BALDWIN's[1] method of representation shows the changes involved:

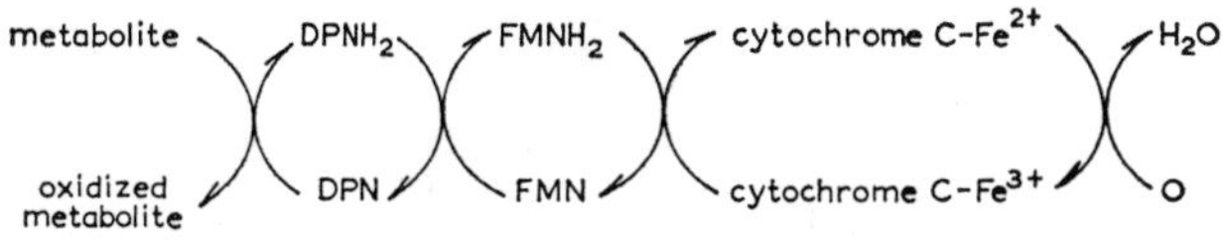

The redox potential

It is evident from the above that these various coenzymes have different relative tendencies to act as reducing or oxidizing agents: the greater the tendency of a reducing agent to lose its hydrogen, the more powerful it is, *viz.*, it exerts a greater hydrogen pressure. This hydrogen pressure can be quantitatively measured by a method based on the fact that some substances are known which will impart their hydrogen to metallic gold or platinum. An example of such a substance is a solution containing ferrous and ferric ions. The Fe^{2+} ion has the tendency to release electrons, thereby being converted into Fe^{3+}, ion, while the latter tends to receive electrons and thus changes to the Fe^{2+} ion:

$$Fe^{2+} \quad \underset{+e^-}{\overset{-e^-}{\rightleftarrows}} \quad Fe^{3+}$$

Hydroquinone, which is easily oxidized into quinone, is another such oxidation–reduction system.

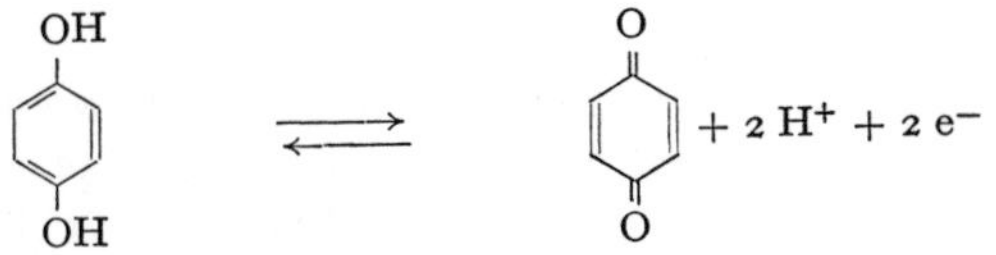

The potential of such systems can be measured if a platinum electrode is dipped into the system and the hydrogen pressure compared with a standard oxidation–reduction system of a known potential. One such standard cell is obtained by bubbling hydrogen through distilled water at a pressure of I atm, when some of its atoms are adsorbed on the electrode and are dissociated into equal quantities of ions and electrons. A glass electrode may be used instead of the hydrogen cell.

The standard cell and that containing the oxidation–reduction system under investigation are connected by a salt bridge, namely a tube containing KCl in an agar-agar gel, which permits the migration of ions but prevents interaction between the adjacent systems. The difference in the hydrogen or electron pressures between the standard cell and that of the given system is measured by a potentiometer, as shown by the schematic representation in Fig. 49.

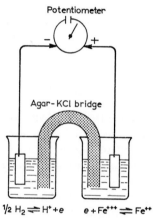

Fig. 49. Schematic assembly for measuring the redox potentials.

The oxidation–reduction (O–R) potential, often called the *redox potential* is, therefore, the potential difference (the difference in hydrogen tension) between the Pt electrode and the hydrogen electrode (or the glass electrode). The unit now accepted (DIXON[2]) is termed the *rH*, which is the logarithm of the hydrogen pressure (P_H) with a negative sign:

$$rH = -\log_{10}P_H$$

The *rH* scale runs from zero ($rH = 0$) when the hydrogen pressure is one atmosphere to the value of $rH = 41$ at I atmosphere pressure of oxygen. Whenever possible, the measurements should be made at pH 7, however, if this is impractical the measurements should be made at a given constant pH and the rH corrected accordingly: by adding 0.06 volt to the value of rH for every unit of pH smaller than 7 or subtracting 0.06 volt for every pH unit higher than 7.

For a mixture of hydroquinone and quinone, for instance, in equal proportions at pH 7 the hydrogen tension is $1 \cdot 10^{-23}$, hence $rH = 23$. Table X gives a few examples of approximate rH values.

TABLE X

Substance	rH
Fruit juices	22–23
Yeast suspensions (in active fermentation)	9
Lactobacilli	5–12
Anaerobic fermentation (bact. E. coli)	0
DPN and TPN dehydrogenases	8
Flavoproteins (FMN and FAD)	14
Cytochrome c	23

The climacteric cycle

So far, the discussion has been concerned with biological oxidations in living matter. The position is entirely different when the living cell is ruptured or even when it has been detached from its living source, as is the case when

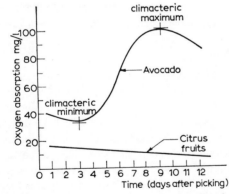

Fig. 50. The climacteric respiration cycle of fruits after picking[2a].

fruits are picked from the tree. Under these circumstances, the fruits continue to respire (to absorb O_2 and to expel CO_2), some of them at a greatly accelerated rate going through the so-called *climacteric cycles*, as shown in Fig. 50.

References p. 301

As can be seen from Fig. 50, the avocado fruit reaches a minimum in absorbing oxygen 2–3 days after picking; however, very soon the absorption of oxygen increases considerably, reaching a climacteric maximum after approx. 10 days. At this stage the fruit reaches its full maturity and after this is apt to deteriorate quickly unless it is stored under special conditions of low temperature and controlled atmosphere. Most fruits, such as apples, pears, bananas and all deciduous fruits, behave very similarly to the avocado. Citrus fruits, after picking, are a distinct exception to this kind of behavior. The factors which distinguish citrus from other fruits in respect to oxidation will be seen presently.

Fig. 51 shows the arrangement of the simple equipment necessary for measuring the climacteric cycle of fruits. The entering air measured in a flow meter, dried and freed from CO_2 comes in contact with the fruits. The amount of CO_2 absorbed by NaOH in the measuring flask is then determined.

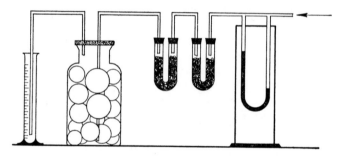

Fig. 51. Apparatus for measuring the climacteric cycle.

The ruptured plant tissue

The foregoing discussion relates to oxidation phenomena in the unbroken living cell. There, the various biochemical reactions are reversible and are regulated by the requirements of the living matter. However, when the tissues are ruptured or when they undergo some physiological change, such as at the post-maturity stage or upon freezing, these various biochemical reactions suddenly proceed in one particular direction, and at an accelerated pace. For instance, the tannin substances in a pear would normally decrease slowly in the fruit on the tree during the weeks approaching maturity. If, however, the same fruit is crushed into pulp, the tannin content will rapidly decrease and probably disappear in a few hours. Indeed, this phenomenon is made use of in industry in order to eliminate the pronounced astringency of fruit juices caused by tannins.

Another salient example is the decrease of malic acid in crushed apples, which is apparently caused by the release of the enzyme *malic acid dehydro-genase* (this reaction being the last step in KREBS' respiration cycle, see Chapter 18).

Table XI shows the disappearance of malic acid in apple juice.

TABLE XI

Stage	Malic acid (g/l)
Immediately after pressing	8.8
Juice pressed 24 h after disintegration of fruit	5.1
Pressed after 48 h	3.7

One of the very well known phenomena in daily life is the quick browning of fruits such as apples, bananas, avocado or of potatoes when peeled or cut and exposed to the air. This is caused by enzymatic oxidation, which will be

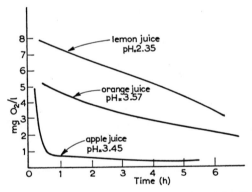

Fig. 52. Oxygen absorption by various juices[26].

discussed presently in detail. But even before this takes place, the plant tissues combine rapidly with the dissolved oxygen, as shown by the following experiment (Fig. 52). In this experiment, various juices were shaken with oxygen, at the time, $t = 0$, for one minute. The remaining oxygen in the juices was measured at various time intervals by a polarographic method.

The curves in Fig. 52 clearly show that:

(a) all fruit juices undergo oxidative processes after their extraction;

(b) while in citrus juices the disappearance of oxygen is slow, in apple juice the bulk of the oxygen disappears in the first half of an hour;

References p. 301

(c) citrus fruits, which do not brown in the air, conduct themselves in this case very similarly during the climacteric cycle, mentioned earlier; in both cases their rate of combining with molecular oxygen is more steady, while the rate of both respiration and of oxidation in apples and, in fact, in all fruits subjected to enzymatic browning is much faster.

Enzymatic browning

The recognition of the enzymatic nature of this type of browning in certain fruits should probably be ascribed to LINDET[3] as far back as 1895. However, it was ONSLOW[4] who showed, in 1920, that the enzymatic darkening of plant tissues in air is due to the presence of o-dihydroxy-phenol derivatives such as catechol, protocatechuic acid, and caffeic acid as well as hydroxy-gallic acid esters of caffeic acid, such as chlorogenic acid, which is widely distributed in many fruits and especially in potatoes and sweet potatoes (see page 271).

OH
OH

catechol

All these and other phenolic substances of similar structure, including the tannins, are abundant in nature and are probably formed by the breakdown of anthocyanins and flavanoids.

ONSLOW made a systematic investigation of many fruits and vegetables and divided them into two groups: those containing catechol substances as well as the appropriate enzymes, to which she gave the name *oxygenases*, and those plants lacking *oxygenases* and catechol compounds, which she named *"peroxidase plants"*. To the first group belong the following fruits: apples, peaches, apricots, bananas, cherries, grapes, pears, strawberries, figs and, of the vegetables, potatoes and red beets. The *peroxidase* group of fruits comprise the various citrus fruits, pineapple, melon, black and red currants and most other berries.

More recent investigations have shown that the enzymes *peroxidase* and *catalase* are always present in both groups, while the *"oxygenases"* are absent in the second group. The divison into two distinct groups is probably not quite correct, for while in the second group neither the enzyme nor the phenolic compounds are present, there are cases in which only one of the essential requirements is missing. Such is the case with the Sunbeam peach, for instance, which has been shown[5] to be deficient in phenolic substances, although the normal enzyme was present.

The enzymes responsible for the enzymatic browning have been assigned different names: the name *oxygenase* is no longer used, instead *phenolase*, *polyphenolase* and *polyphenol oxidase* are applied. This entire class of enzymes is characterized by possessing Cu as their prosthetic group, and comprises a number of *phenolases*:

(a) *Tyrosinase*—a monophenol *oxidase* capable of catalyzing the amino acid, tyrosine, into *o*-quinone-phenylalanine. Tyrosine undergoes initial hydroxylation with the formation of 3,4-dihydroxyphenylalanine (DOPA), which is further oxidized:

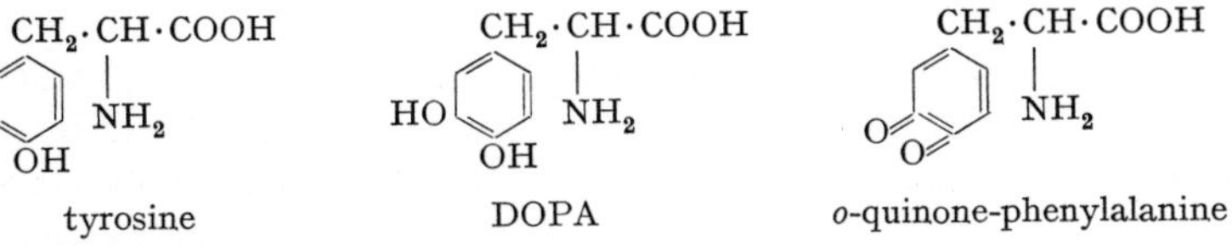

tyrosine   DOPA   *o*-quinone-phenylalanine

(b) *Catecholase*—a polyphenol *oxidase*, which catalyzes the oxidation of catechol and other similar phenolic compounds:

(c) *Laccase*—also a polyphenol *oxidase* catalyzing the oxidation of laccol, a phenolic substance found in Japanese latex, which turns black on oxidation:

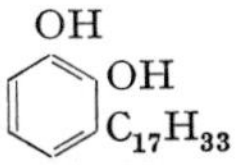

laccol

Laccase is also active with diphenols in the *para* position, but does not act with monohydric phenols. It is important to note that, as long as indivudal *phenolases* have not been isolated and crystallized, one cannot be sure that some of them are not mixtures of several *phenolases*. So far, we know that the source of the *phenolases* is often responsible for their mode of action. An excellent summary of all this work is presented in the review by JOSLYN AND PONTING[6].

(d) *Ascorbinase*—is also a Cu-containing oxidative enzyme, catalyzing the oxidation of ascorbic acid (vitamin C) into dehydroascorbic acid (see Chapter 14).

References p. 301

The second group of oxidative enzymes found in practically all plant tissues, *peroxidase, catalase* and *cytochromes* have been found now not to take part in enzymatic browning. *Peroxidase* is capable of oxidizing phenolic substances only in the presence of H_2O_2. All these enzymes contain the same prosthetic group, iron porphyrin, with a different apoenzyme. The apoenzyme of *peroxidase* contains the amino acids histidine, lysine, arginine and a polysaccharide. The structural formula of the prosthetic group and its linkage to the protein are given in Chapter 12, page 158.

Properties of oxidative enzymes

An extract of *phenolases* is usually obtained by macerating the plant tissue, such as potato skins, with 50 % acetone in water at 0°C, then storing it at a very low temperature (— 60 to — 75°C). The purification of these enzymes is usually done by fractional precipitation in ammonium sulfate solutions. Two methods can be used for determining which substrates are affected by a given *phenolase*: either the substrate is oxidized first and the oxidized products are then separated chromatographically, or the reverse is carried out—a chromatogram of the substrate is prepared and then sprayed with the enzyme suspension.

TABLE XII

Enzyme	Temp. range of activity (°C)	Optimum temp. (°C)
Apple *phenolase*	5–65	40.0
Olive *oxidase*	5–40	31.5
Grape *peroxidase*	0–40	36.3
Guava *peroxidase*	5–50	50.0

The *phenolases* are not stable even at comparatively low temperatures. *Peroxidase*, on the other hand, is one of the most stable enzymes, and its inactivation takes a long time. The Table XII gives a few examples of the temperature range of the optima for the activity of these enzymes.

At a temperature of 85–95°C all the *phenolases* are inactivated in a short time, while it sometimes takes as long as five minutes to inactivate *peroxidase*. When using the blanching process for the inactivation of these enzymes before processing fruits, there is always a struggle to achieve complete inactivation without injuring the flavor and texture of the final product, each case must then be judged on its own merits: for instance, insufficient blanching of cut fruits intended for freezing may result in discoloration of the inner layers which still contain active enzymes.

Besides heat, these enzymes can also be inactivated by the presence of ions of heavy metals, halogens, sulfites, cyanides, ultrasonic and radio waves of high frequency. The halogen salts and sulfites are most frequently applied for practical use in the food industry. Only $1 \cdot 10^{-2}$ M NaF will completely inactivate grape *peroxidase*, and 0.1 N NaCl will reduce the activity of the enzyme by 78 %. This is why sodium chloride brines are used for dipping sliced potatoes just before they are dehydrated.

Sulfur dioxide in its gaseous form or as sulfites is widely used in cut fruits and some vegetables to prevent their browning immediately after slicing and before dehydration or freezing. It must be remembered, however, that only free SO_2, and not its bound form, is capable of preventing browning (see Chapter 5).

In addition, the pH of the plant tissue plays an important role in the browning phenomena, as in all other enzymatic reactions: lowering the natural pH will often appreciably decrease the rate of browning. In apples, for instance, the optimal pH for brown discoloration is 4, while at pH 3.7 the rate of browning is greatly diminished, and at pH 2.5 it nearly ceases. In plums, the optimal pH is 7, at pH 3.0 the *phenolase* activity is only 12 %, and at pH 2.5 it stops completely. The influence of pH in reducing the rate of browning is widely used in the food industry when fruits, such as apricots or peaches, after lye peeling, are immersed immediately into citric acid solution in order to reduce their pH to their normal value of 4. A mineral acid is, of course, even more effective and pure phosphoric acid is, therefore, often used. JOSLYN AND HOHL[7] proposed the use of a solution of 0.5 % citric acid and 0.03 % of ascorbic acid to prevent browning in cut fruits intended for freezing. In this case, ascorbic acid plays the part of the antioxidant.

The reason why the presence of *phenolase* enzymes *in situ* does not cause browning was for some time explained by the supposition that the chromogen (the phenolic substrate) and the enzyme find themselves enclosed in different cells of the fruit and their interaction does not begin until the cells are ruptured, when both have a chance to mix. However, this supposition is untenable and SZENT-GYÖRGYI[8] first gave the true explanation: all these biochemical reactions, while in the cell, are reversible reactions, the oxidation of the chromogens and their reduction both running simultaneously. When, however, the cell organization is disrupted, the reaction proceeds rapidly in one direction. After all, this oxidation system requires three components: the chromogen, the *phenolase* as well as oxygen. According to this investigator, disintegrated potato pulp is capable of absorbing 15 times as much oxygen for the oxidation of its chromogens as it requires for normal respiration.

In connection with this ability of crushed fruits to absorb oxygen, it is of great interest to mention here some results of experiments which also indicate clearly the location of the oxidative enzymes. Contrary to such enzymes as *phosphatase* in milk which are dissolved in the substrate, the *phenolases* are mostly adsorbed on the solid tissues and, when these are filtered off from the juices, the rate of oxidation decreases considerably. Fig. 53 shows the results of experiments[9] with apple juice, which has been

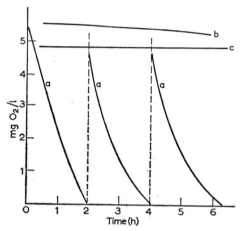

Fig. 53. Loss of oxygen in apple juice (a = juice with natural pulp, b = filtered juice, c = after enzyme activation)[15].

impregnated with oxygen every two hours. Natural juice ("a"), containing a normal amount of pulp, lost all of its oxygen in about two hours and continued to lose it even when impregnated anew. In contrast, EK filtered* juice ("b") lost its absorbed oxygen only very slowly, while pasteurized juice with pulp ("c") did not undergo oxidation because of enzyme inactivation.

These experiments also clearly suggest that the *phenolases* are mostly adsorbed on the pulp.

Mechanism of enzymatic browning

Probably the most striking property of the two groups of oxidative enzymes is their characteristic feature of slowing down and ultimately stopping the enzymatic activity as if it had been somehow "poisoned". Such inhibition of enzymes by the resulting reaction products is not uncommon in biochemistry. LuVALLE AND GODDARD[10] suggested a mechanism based on the formation of a free radical capable of forming an inactive enzyme peroxide; in the following scheme, SH_2 is the substrate, S = the oxidized substrate and E = the enzyme:

---

* Juice filtered through a very compact Seitz filter EK (*Ent*K*eimungs Filter) capable of retaining yeast.

(1) $SH_2 + E \rightleftharpoons E \cdot SH_2$ (substrate–enzyme complex formation)

(2) $E \cdot SH_2 + O_2 \rightleftharpoons SH_2 \cdot E \cdot O_2$ (the two combine with oxygen)

(3) $SH_2 \cdot E \cdot O_2 \rightleftharpoons S + H^+ + HO_2^- \cdot E$ (the triple complex breaks up into oxidized substrate, a proton and a free radical)

(4) $HO_2^- \cdot E + SH_2 \rightleftharpoons HO_2^- \cdot E \cdot SH_2$ (the free radical forms a new complex with the substrate)

(5) $HO_2^- \cdot E \cdot SH_2 \longrightarrow E + S + H_2O + OH^-$ (the new complex breaks up)

(6) $HO_2^- \cdot E \longrightarrow HE \begin{matrix} O \\ | \\ O \end{matrix}$ (however, the free radical of the enzyme may also form an inactive peroxide)

In elucidating the mechanism of the enzymatic browning reaction, many theories have been offered to cover the various stages of oxidation as well as the formation of the melanoidins, the complex brown end-products. None of these proposed theories completely answers the actual data assembled by a large number of investigators except that this intricate mechanism must involve initial enzymatic oxidation of the o-benzene derivatives, a further non-enzymatic oxidation followed by some non-oxidative transformations and final polymerization, the total oxygen absorbed during this browning process being in the range of 2.34–3.35 atoms of oxygen per mole of catechol:

(a) initial hydroxylation, as in the case of tyrosin to DOPA

(b) oxidation to o-quinone, which, at this stage, requires only one atom of oxygen

(c) secondary hydroxylation

(d) with possibly some interchanges or intramolecular rearrangements

(e) final color formation due to polymerization possibly into one of the several proposed forms

(The above is an adaptation from the review of JOSLYN AND PONTING[6].)

While investigating the presence of phenylalkylamines in some broom plants CORREALE AND CORTESE[11] found that the mechanism of tyrosine oxidation is quite different from that assumed earlier. According to these investigators the decarboxylation of tyrosine is taking place before the oxidation of tyramine. The same has been shown by GRIFFITHS[12] in bananas. Moreover, using[14] C-labeled materials BUCKLEY AND TOWERS[13] identified a dihydro indol compound as the final product of tyrosine oxidation. These recent findings can be summarized as follows:

REFERENCES

[1] E. BALDWIN, *Dynamic Aspects of Biochemistry*, 3nd edn., Cambridge Univ. Press, 1957.

[2] M. DIXON, *Multi-Enzyme Systems*, Cambridge Univ. Press, 1949.

[2a] J. B. BIALE, Postharvest physiology and biochemistry of fruits, *Plant Physiol. Ann. Rev.*, 1 (1950) 183.

[2b] H. LÜTHI, *Schweiz. Z. Obst- u. Weinbau*, 63 (1954) 455.

[3] M. LINDET, Sur l'oxidation du tannin de la pomme à cidre, *Compt. rend.*, 120 (1895) 370.

[4] M. W. ONSLOW, Oxidizing enzymes. III. The oxidizing enzymes of some common fruits, *Biochem. J.*, 14 (1920) 541.

[5] Z. I. KERTESZ, The oxidase system of a non-browning yellow peach, *N.Y. Agr. Exptl. Sta. Tech. Bull.*, (1933) 216.

[6] M. A. JOSLYN AND J. D. PONTING, Enzyme-catalyzed oxidative browning of fruit products, *Advances in Food Research*, 3 (1951) 1.

[7] M. A. JOSLYN AND L. A. HOHL, The commercial freezing of fruit products, *Calif. Agr. Exptl. Sta. Bull.*, (1948) 703.

[8] A. SZENT-GYÖRGYI, *Studies on Biological Oxidation and Some of its Catalysts*, Williams and Wilkins Co., Baltimore, 1939.

[9] HANS LÜTHI, *Symposium of the Intern. Fruit Juice Union, Paris, 1951*.

[10] J. E. LUVALLE AND D. R. GODDARD, The Mechanism of Enzymatic Oxidations and Reductions, *Quart. Rev. Biol.* 23 (1948) 197.

[11] P. CORREALE AND I. CORTESE, Untersuchungen über die Biogenese der Phenyl-alkylamine des Besenginsters (*Sarothamnus seoparius*), *Naturwissenschaften* 41 (1954) 457.

[12] L. A. GRIFFITHS, Detection and identification of the polyphenoloxidase substrate of the banana, *Nature* 184 (1959) 58.

[13] E. H. BUCKLEY AND G. H. N. TOWERS (United Fruit Co), private communication.

SELECTED BIBLIOGRAPHY TO CHAPTER 19

BATE-SMITH, E. C. AND T. N. MORRIS, The nature of enzymic browning, in *Food Science*, The University Press, Cambridge, 1952, p. 55.

BIALE, J. B., Postharvest physiology and chemistry, Chapter 4 in W. B. SINCLAIR, *The Orange, its Biochemistry and Physiology*, Univ. Calif. Press, 1961.

CLARK, W. M., *Topics in Physical Chemistry*, Williams and Wilkins Co., Baltimore, 1948.

HENZE, R. E., Inhibition of enzymatic browning of chlorogenic acid solutions with cysteine and glutathione, *Science*, 123 (1956) 1174.

JOSLYN, M. A. AND J. D. PONTING, Enzyme-catalyzed oxidative browning of fruit products, *Advances in Food Research*, 3 (1951) 1.

ONSLOW, M. W., *The Principles of Plant Biochemistry*, Cambridge Univ. Press, 1931.

PONTING, J. D., The control of enzymatic browning of fruits, in H. W. SCHULZ, *Food Enzymes*, Avi Publishing Co., Westport, Conn., 1960.

CHAPTER 20

NON-ENZYMATIC BROWNING

The Pandora box

In addition to the darkening of fruit products caused by enzymes, as discussed in the previous chapter, numerous browning phenomena of a purely chemical nature occur very often during food processing and storage. With the exception of such desirable phenomena as the brown color of beer, bread crusts, maple syrup, coffee, etc., all other browning of food products is undesirable, unsightly and is a distinct sign of deterioration of the flavor and of the nutritional value of the food in question. Examples of such discoloration are numerous, they appear in dry egg and milk powders, in dehydrated fruit, in concentrated and sweetened fruit juices, especially in lemon and grapefruit, in starch and protein hydrolyzates, etc.

Although many aspects of these phenomena have not been thoroughly elucidated, especially as far as the later stages of melanoidin formation are concerned, three distinct mechanism are now known to be involved in the non-enzymatic browning of foods and food products: (a) the MAILLARD reaction or the melanoidin condensation, (b) the ascorbic acid mechanism, and (c) the active aldehyde theory. There is no doubt that in foods which are very complex systems, combinations of all three paths often occur.

The MAILLARD *reaction*

The condensation of sugars with amino acids and proteins was first studied by MAILLARD[1] in 1912. It is now generally known that aldehydes, ketones, and reducing sugars combine readily with amino acids, peptides and proteins in accordance with the aldol condensation to form first a Schiff's base and then an N-substituted glycosylamine (see formula on p. 303).

Obviously, only such carbohydrates which have a free carbonyl group can combine with the amino compounds. A discussion was given in Chapter 5 regarding the open-chain aldehydic form of the sugars and its slow combination (at ordinary temperatures) with sulfites to form hydrosulfonic acids. KATCHALSKY[2] has shown that the rate of formation of brown melanoidins depends on the concentration of this aldehydic straight-chain form of the sugars. Hence, any sugar in which the functional carbonyl group is somehow

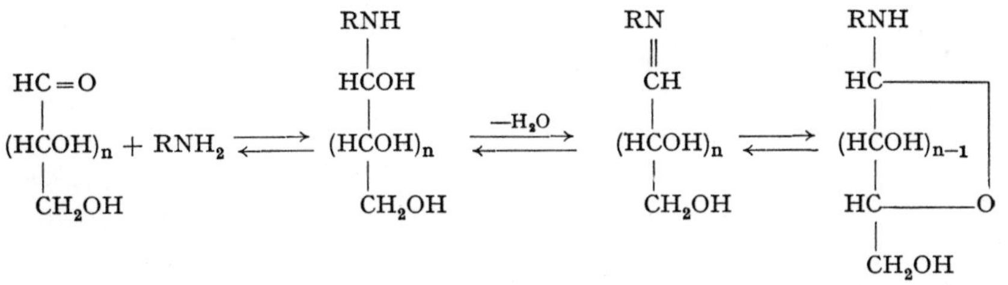

RNH   RN   RNH

$$
\begin{array}{l}
\text{HC}=\text{O}\\
|\\
(\text{HCOH})_n + \text{RNH}_2 \rightleftarrows\\
|\\
\text{CH}_2\text{OH}
\end{array}
\quad
\begin{array}{l}
\text{RNH}\\
|\\
\text{HCOH}\\
|\\
(\text{HCOH})_n\\
|\\
\text{CH}_2\text{OH}
\end{array}
\xrightarrow{-\text{H}_2\text{O}}
\begin{array}{l}
\text{RN}\\
\|\\
\text{CH}\\
|\\
(\text{HCOH})_n\\
|\\
\text{CH}_2\text{OH}
\end{array}
\rightleftarrows
\begin{array}{l}
\text{RNH}\\
|\\
\text{HC}\!\!-\!\!\!\rule{0pt}{1ex}\\
|\\
(\text{HCOH})_{n-1}\\
|\\
\text{HC}\!\!-\!\!\!\text{O}\\
|\\
\text{CH}_2\text{OH}
\end{array}
$$

 sugar amino   addition   Schiff's   N-substituted
     comp.   product   base   glycosylamine

blocked will not combine with the amino compound. This is the reason why sulfites usually inhibit this type of browning; in fact, as can be seen from the following reaction formulae, there is a free position for the aldol condensation to take place but further formation of the Schiff's base is hindered:

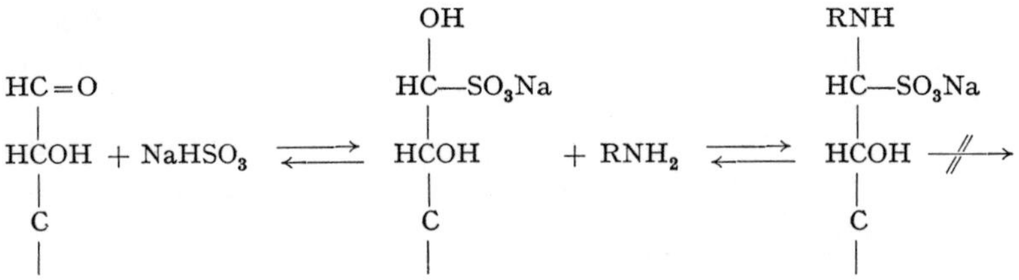

$$
\begin{array}{l}
\text{HC}=\text{O}\\
|\\
\text{HCOH} + \text{NaHSO}_3\\
|\\
\text{C}\\
|
\end{array}
\rightleftarrows
\begin{array}{l}
\text{OH}\\
|\\
\text{HC}\!-\!\text{SO}_3\text{Na}\\
|\\
\text{HCOH}\\
|\\
\text{C}\\
|
\end{array}
+ \text{RNH}_2 \rightleftarrows
\begin{array}{l}
\text{RNH}\\
|\\
\text{HC}\!-\!\text{SO}_3\text{Na}\\
|\\
\text{HCOH} \;\;\not\!\!\rightarrow\\
|\\
\text{C}\\
|
\end{array}
$$

Pure fructose does not condense with amino compounds, as has been shown by KATCHALSKY. Similarly, it does not combine with sulfites, as has been shown by BRAVERMAN[3], the reason most probably being the abnormal behavior of fructose during mutarotation.

The second step is the so-called AMADORI rearrangement, which consists of the isomerization of the N-substituted aldosylamines into N-substituted 1-amino-1-deoxy-2-ketose:

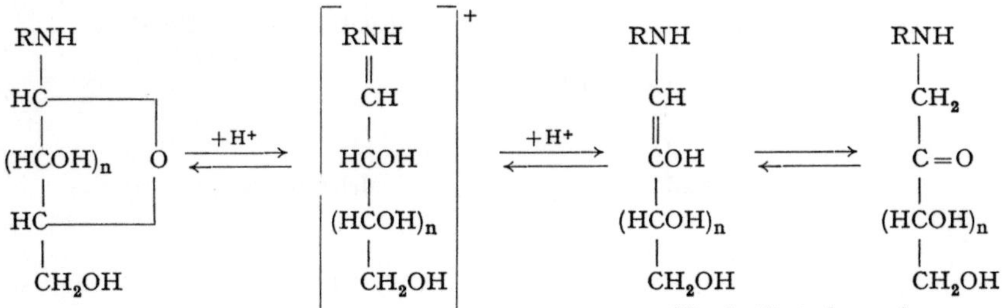

$$
\begin{array}{l}
\text{RNH}\\
|\\
\text{HC}\!\!-\!\!\!\rule{0pt}{1ex}\\
|\\
(\text{HCOH})_n\;\;\;\text{O}\\
|\\
\text{HC}\!\!-\!\!\!\rule{0pt}{1ex}\\
|\\
\text{CH}_2\text{OH}
\end{array}
\;\underset{\longleftarrow}{\xrightarrow{+\text{H}^+}}\;
\left[
\begin{array}{l}
\text{RNH}\\
\|\\
\text{CH}\\
|\\
\text{HCOH}\\
|\\
(\text{HCOH})_n\\
|\\
\text{CH}_2\text{OH}
\end{array}
\right]^{+}
\;\underset{\longleftarrow}{\xrightarrow{+\text{H}^+}}\;
\begin{array}{l}
\text{RNH}\\
|\\
\text{CH}\\
\|\\
\text{COH}\\
|\\
(\text{HCOH})_n\\
|\\
\text{CH}_2\text{OH}
\end{array}
\;\rightleftarrows\;
\begin{array}{l}
\text{RNH}\\
|\\
\text{CH}_2\\
|\\
\text{C}=\text{O}\\
|\\
(\text{HCOH})_n\\
|\\
\text{CH}_2\text{OH}
\end{array}
$$

                 N-substituted 1-amino-
N-substituted   cation of   1-deoxy-2-ketose
glycosylamine   Schiff's base (enol form)   (keto form)

References p. 312/313

In these first two stages of the melanoidin condensation, all the reactions are reversible and the products are colorless.

The third step in the MAILLARD reaction is the STRECKER degradation, *viz.*, the loss of a molecule of CO_2 from the system. By using an isotope tracing technique, it has been demonstrated that 90–100 % of the expelled CO_2 originates from the amino acid moiety and not from the sugar residue. At this stage of the reaction, discoloration begins to appear and spectrophotometric measurements show a strong absorption maximum in the region of 2770–2850 Å, *i.e.*, the region of furfural.

What exactly follows is not quite clear. At this stage a number of reactions could take place: an aldol condensation, polymerization of aldehyde amines, and the formation of heterocyclic substances, such as pyrroles, pyridines, amidaldoses, etc. All these are mainly assumptions based on several known facts: that the aldol, $CH_3CH \cdot (OH) \cdot CH_2 \cdot CHO$, turns brown immediately on coming into contact with glycine, and that even the simplest aldehydes, such as an acetaldehyde, form brown complexes with NH_3. In addition, it has been found that the precursors of the colored pigments are fluorogens, namely substances causing strong fluorescence.

Sulfur dioxides and sulfites, if added at the stage of the formation of fluorogens, are still able to arrest browning; however, the brown pigments appear, the addition of sulfites will not prevent their further development.

The ascorbic acid browning mechanism

Browning in citrus juices, especially in concentrates and more specifically in lemon and grapefruit concentrates, has been found to be caused by the decomposition of ascorbic acid. JOSLYN has demonstrated that this kind of browning takes place only after the bulk of ascorbic acid has disappeared. In fact, if ascorbic acid is heated with an acid, it is finally transformed into furfural with the formation of CO_2. The following shows the formation of furfural by dehydration of 2-keto-3-keto-hexuronic acid with the closure of the furfural ring:

$$CH_2(OH) \cdot CH(OH) \cdot HC \cdot C\text{---}OH$$
$$O{<} \quad \|$$
$$C \cdot C\text{---}OH$$
$$\|$$
$$O$$

ascorbic acid

$$\rightleftharpoons$$

$$CH_2(OH) \cdot CH(OH) \cdot HC \cdot C = O$$
$$O{<} \quad |$$
$$C \cdot C = O$$
$$\|$$
$$O$$

dehydroascorbic acid

$$\downarrow$$

$$CH_2(OH) \cdot CH(OH) \cdot CH_2 \cdot C = O$$
$$|$$
$$HOOC \cdot C = O$$

2-keto-, 3-keto-hexuronic acid

or written in a more discernible form:

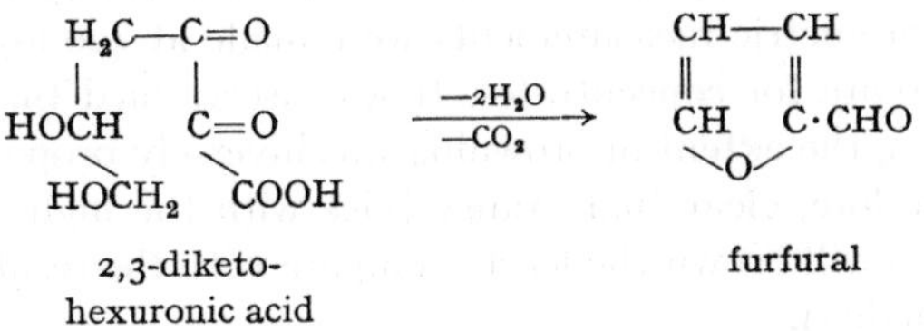

$$
\begin{array}{ccc}
\underset{\substack{| \\ \text{HOCH} \\ \diagdown \\ \text{HOCH}_2}}{\text{H}_2\text{C}-}\overset{\substack{| \\ \text{C}=\text{O} \\ | \\ \text{C}=\text{O} \\ \diagdown \\ \text{COOH}}}{} & \xrightarrow[-\text{CO}_2]{-2\text{H}_2\text{O}} & \underset{\underset{\diagdown \text{O} \diagup}{\text{CH} \quad \text{C}\cdot\text{CHO}}}{\overset{\underset{\|}{\text{CH}-}}{}\overset{\underset{\|}{\text{CH}}}{}} \\
\text{2,3-diketo-} & & \text{furfural} \\
\text{hexuronic acid} & &
\end{array}
$$

Furfural is known to undergo polymerization and browning. Moreover, as an active aldehyde it may easily undergo the MAILLARD reaction even with the very small quantities of proteins or amino acids found in citrus juices. It should be remembered from Chapter 5 that pentoses, when heated with acids, easily undergo transformation into furfural. Also, various reductones possessing the same dienol configuration as the ascorbic acid may follow the same scheme of browning.

While the first experiments, performed with the aim of elucidating the above scheme, were made in the presence of oxygen it was soon shown that juices from which oxygen had been completely excluded, or dehydrated fruits packed *in vacuo* or in an inert atmosphere, all underwent browning. When ascorbic acid was heated in a sealed tube together with some citric acid both in the presence of oxygen and under reduced pressure of 0.075 mm Hg—browning took place in both cases at the same rate[4]. The fact that the browning of citrus juices is mainly caused by the degradation of ascorbic acid has received further confirmation from MOORE[5] who showed that additional quantities of ascorbic acid in the juices increased the formation of the brown pigments even more.

The auto-oxidation of ascorbic acid has been dealt with previously (see Chapter 14). Suffice it to say that even minute quantities of oxygen, normally acquired in any operations concerned with the preparation of foods, are able to start the chain of auto-oxidation, whether it is propagated by flavonoids or otherwise. From then on, there is no escape from further breakdown of ascorbic acid with the resulting browning. The most important things about these browning phenomena in citrus juices are their dependence on the pH, and on the degree of concentration. In the citrus industry, concentrates are prepared for the market both pasteurized in cans or preserved in barrels with SO_2. While orange concentrates with a pH around 3.4 do not tend to darken quickly if kept in the cool or if preserved with SO_2, grapefruit (pH = 2.9) and lemon (pH = 2.15) concentrates darken very quickly even if preserved with SO_2. The effect of pH on the extent of browning has been measured[6] both on straight juices and on their 60° Brix concentrates. These samples were brought up to various pH within the range of citrus juices either by citric acid or by sodium bicarbonate. After storage for 30 days at 30°C, spectrophotometric measurements were made at 420 mμ for straight juices and at 560 mμ for concentrates. It was ascertained that, within the range of pH 2–3.5, the extent of browning was inversely proportional to the pH. It was, therefore, clear that orange juice with the highest pH among other citrus juices will brown the least. Compare with the results on glucose browning (see further).

The active aldehyde theory

The third possible mechanism of non-enzymatic browning is the dehydration of sugars with the resulting formation of very active aldehydes. Mention has already been made of the formation of furfural in acid solutions; however, hexoses as well as all uronic acids are broken down easily when heated in an acid medium, as is the case, for instance, during acid hydrolysis of starch for the manufacture of glucose syrups containing dextrins or in the brewing of beer, etc. All these products are brown and are due to the so-called "caramelization" of sugars, even in the absence of proteins or amino acids. WOLFROM[7] offers the following scheme for such caramelization phenomena, which are due to the formation of HMF, hydroxymethylfurfural:

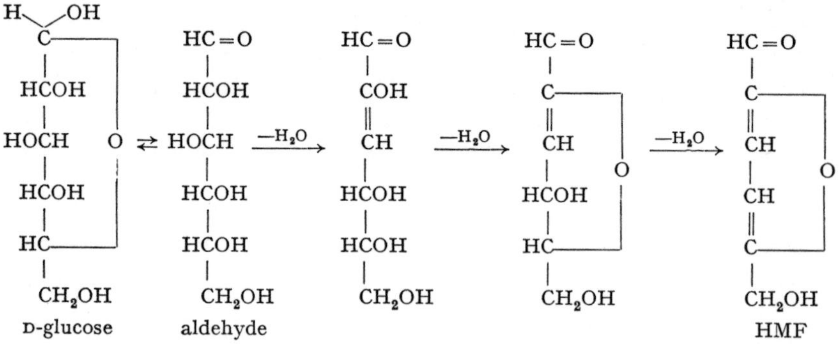

or in another presentation:

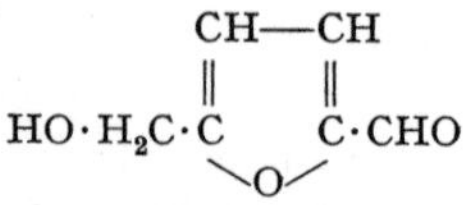

hydroxymethylfurfural

Hydroxymethylfurfural, as such, is capable of polymerizing and, in addition, as a very active aldehyde, of readily combining with amino compounds if present even in very small quantities.

By using cathode rays as a tool for studying cases of non-enzymatic browning, PROCTOR AND GOLDBLITH[8] demonstrated that HMF is by no means the sole compound responsible for the browning of dried fruits: another compound with a maximum absorption at 265 mμ was found. GOLDBLITH also showed that irradiation of powdered sucrose resulted in the presence of a substance with the same U.V. absorption maximum at 265 mμ.

D-Galacturonic acid can also result in brown pigments, however pectin, in its different forms, does not brown before being cleaved into its galacturonic acid monomers.

In all these systems lacking amino groups, browning of the sugars, polysaccharides and polyhydroxy acids can proceed without catalysts at rather high temperatures, however, in the presence of phosphates and a number of carboxylic acids, acting as catalysts, these reactions proceed very quickly, just as in the case of MAILLARD reactions. Malic acid has been found to be the most active of all carboxylic acids in accelerating browning.

The above reactions, based on the formation of active aldehydes, proceed under acid conditions. It will be remembered, however, that in alkaline media the 1,2-enolization of reducing sugars (the LOBRY DE BRUYN–ALBERDA VAN EKENSTEIN rearrangement) causes the formation of a very labile configuration capable of rapid oxidation and subsequent browning:

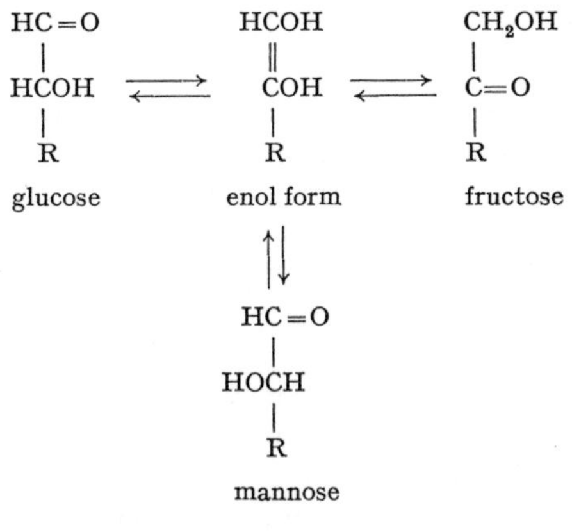

$$
\begin{array}{ccccc}
HC=O & & HCOH & & CH_2OH \\
| & & \| & & | \\
HCOH & \rightleftarrows & COH & \rightleftarrows & C=O \\
| & & | & & | \\
R & & R & & R \\
\text{glucose} & & \text{enol form} & & \text{fructose}
\end{array}
$$

$$
\begin{array}{c}
\updownarrow \\
HC=O \\
| \\
HOCH \\
| \\
R \\
\text{mannose}
\end{array}
$$

In this case the browning will follow the path of the ascorbic acid and of other substances with dienolic configurations.

The influence of pH on this type of browning has been studied[9, 10], among other factors, in a number of commercial glucose syrups, and the results confirmed earlier findings in other products mentioned above under the ascorbic theory.

References p. 312/313

The curves in Fig. 54 show the extent of browning (measured spectro-photometrically in U.V. light and expressed as the extinction coefficient of a 50 % solution at 420 mμ) and the contents of HMF (expressed as the difference between $\epsilon^{5\%}$ at 284 mμ and at 245 mμ) at different pH values.

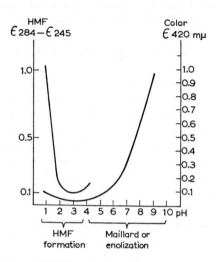

Fig. 54. Browning and HMF contents of glucose syrups at different pH.

The process of conversion of starch into glucose and other carbohydrates by acid hydrolysis is always accompanied by the formation of HMF and subsequent browning; a similar reaction takes place on storage at pH 1. At pH 2–5, browning is accompanied by the formation of HMF, which decreases with increasing pH. The color is at a minimum at about pH 3 and intensifies gradually with increasing pH. At pH 5–6, the formation of HMF seems to be arrested, which is explained by the fact that the rate of HMF formation is gradually exceeded by the rate of its polymerization or by its entering the MAILLARD reaction. With increasing pH, the browning due to HMF is accompanied or replaced by the MAILLARD reaction or by other mechanisms not based on the presence of amino groups, such as enolization or formation of reductones.

The HODGE *scheme*

An attempt to summarize the existing knowledge about various types of browning, including enzymatic browning, was made by HODGE[11] as shown in Fig. 55.

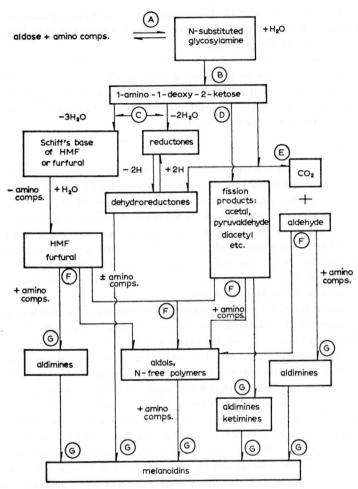

Fig. 55. The HODGE scheme for browning reactions.

In this scheme the encircled letters denote the following reactions:

(A) The MAILLARD reaction;

(B) The AMADORI rearrangement;

(C) Dehydration conversions of sugar addition products or of ascorbic acid into reductones or dehydroreductones and into furfural and hydroxymethyl-furfural (HMF), as well as the loss of the amino groups;

(D) Fission products such as acetal, diacetyl, pyruvaldehyde, etc.;

(E) STRECKER degradation with the loss of CO_2 from the amino acid moiety;

(F) Reactions concerning the recombination of amino acid groups or other nitrogenous residues with carbonyl groups and formation of aldimines, etc., or the formation of N-free polymers;

(G) Final polymerization with the creation of melanoidins.

HODGE also includes in his general scheme the catechols and similar phenolic substances which are substrates for enzymatic browning, his point of view being that catechols are not different from any other dienolic compound such as ascorbic acid or other reductones.

Recent theories

In a recent comprehensive review of the MAILLARD reaction, ELLIS[12] points out that the results of the numerous investigations into the mechanism of this reaction support one of two main theories. The first assumes the formation of *glycosylamines* which undergo the AMADORI rearrangement, as described above. The many investigators who support this mechanism have also found that optimum conditions for the occurrence of the MAILLARD reaction are: (a) a fairly low water content; (b) a pH between 7 and 10; and (c) a high temperature. However, we are well aware that browning also occurs under much milder conditions.

The second theory for the mechanism of the browning reaction is of a more recent origin[13] and maintains that the color formation and the MAILLARD reaction are two separate and distinct processes. According to this school of thought, browning is due to the effect of pH on the sugar and can occur over a wide range of pH, whereas the MAILLARD reaction proceeds only in alkaline media. It has been observed that when sugars plus amino acids were heated in the absence of added buffers, there was no decrease in amino nitrogen. In alkaline buffers, however, the pH decreased as well as the content of amino nitrogen, and the formation of color proceeded, as shown by an extra spot on the chromatogram. All these facts indicate that browning and the MAILLARD reaction proceed, in this case, simultaneously. The reaction products in these experiments were shown to be *glyconyl-amino acids* (which had never before been identified as products of this type of reaction). Evidence does not exist to suggest that browning and the disappearance of amino groups do not run parallel. However, it must be noted that all these experiments were performed at a temperature of 120°C and under pressure, while the AMADORI rearrangement takes place at much lower temperatures and at atmospheric pressure.

Both mechanisms result in the formation of water, a fact which may be significant when "dry-state" reactions are considered (because it is well known that, while the browning proceeds rapidly at high concentrations, the reaction stops in the absence of moisture):

$$
\begin{array}{c}
\text{H}\diagdown\ \diagup\text{OH} \\
\text{C}\!\!-\!\!-\!\!-\!\!- \\
| \\
\text{HCOH} \qquad + \quad \text{R}\!\!-\!\!\text{COOH} \\
| \qquad\qquad\quad | \\
\text{O} \qquad\qquad \text{NH}_2 \\
|
\end{array}
\qquad
\begin{array}{l}
\text{CO}\cdot\text{NH}\cdot\text{R}\cdot\text{COOH} \qquad + \text{H}_2\text{O} \\
| \\
\text{HCOH} \\
| \\[4pt]
\text{HCONH}\cdot\text{RCOOH} \\
\| \qquad\qquad\qquad\quad + \text{H}_2\text{O} \\
\text{COH} \\
|
\end{array}
$$

Generalizations regarding the MAILLARD reaction cannot be made because of the variation in the behavior of different amino acids and because of the profound effects of comparatively small changes in experimental conditions, especially in natural systems where browning may be further complicated by the high degree of coloring which is produced by the presence of other compounds such as ascorbic acid, uronic acids, non-nitrogenous carboxylic acids, phenols, proteins, etc.

Methods for preventing browning

On the strength of the above discussions, it is evident that in such complex systems as foods it is very difficult to suggest general methods for the prevention of non-enzymatic browning. It will be attempted here only to indicate some possibilities; however, the application of each must be judged separately on its own merits.

(1) Some general precautions can be taken in preventing or at least greatly decreasing the rate of browning. The most helpful method is to refrigerate the foods subject to this type of change. Lowering the temperature, generally slows down all chemical reactions especially this type of browning.

(2) Similarly, the presence of sulfites, as already explained, will hinder the MAILLARD reaction.

(3) Lowering the pH of the product may again be of use if the main cause of browning is the melanoidin condensation. (Dried egg powder, for instance, is often made after the addition of HCl with subsequently admixing of the powder with some Na_2HCO_3: the excess acid will then combine with the bicarbonate of soda to form NaCl.)

(4) Lowering the concentration of the final product sometimes decreases the rate of browning. (Grapefruit and lemon juices are often concentrated at a ratio of only 4:1 instead of 6:1 which is usual for orange juice.)

(5) Because the MAILLARD reaction requires a free carbonyl group in the sugars, it is sometimes possible to prevent browning of certain food products by using sucrose instead of reducing sugars, provided, of course, the sucrose will not undergo inversion in the final product during storage.

References p. 312/313

(6) Fructose, as previously mentioned, does not enter into combination with amino acids easily and may probably also be used with the same effect.

(7) When the sugar constitutes only a negligible part of the product, such as is the case with eggs or meat, it can be removed by fermentation. (Eggs are sometimes subjected to fermentation by yeast before drying them into powder. Similarly, it has been suggested[14] that meat may be fermented before dehydration; ground meat (1/8″) with 5% yeast added is claimed to be well preserved after dehydration.)

(8) Another successful method[15] of removing small quantities of sugar is the use of a mixture of two enzymes, *glucose oxidase* and *catalase* (now commercially available under the name of DeeO). The *oxidase* converts glucose into gluconic acid (which does not combine with the amino groups) and hydrogen peroxide, while the latter is converted into water and oxygen by *catalase*:

$$R \cdot CHO + O_2 + H_2O \xrightarrow[\text{oxidase}]{\text{glucose}} R \cdot COOH + H_2O_2$$

$$H_2O_2 \xrightarrow{\text{catalase}} H_2O + \tfrac{1}{2}O_2$$

The same procedure is used now also in lowering the oxygen content in the headspace of bottled products.

(9) As far as the proteins part in the MAILLARD reaction is concerned, there are probably also some possibilities. It has been shown that only soluble proteins are involved in browning: Sorghum starch, for instance, with a total protein content of 1 % but with a low soluble protein content of 0.01 % has been found to be much preferred to cornstarch for the preparation of glucose syrups since the latter, although comparatively low in total protein, has a high soluble protein content (0.07 %).

(10) In many cases, the greater part of the proteins can be removed through coagulation by heat or by absorption on activated carbon.

REFERENCES

[1] L. C. MAILLARD, Action of amino acids on sugars, *Compt. rend.*, 154 (1912) 66.
[2] A. KATCHALSKY, Interaction of aldoses with α-amino acids or peptides, *Biochem. J.*, 35 (1941) 1024.
[3] J. B. S. BRAVERMAN, The mechanism of the interaction of SO_2 with certain sugars, *J. Sci. Food Agr.*, 4 (1953) 540.
[4] M. P. LAMDEN AND R. S. HARRIS, Browning of ascorbic acid in pure solutions, *Food Research*, 15 (1950) 79.
[5] E. L. MOORE, W. B. ERRELEN JR. AND C. R. FELLERS, Factors responsible for the darkening of packaged orange juice, *Fruit Products J.*, 22 (1942) 100.
[6] Z. BERK AND J. B. S. BRAVERMAN, Some observations on non-enzymatic browning of citrus concentrates, *Symposium of Fruit Juice Concentrates, Fruit Juice Union, Bristol, 1958.*

[7] M. L. WOLFROM, R. D. SCHULTZ AND L. E. CALVALIERI, *J. Am. Chem. Soc.*, 70 (1948)
514.
[8] B. E. PROCTOR AND S. A. GOLDBLITH, Electromagnetic radiation fundamentals and
their application in food technology, *Advances in Food Research*, 3 (1951) 119.
[9] R. SCHACHTEL, J. B. S. BRAVERMAN AND W. GROAG, Non enzymatic browning in
commercial glucose syrups, *Bull. Research Council Israel*, C7 (1959) 37.
[10] W. DIEMAIR AND E. JURY, Beitrag zur Veränderlichkeit und Bildung von 5-Hydroxy-
methylfurfural, *Z. Lebensm. Untersuch. u. Forsch.*, 113 (1960) 189.
[11] J. E. HODGE, The chemistry of browning reactions, *J. Agr. Food Chem.*, 1 (1953) 928.
[12] G. P. ELLIS, The Maillard reaction, *Advances Carbohydrate Chem.*, 14 (1959) 63.
[13] L. J. SCHROEDER, M. IACOBELLIS AND A. H. SMITH, *J. Biol. Chem.*, 212 (1955) 973.
[14] R. L. HENDRICKSON, Dehydrated pork studies, *Food Technol.*, 9 (1955) 290.
[15] R. L. HENDRICKSON, *Food Technol.* 10 (1956) 1.

SELECTED BIBLIOGRAPHY TO CHAPTER 20

DANEHY, J. P. AND W. W. PIGMAN, Reactions between sugars and nitrogenous com-
pounds and their relationship to certain food problems, *Advances in Food Research*, 3
(1951) 241.
ISBELL, H. S. AND H. L. FRUSH, Reactions of the glycosylamines, *U.S. Atomic Energy
Comm. Rept. No. NBS–5352*, National Bureau of Standards, Washington, 1957.
JOSLYN, M. A. AND J. B. S. BRAVERMAN, The chemistry and technology of the pretreat-
ment and preservation of fruit and vegetable products with sulfur dioxide, *Advances in
Food Research*, 5 (1954) 97.
STADTMAN, E. R., Nonenzymatic browning in fruit products, *Advances in Food Research*,
1 (1948) 325.

SUBJECT INDEX

(* = Chemical formulas are designated in this index by asterisks)

PRINTED IN THE NETHERLANDS
BY DRUKKERIJ MEIJER, WORMERVEER/AMSTERDAM